MODERN
ENGINEERING
THEORY AND PRACTICE

CIVIL : MECHANICAL
ELECTRICAL : CHEMICAL
AERONAUTICS

Advisory Editor
PROFESSOR HYMAN LEVY
M.A., D.Sc., F.R.S.E., *Professor
of Mathematics, University of
London*

Edited by
C. E. G. BAILEY, B.A. (Oxon.)
A.M.I.E.E., A.M.I.R.E.

ODHAMS PRESS LIMITED
LONG ACRE, LONDON, W.C.2

INTRODUCTION

SUPPOSE that the well-known fictitious situation had come about in which you found yourself planted some centuries back " in the Court of King Arthur." Like Mark Twain's Yankee, you found yourself out of place and decided to make an impression by some such piece of twentieth-century magic as building a motor-car or setting up a crude telephone system. You would probably find yourself brought to a premature standstill—for lack of *materials*. There would be no petrol, no acid for batteries : iron which made good armour would be useless for a crankshaft, and pure copper and the right sort of enamel would be lacking for winding magnets.

You find yourself to-day in circumstances far less solitary. You have only yourself to instruct and convince : if you become an engineer you will draw continually on the experience of thousands of others. Still your understanding of engineering will be based on your knowledge of the properties of engineering materials, and when you start this book you should bear this in mind, and first read one of the sections in which they are described.

If this is your first introduction to engineering, you will find these materials and the machines fashioned from them described in the section on Mechanical Engineering (*The Science of Machines*). You will find here descriptions of the way in which steel or aluminium or bakelite is pressed, turned, moulded into machinery. You will find, too, an account of the way in which energy is put into machines, to make them turn, or travel, or fly : and this leads to a description of modern steam engines, petrol engines, steamships and aircraft.

Those works of engineering such as roads, bridges and tunnels which have only to stand still are described in the section on Civil Engineering (*Building the Modern World*). Here materials and their shapes are everything, and the different potentialities of steel, brickwork, concrete and other substances are explained in greater detail.

5

But with all the materials we have named, we have hardly glanced at the world's storehouse, and in the Chemical Engineering section (*The Great Chemical Industries*) you may see a glimpse of the new range of solids, acids, fuels and explosives which will shape the designs of the mechanical engineer of to-morrow.

The section on Electrical Engineering (*Electricity in Harness*) should probably be left till the last. Here it is shown how a few simple devices, a glowing filament, a bobbin wound with wire, are specialised, combined and developed till they serve such widely different purposes as the operation of a pocket torch or a lighthouse lantern, a tramcar, a door-bell, or an automatic telephone exchange.

At the end of the book there will be found a section on *The Choice of a Career* for those who take engineering seriously, and a section on the growth of engineering (*How Man has begun to build a New World*) is at the beginning for those who like to speculate on how it all came about.

CONTENTS

CONTENTS

Page

by E. O. Taylor, B.Sc., A.C.G.I., D.I.C., A.M.I.E.E.

by A. D'A. Hodgson, A.M.I.E.E., A.M.I.R.E.

HOW MAN HAS BEGUN TO BUILD A NEW WORLD

by C. E. G. BAILEY, B.A.(Oxon.), A.M.I.E.E., A.M.I.R.E

THE world as we know it, the world as the earliest men surveyed it, is filled with manifestations of energy and matter in contrasting forms. Fluid water in ton masses sluices over solid rock : wind twists and bends trees : the sun's heat dries up mud, hardens and cracks the earth. The waterfall, the wind in the trees, the sun's heat are all manifestations of the physical forces of nature. The realm of engineering is the realm in which these forces are examined, classified and correlated in a special way, and applied to fulfil certain needs of mankind. The special classification is the method of science, and the application is the method of engineering.

Science and engineering have this much in common : they are both processes of simplification, of stripping away unessentials. Perhaps it may not be obvious that so intricate a thing as a power station switchboard is a simplification of nature, but if a firm gives an order it can be supplied with thirty switchboards in a week, whereas all the manufacturers in the world could not in a century build the bough of a tree out of chemical raw materials.

Let us take a concrete example of the process of simplification. When the primitive hunter wanted to make a bow, he went to a tree whose wood had all the properties required ; it was supple, springy, and certain branches had more or less the right length and thickness. But attached to any one of these branches were twigs, leaves, bark, in fact, all the rest of the tree, the ground, and the whole of the rest of nature. He cut off his branch, trimmed away unessentials, and had his bow. In this example is summed up every problem of engineering. Natural forces are not produced by the engineer, they are all displayed in one corner or another of the universe. But they are on too large or too small a scale, or too far away, or too much involved with one another for his immediate use. Man casts and bores cylinders to contain steam, draws and insulates wires to conduct electricity, moulds tyres to

11

enclose compressed air, and then steam, air and electricity fulfil his economic needs.

With the development of engineering comes a new complexity, the machine. But this does not destroy, rather it emphasises, the foregoing argument. A modern Diesel power plant, for example, is by no means simple. The engine consists of thousands of parts ; each must be minutely specified, exactly made. Yet it can be regarded and summed up in a fairly simple manner : an engine operated by the burning of hydrocarbons in air, ignited by the heat of compression : so many cylinders, so many horsepower, so much weight : the result of the instructions contained in several hundred drawings and specifications. Also the problems of its design are a series of questions which can be answered one at a time : the problems of pistons and crankshafts, of strength and balance : the hard steel of the cylinder, the light rigid steel of the connecting rods, the uniform steadily burning oil for combustion, the resistant oil for lubrication. These are questions of mechanics, properties of materials, and chemistry ; they are answered to a certain extent in the various sections of this book, and are the subject of detailed study by thousands of expert engineers.

But now the question arises : if the methods of engineering are ones of simplification, if the human mind has always tended to simplify the universe in just this way, why did engineering never develop in past ages to the extent it has developed in the last two centuries ? We now live in an age of engineering—why not in an age of agriculture, or an age of athletics ? The answer is that the urge, the economic necessity, to extend the scope of manual labour by the aid of machinery, together with the social structure on which a machine civilisation could be built, never existed together before. In order to study the roots of this machine civilisation, we shall have to examine the social structure of the last few centuries.

LIFE IN A MECHANISED SOCIETY—LIVING BY PROXY

WE live in an Age of Engineering. While most of us would give a glib assent to this proposition, we hardly realise how much we are in fact dependent, throughout the whole range of our activities and experiences, on the engineer and the expert : the man who invents the machines and the techniques, and the man who has learnt how to work them.

Compared with our cave-dwelling ancestors, compared with the Esquimaux or even with modern Finnish peasants, we live by proxy, each of us tied up to some thousands of other people. It has even become vital to our mental and physical health that, at intervals, we should remind ourselves of the time when we wrested our food and housing from the earth with our two hands, and whatever tools and weapons they could immediately devise. Hence some popular forms of play; hunting, camping, scouting and gardening. All of these have perhaps the same psychological value; they give us a sense of our continuity with the human race.

But however much some of us may need a certain amount of romance to balance us, the fact is that nearly every department of life as we lead it to-day is in some degree mechanised or dependent on mechanisation. Very few economic activities which procure the doer a livelihood or status in the world remain highly individual; most are based upon a wide co-operation. Take a small common object, a cigarette for example, and consider the range of machines, machine-tools and modes of transport, as well as the number and distribution of workers that are necessary to produce it.

There are cutting machines, drying chambers, dust extractors for treating the tobacco leaf. There are rolling machines that include " guillotines " for cutting the paper to the right length, blanking machines for the cardboard cartons, printing machines for these and the cigarette cards, counting and packing machines, vans, railway trucks, conveyors for transporting raw materials and distributing the product. Now step up one rank in the army of machines. There are gear-cutting lathes for making the teeth of the wheels used in the machinery, milling machines for planing the framework, drills for inserting the bearings. There are oil refineries for purifying the oil to lubricate the machinery, electrical generating stations to make the power to run them, winding machines to put the copper wire on the meters to measure the current taken. . . . Rank and file, the army is unending.

MACHINE-MADE ART WHICH THE PUBLIC ENJOYS

EVEN those highly individualised activities art and literature are affected. Mechanical technique has put them on a co-operative basis; radio and the cinema are obvious examples. But think how the poet-painter William Blake produced his books as author, printer and illustrator all in one; and think how a modern publication is produced. It is interesting that at present, especially in Europe and America, the highly mechanised forms of art and entertainment are by far the most popular. The reason for this may be purely economic. It may be merely that entertainment which has been largely mass-produced in a factory is all that the public can get, because it is all that the public can pay for ; or there may be a genuine development in the human mind. We cannot at present tell. Possibly Russia may give the answer sooner than any other European country, because her industries have only to fulfil a need, not to make a profit ; and so " unprofitable " enjoyments like group-music are making headway there.

But it will be impossible in our lifetime to assess the human results of mechanisation, because we are in transition. We are only just beginning to find out what we can do with mechanisation, and it would be possible to take too gloomy a view. Transition after all surely means that humanity is gaining as well as losing capacities. We human beings, with all the elaborate techniques at our disposal, are really engaged in making a home in the world. Unless a war, which these same techniques would make abnormally destructive, ends us and all our techniques, we shall go on till we succeed, which means that the lot of our descendants will not be less satisfying than our own.

NEW CONDITIONS WHICH FOSTERED INVENTIONS

THE fact that most of the things we eat, wear and use are the products of wide co-operation, has reacted upon the whole process of invention. The inventor is less and less of a discoverer, less and less of a creator in the full and most exciting sense of the word. He becomes more and more an adapter, an improver of inventions that have been useful for a long time already. This is the natural result of the way in which our engineering civilisation has grown to its present complexity and inter-dependence. For engineering has grown as the result of the engineer's, the workman's attempt to make his job easier. The scientific principles involved are in many cases of ancient date. Why then has there never yet been, as far as we know, a mechanised civilisation like our own ?

We are told at school that James Watt invented the steam-engine towards the end of the eighteenth century. Actually there is a description of a primitive steam-turbine in the

Pneumatica, a book written by Hero of Alexandria who was born one hundred and thirty years before Christ. He called it an æolipile, and it may possibly have been used for opening the doors of a shrine, thus giving an appearance of magic or divinity, but it certainly was not used for lightening the necessary labour of man. And after this and one or two primitive engines of the same sort, there is no record of a power engine adapted to any useful purpose till Ramsay's patent, granted in England in 1630, " for raising water with the aid of fire."

Why is this ? Surely it is man's first and most natural impulse to lighten his necessary labour. Why should the Greeks and the Alexandrians have lacked this impulse, have thought it not worth their while to follow the lead which Hero had given them ?

A piston-engine, invented by Thomas Newcomen, was being used for pumping mines in 1711. There is a story that a lazy boy called Humphrey Potter, whose duty it was to open the valves of the engine, found a way of making the engine self-acting (and of saving himself trouble) with pieces of string. Now the development of the boy's invention was favoured by factors which were lacking in Hero's time. First, the boy was working on the job—he had his heart in making it easier. Secondly, the job was on a fairly broad economic basis by this time. A number of people who had money to use in a productive way were interested in making the job easier, because this implied a saving in man-power, resulting in greater cheapness, and a far larger field of consumption. Thus the steam-engine was developing between the times of Hero and Humphrey. A big change took place during those centuries. The social conditions which would make the steam-engine useful on a large scale were slowly ripening.

SEEDS SOWN BY HISTORY FROM WHICH ENGINEERING SPRANG

WE take as our standpoint here that the foundation of all life is economic. " Economy " is strictly the law and order of the habitat or household ; the attempt of the living organism to understand the laws or material conditions of its successive environments ; to employ usefully those laws which are favourable to its own existence (or in many cases its existence as a member of a family or clan) ; and to avoid and circumvent the operation of those which are hostile. Individuals, according to their own views, are probably always trying to harmonise and fulfil their greatest possible range of needs. And, in so far as we can consider it as a whole, this is probably true of any given society.

But up to the present it has been very difficult justly to consider any society known to us as if it were a whole. All of them have in fact consisted of different groups or clans of human beings living in very distinct material conditions and therefore moulding their lives and outlooks on widely different experiences of the world. It is too easy to talk of the glory that was Greece and the grandeur that was Rome. What else were Greece and Rome besides glory and grandeur ? More precisely, they were in their special ways, intellectual civilisations of unusual brilliance, based upon war and slavery.

Here, to begin with, we have three very different types of human being, the " hind " (slave, serf and hired worker), the artist-thinker and the soldier : the man who only produces and reproduces life and its material conditions, the man who contemplates the result, and the man who destroys it. It is quite clear to any of us, even in our own day and experience, that the attitude of these three towards life, towards " economy," the whole rule and management of living, eating, sleeping, playing, loving, will be radically different.

To the hind who is always limited and biassed in these activities by the fact that he is tied to the soil or to his master's service, while no part of the twenty-four hours is strictly his own, life will be a mystery he has no time to investigate, a curse he has no room to escape. The soldier's attitude towards life and the means of life, towards persons and property, is likely to be at best a playful and childish disrespect. The artist and thinker, while he may understand and even be grateful that the work of the hind and the soldier keeps him comfortable and secure while he pursues his thoughts, will be unlikely to devote many of them to improving material conditions, certainly not while these conditions remain stable. For him, as for the soldier, the problem does not arise.

Therefore there can be no answer to the hind's practical question—how to lessen his toil, in increasing and maintaining life and the means of life—except the answer of the priest : " Perform these rites, give to the gods and to us our due proportion of the fruits of your labour, and you shall prosper." The priests, we must remember, had originally a mystical economic function of increasing all forms of fertility.

All this is not to deny the function of individual genius in reshaping human conditions. The genius of Aristotle, who devoted most of his purely scientific work to compiling and arranging facts, could no doubt have forestalled a great part of our modern technological achievement, if the problems had presented themselves to him as urgent practical necessity. But until some degree of fusion, of melting down of all these different types of men, the thinker, the soldier and the hind took place, this could hardly be. There can only be a remarkable technical advance when the majority of men stand in a useful relation to the means of production and have some degree of freedom and enlightment ; when in fact a unified society already exists in germ. This is what the breaking-down of feudal conditions in Europe really meant.

LIFE IN THE MIDDLE AGES : PRODUCTION BY HAND

LIVING in a world which has been materially unified by the engineer and the machine, it is not easy for us to picture these mediæval and feudal conditions as they were. Certainly the Holy Roman Empire provided the world with a unity of idea which we have lost or mislaid to-day, and the unity of idea must have given all classes some feeling of common purpose. In theory at least, the hind, the soldier and the scholar had each a social status, and, within limits, a duty to each other. Though the division of work within it was not less rigid, the " City of God " (to extend St. Augustine's name for the Church to the whole social, political and religious order of the Middle Ages) was in this respect more advanced in humanity than the Greek City State.

Land transport and communications were very poor. The " A " road of the fourteenth century was one on which three horses could travel abreast, where " a bride could ride by without touching the funeral cart." Commodities were carried in packs at a speed which did not exceed five to seven miles a day. Water transport was, of course, more advanced. By hugging the shores of the Mediterranean, sailing by the church-spires on land, men in ships had given Europe the semblance and forecast of a material unity from the days of the Phœnician sailors who brought saffron to our Cornish shores. But sea-travel remained till a late date, as we can tell from literary references alone, hazardous and not to be lightly undertaken.

The problem of material unity, the whole question of the distribution of people and products, which we look to our engineers to solve, had therefore hardly arisen. Throughout the Middle Ages, the ordinary human being had a circumscribed status and function in society. If a peasant, he lived on a manor. He sowed, reaped and harvested for himself, but a certain proportion of his harvest and a certain number of his working days were due to his lord. His lord had in theory the duty of defending him, and to some extent of representing his interests in the larger world. The " manor " was a social as well as a geographical expression. It symbolised the relationship between classes and the " economy " of the time ; and though the system was full of abuses, in its heyday we must suppose that it worked.

If, on the other hand, the average human being was a town-dweller, he worked at a " craft " as a member of a " guild." He went through the stages of apprentice, journeyman, and if he was lucky, master. He became highly skilled according to the standards of the time. His relation with the senior and junior members of his guild was a personal one ; he was regarded as a human being, not merely as an employee, and his social welfare was of some importance. The guilds probably had some of the characteristics of Masonic Lodges and Benefit Societies, apart from their industrial aspect. But tradition lay heavy upon them, there was no exchange of ideas and techniques or division of labour between guilds, and the individual workman had no chance to look abroad or to gain other kinds of skill and experience. Producers, both agricultural and industrial, were very much bound to their means of production, and as we should expect the first impetus to production in a larger and technically more efficient way came from another class of men, less restricted in their material opportunities for experience.

THE NEW ORDER BEGINS : THE RISE OF MERCHANT ADVENTURERS

THESE were the merchants, speculative adventurers, as many of our big financiers are to this day. Because of the difficulties of transport, the earliest commerce was in small luxury articles like gloves, or in necessities like salt, which had great value in small bulk. These the merchants bought very cheaply abroad where they were common and insignificant, and sold at enormously high prices at home where they were rarities. The heroes of this mercantile class, however different they may appear to the romantic historical eye, were in fact men like Columbus, Cortes, Drake and Clive, who in giving expression to their adventurous temperaments or patriotic and religious zeal, were in practice making it possible for merchants to acquire those large personal fortunes which, when technology was ready, would be used to found large-scale industry at home in Europe.

But money without political power is as useless as money when there is no food to buy. The merchant class, by which we mean all those people whose function in society was owning, organising, distributing or lending, instead of directly producing the goods and wealth by which society lived, had to become the real rulers before their money could breed on a grand scale and fertilise an industrial European civilisation whose technical possibilities were only latent. This meant an attack on the prevailing system of ideas, both religious and political, and as a beginning the sixteenth century Reformation in Europe and the seventeenth century revolutions in England.

This is not to deny that men like Luther were inspired with a sincere hatred of the corruption of the Roman Catholic church and a genuine Protestant passion for direct personal communication with God ; that the militant Puritans in England were really repelled by Charles the First's claim to Divine Right over their consciences and fortunes ; or that the Anti-Jacobites who fetched over William of Orange to rule us in 1688 were enraged at James II's favouritism to Papists. Certainly a large share of the revolutionary and reforming energy of the world has always been provided by the idealists and the zealots ; hence the popular appeal of the Great War.

But we have to remember that the Church of Rome which sold indulgences, also set her face against usury, that is, lending for profit ; and that the Divine Right of a king also covered his financial irresponsibility. These two facts alone insured that the Lutheran Reformation and the Revolution by which we cut off Charles' head, had a wider appeal than the disinterested passion of a few idealists, and found a backing in the money and power of the rising mercantile class.

TOWNS AND TRANSPORT SYSTEMS MADE BY THE MERCHANTS

IN England, the political and economic power of the Church of Rome was broken before the full religious effects of the Reformation were felt. Henry VIII, that astute materialist, preferring his own judgment in matrimonial causes to the

Pope's, set himself up as head of an independent State Church. With the help of Thomas Cromwell, he seized the monastic lands. In this way, and by founding the British Navy, he prepared for the glorious expansion of the age of Elizabeth.

The seizure of Church lands meant the beginning of large-scale agriculture. The Church had acted, however poorly, as a feudal landlord ; in theory at least it had a charitable duty towards the poor peasants who lived and worked upon its land ; but the new big secular landlords were to feel no such responsibility. Gradual enclosure of the peasant's lands was to complete what Henry had begun. The Statute of Labourers in 1562, which regulated the migration of labour and of the unemployed between parishes, and the Poor Law passed in the same year, show how far the enclosures and monopolistic agriculture had progressed by the Elizabethan age.

By thus separating the peasant from his land, the new proprietors created a big reserve of labour and a drift towards the towns. In 1694, the Bank of England was founded ; so that we may say that by the end of the seventeenth century all the most important economic and political factors for a big industrial and technological expansion were present in this country ; the foundations of the Age of Engineering were well and truly laid.

As we have seen, the first and most important technical problems which the merchant called upon the engineer to solve were connected with shipping and transport. By the end of the fifteenth century, commercial enterprise had already progressed so far that there was a famine in gold ; there was not enough money to go round. Hence a big incentive to our American expansion on the one hand, and on the other, a focussing of attention on the problems of mining and metallurgy. War, moreover, early became highly technicalised, a matter for the engineer, and brought about a great development of iron and copper mining.

Thus one of the earliest and greatest of engineering advances was in mining. The cutting of galleries in the mines alone demands high skill and knowledge. By the end of the fifteenth century, there were scientific engineers at work in the mines, and since, as the mines were deepened, the problem of removing water arose, there were already sixteen known water-raising machines, worked by horse and mule, wind and water-power. Smelting furnaces, stamping mills and machinery for dividing metals were also at work.

THE LOOMS START: INDUSTRY AWAKENS

DURING the next centuries, all the elements for the enormous technological expansion which was to take place during the nineteenth and twentieth centuries were being amassed, rather than organised or understood. Weaving and spinning developed early on a technical basis, and by the eighteenth century had also progressed fairly far beyond the individual handicraft stage in industrial organisation. Hargreaves' " spinning-jenny " had been superseded by Arkwright's " mule." The threads spun by Hargreaves' machine were not sufficiently tough and hard to be used except as weft, and only twenty or thirty of them could be spun at a time. Arkwright's " mule " could spin any number of threads of any degree of toughness and durability.

Land and water ways of communication were also developing and by about 1820, as we find from the notes of a German visitor to this country, the English highway system was an example to the rest of the world. He speaks of driving in a mail-coach along the " magnificent and perfectly level highways, swiftly and without any vibration." It is only reasonable, however, to suppose, after experience even of the latest versions of the London motor-bus, that tolerance of physical discomfort was high in those days. Also by about 1830, the British canal system was complete. Better distribution of the coal which was becoming essential to all industries was the main object in the construction of this fairly intricate system. Altogether, an angel looking out of heaven in the early years of the nineteenth century to study the map of England would have found the country a busy and complicated organism. But being gifted with foresight, he would perhaps have noticed a certain placidity, a brooding quality in the landscape. What was lacking ?

If we glance back at some of the inventions we have mentioned : pumps, spinning jennies, looms and so on, we see that these reached a high degree of complication while the energy that worked them was still mechanical—in the strict sense of the word. The early engines were worked by pushing and pulling done by horses, wind or water, instead of men, or by some relatively simple technique of multiplying hand and foot labour, as in Hargreaves' spinning-jenny, patented in 1770, which span twenty to thirty threads with the labour previously required for one. The machine in these cases was only a glorified hand tool, the amount of work it could produce being only a recognisable multiple of the work done by the woman at her solitary spinning wheel, or the man at his pick and shovel.

COAL AND STEAM : THE NEW PROMETHEANS

WIND and water are at best staid and unimaginative servants of the craftsman. What a difference when the new industrial Prometheus brought down fire ! The application of steam-power to mechanised production was the next big advance in the revolution in industry, and an absolute change in principle.

If I can multiply the strength of my own hand and arm, or of my horse, or of the wind, by distributing the effort over a structure of wood and metal, there is nothing in principle so very new or surprising about this ; but if I can persuade the demon of fire to enter into a relationship with water or air or both, in which no apparent effort is involved and to which I stand passive, there *is* something new and remarkable about this ; a real transformation of one kind of energy, heat, into another, mechanical movement. Of course the thing not only seems outside my control, it *is* outside, at present, as we see from the course which productive civilisation has taken. Thermal energy, in the form of fire, took charge of industry for us, and produces all the goods and services which we need, with the utmost generosity ; but it leaves the difficult problem of sharing these goods for us to solve.

The detailed development of the application of power to industry will be traced for you in other parts of this book. Naturally there was no sudden complete transformation. The eighteenth century was a period of transition in which old forms of production were being used side by side with the latest technical devices. Indeed, until 1830, no single British industry had passed through a complete technical revolution, not even the weaving and spinning industry, which, after mining, was technically the most developed. For instance, while there were about fourteen steam-loom factories in Manchester, Salford and Middleton in 1818, in 1824 there were still plenty of wooden spinning-jennies turned by hand in the Lancashire mills.

The application of engineering technique to industry throughout the whole of the eighteenth century was in fact departmental, chiefly because demands were constantly changing. The primary metallurgical industries had nearly completed the first of their technical revolutions by 1825–30, that is, all blast-furnaces were worked by steam by that date, although no farther back than 1788 there had still been 26 of the old charcoal furnaces operating in Great Britain.

THE WEB OF STEEL IS SPUN

THE main reason for this rapid progress was a long sustained demand for munitions during the Napoleonic wars. It is interesting to note that during the eighteenth century the iron foundry was almost identified with the casting of cannon ; but after 1830, experiment in the civil uses of iron was greatly extended—in the new gas and water mains, in cables and bridging material and, very importantly, in railways. The production of steel rails, an essential step in railway engineering, needed considerable experiment. As late as 1770–80, Sheffield itself, inseparably associated with steel production in most of our minds, was importing its fine steel from Germany. Its own production was limited to a sort known as " blister " steel. The appearance which gave this steel its nickname was caused by the irregular absorption of carbon.

The first perfectly uniform steel was produced by Benjamin Huntsman, a Sheffield worker, in 1740. However, the railway industry did not have to wait for the steel rail, but received a notable technical impetus from the perfecting of wrought iron rails. The use of wooden and cast-iron rails was the weakest spot in railway development in the eighteenth and early nineteenth centuries, since they lacked the toughness and durability which would make the railroad a cheap means of transport for heavy goods over long distances. The railroad, in fact, which began as an accessory to the coal-pit, for a long time lagged behind the canal as an important means of inland transport. It is amusing to reflect when one watches the leisurely progress of a horse along a tow-path, that this is the speed at which our great-grandfathers were still content to receive their goods and raw materials.

For in spite of Stephenson's triumph at the Rainhill locomotive trials, expert opinion of the industrial importance of the locomotive steam-engine was and remained low. At Rainhill it appeared that a locomotive engine could only save 30% of cost. " Not 30%," wrote the gloomy Galloway in 1830, in his work On The Steam-Engine, " and that on a line

made to carry coals, where fuel costs would be negligible."
The alternative to a locomotive engine, we may add, was an
engine hauled to its destination by a cable. Galloway continued in a circumstantial and convincing way :

> " These locomotive engines have been long in use at
> Killingworth. But notwithstanding the great exertions on
> the part of the inventor, Mr. Stephenson . . . there cannot
> be a better proof of the doubts entertained regarding their
> utility, than the fact that it has been determined that no
> locomotive engine shall be used on the projected railway
> between Newcastle and Carlisle."

Mr. Galloway was wrong. By 1835, locomotives were pretty
well established on the new public railways, and by 1843 there
were 1,900 miles of finished line in Great Britain. In another
five years nearly as much line was equipped with the electric
telegraph, with which the Great Western railway had decided
to experiment.

THE BIRTH OF MODERN ENGINEERING

THESE are a few examples of how engineering technique
hastened the development of specialised industries. What
factors were lacking to complete the transformation of society
from one in which individual man-power and its extensions
were of major importance, to one in which the guarantee of
the foundation of material life should be the technique of
the engineer ?

First of all, the engineer himself had to evolve. The
eighteenth century never quite made up its mind what it
meant by an engineer. For a long time he was little more
than a pump-maker. In a work called the *London Tradesman*,
published about 1750, the author, Campbell, defines a millwright as an ordinary craftsman who needs less money to set
up in business than a plumber (though actually men like
Brindley, a millwright making 3s. 6d. a day and Telford, a
stonemason, created the profession of civil engineer as we
know it to-day). Campbell, however, had the germ of a
notion of what we mean by a mechanical engineer. He says :

> " The Engineer makes Engines for raising of Water
> by Fire, either for supplying Reservoirs or draining Mines.
> . . . The Engineer requires a very mechanically turned
> Head. . . . He employs Smiths of various sorts, Founders
> for his Brass-work and a Class of Shoemakers for making

his Leather Pipes. He requires a large Stock (i.e. Capital) to set up with and a considerable acquaintance among the Gentry. . . . He ought to have a solid not a flighty Head, otherwise his Business will tempt him to many useless and expensive Projects. The Workmen . . . earn from fifteen to twenty shillings a week and the Foreman of a Shop who understands finishing of the common Engines, may earn much more."

It is worth mentioning that in these little " Shops " of the makers of " Fire " or Steam-engines, steam was not employed. Matthew Boulton, who partnered the famous James Watt in making boilers at Glasgow, was advanced, before 1770, in using water-driven plant.

A NEW SPECIALIST APPEARS TO MAKE THE MACHINES

THIS brings us to the next great step in developing the equipment of an engineering world. Till the first decades of the nineteenth century, manufacturers made their own machinery as they required it. The first wooden textile machinery was made to order by a variety of mechanics, loom-makers, clock-makers, cabinet-makers. By about 1830, the mechanical engineer, as we know him, the professional purveyor of machines made with the help of other machines, was coming into existence. Soon afterwards, just as the eighteenth century had to make up its mind as to what it meant by an engineer, the nineteenth century had to decide what it meant by a " tool." There is an explicit reference to this problem in the Report of the Select Parliamentary Committee of 1841, on the *Export of Machinery*, which redefined a tool for the benefit of the gentlemanly non-technical intelligence of honourable members.

Clearly by this time a tool was very much more than the extension of a man's right hand. A situation, as we know, must be well developed before it receives the official notice of a Parliamentary Committee. We must therefore suppose that the modern phase in engineering when anything from a hundred-ton press to a gimlet is called a " tool " in the shops, was well begun by this time.

The work of Bramah, known as the universal inventor (he invented, among other things, the hydraulic press, the publican's pull-over bar-room tap, and the water-closet) may be considered as the starting-point of this latest and very important development of engineering. He lived during the last

half of the eighteenth century and the first years of the nineteenth, beginning as a cabinet-maker. He devised a set of
machine-tools to make the locks which he had invented.
With Henry Maudslay, one of the earliest " big " London
engineers, that is, employer of relatively large numbers of
people, he also evolved a heavy screw-cutting lathe. But
Richard Roberts, one of Maudslay's mechanics who was to
do important work in developing the machine-tool, and who
arrived in Manchester in 1816, tells us that the " whole of
the Machinery was executed by hand." A great change took
place during Roberts' lifetime in Manchester. Fairbairn,
during the next twenty years, we are told, built up a firm
which would turn you out an equipped mill " for any price,
trade, site or motive power."

THE BEGINNINGS OF STANDARDISATION

THE real difficulty in large-scale production of machinery
was the lack of instruments of precision, and therefore
of standardisation of manufacture. About 1830, a new idea
was introduced when Roberts made standard templates
(patterns of gauges, usually of thin board or metal plate,
used as guides in cutting or drilling metal, wood, etc.) to help
his workmen in reproducing the parts of his automatic spin-
ning-mule. We may add a note on the origin and the commercial success of this spinning-machine. In 1825, the
spinners struck in Manchester. Roberts' self-acting mule
which, of course, still further cut the necessary man-power,
was the employers' answer ; and it was the brisk demand for
duplicates of his machine which turned Roberts' attention
to the problem of producing standard parts.

In 1833, another of Maudslay's mechanics, Joseph Whitworth, set up in a small way in Manchester, and in his spare
time engaged in the work of perfecting measurements and
precision in engineering by means of surface plates and of
gauges. Though standardisation, of course, was still a long
way off, Whitworth proposed a " system by which uniformity
would be secured in the dimension and fitting of machinery
and especially with regard to screws : fixing thus their exact
diameters and pitch—a process which would have the effect
of making the construction, application and repair of all work
into which screws enter, vastly more expeditious than it now
is." Nowadays, Whitworth's system is world-wide, and
standardisation is so highly developed, that not only articles

of comparative complication such as sparking-plugs for cars and bases for wireless valves are at least nationally standardised, but also British and American standard specifications are drawn up for all sorts of raw materials, steel, rubber, paper and so on.

The modern phase of industry, as we have indicated, depended on the establishment of the machine-tool and of the mechanical engineer proper. He is the man who designs the plant which manufactures the tools which produce and pack the brands of articles, the tinned foods, patent medicines, motor-cars and wireless sets, our necessities or luxuries ; he is in fact the Jack who builds and furnishes the unstable house of our civilisation. As the machine and the machine-tool grew and became standardised, so the organisation of people in industry developed and altered. While men had to make their machines with their own hands, the personal element remained in industry. Man was still more important than the machine. The machine was a Robot which had not learnt its power. It was less automatic, needing an initial push from its master and creator to get going : a mysterious, helpless and erratic object. If it went wrong it might require the day and night attention of several mechanics to put it right. Meanwhile production was held up.

Again, because there was little standardisation and plant was evolved to fit new and growing needs, mechanics were organised in small units. Production was not far removed from the handicraft basis, and the relation between the employer and his mechanics seems to have remained personal and to some extent patriarchal. In the early part of last century the largest employment figures in England were the 140–150 men employed by Herves of Manchester. Power, as we have said, was little used.

THE ENGINEER CAUGHT IN THE COMPLEX MODERN SYSTEM

As we have perfected standardisation, opened up new sources of power in electricity and oil, approached in fact nearer and nearer to perfecting the automatism of the machine, the factory-worker has dwindled in individual importance. He has become more and more an abstract of his own labour-power, more and more the slave of a conveyor belt. What has been the effect of this development on the engineer himself, the man who, because of his greater degree of technical skill and education, still remains something of a personality in industry ? Certainly it has not left him untouched. He is usually working for a salary, and so his position is only a few degrees less precarious than the unskilled worker's. But he is in a peculiarly strong position to form a reliable opinion of economic society, for he combines close contact with actual workshop conditions with his necessary high degree of technical education, an education which of its very nature must develop the abstract and logical powers of the mind.

So we do find that engineers are beginning to be disturbed both at the uses and the limitations that are being imposed upon their researches and techniques. On the one hand we have the human and therefore unwilling engineer tied by a wage to the production of armaments and poison gas. On the other he is headed off the exploration of some technique which might benefit humanity, because there is no immediate prospect of profit, or because his employers have to consider law costs in respect of possible infringement of patents. For the patent situation, an outcrop of the competitive system, is by now so much involved that it is understood only by the expert few.

There is much in the present system which is unnatural and disproportionate and which therefore contains the seeds of its own decay. The same criticism, many people think, applies to the social and economic system which we have sketched for you in so far as it bears upon the present position in engineering and still conditions its development.

LOOKING FORWARDS : WHAT MAY THE WORLD BECOME?

WE have traced the development of this social and economic system, and shown how it is the explanation of the question asked at the beginning of this section—Why did engineering develop as it did ? Why were the last two centuries of all this history of mankind marked out for its sudden, its almost explosive burst of energy ? To the further question— What is the immediate future of our engineering age ?—no detailed answer could be given that might not be contradicted in one week by a startling new development.

In our world of telephones and aeroplanes it is becoming difficult for us to imagine the mental outlook of the seventeenth-century poet who found it natural to write a *Valediction forbidding Mourning* to his wife, when he went to the Continent. We might go so far as to say that the engineer has largely transformed our emotional habits. It is probable that the average human being never at any other time experienced the feeling of security as we learnt it in England during the nineteenth century. Certainly the war and post-war years have taught us all that it was in many ways a false security, that for the less prosperous classes it was near to being a total illusion. But even so, think what such a phrase as the " expectation of life " means now and what it would have meant during the fourteenth century, the century of the Black Death in Europe.

Let us ignore for the moment the bad habits of the machine, its capacity when mishandled and misdirected for dealing death through war and unemployment, and realise the kind of world the engineer *could* create for the average human being.

Given a free hand, the engineer could, in the very near future, supply production and medical science with a technical and chemical basis so developed that the average human being could be born into this world with a legitimate sense of security. His " expectation of life," that is, could exclude three-quarters of our average human fears, disease, starvation, immature death, lifelong separation from friends and kin ; and include a high and guaranteed share of bread, milk, meat, foreign fruits, travel, music, thought, experience and bricks and mortar, for himself and his children. Need we scoff at the kind of civilisation this could mean, or be sceptical of new capacities for freedom even if they are based on telephones, aeroplanes, radio, combine harvesters, and cold storage ?

In the pages which follow, you will be given some idea of the actual working of this complex engineering world of ours which re-presents every moment and department of our lives, and you will see what a vast and interesting material is being collected by technical man as a basis for reconstruction and progress.

BUILDING THE MODERN WORLD:
THE CIVIL ENGINEER AT WORK

by B. G. MANTON, B.Sc.(Eng.), A.M.Inst.C.E., D.I.C.

THE field of work covered by the civil engineer, including the contracting work of railway companies and builders, road, rail, bridge and irrigation schemes of governments and municipal authorities, water supply, sewage disposal and many other activities to which the civil engineer applies his knowledge, is all based on certain fundamentals which are dealt with in the pages which follow.

Surveying is, of course, necessary before any road, rail, or irrigation scheme can be carried out in uncharted country; all building depends on a sound understanding of the theory of structures and structural design, whilst irrigation and drainage schemes, sea defences and docks, lock construction and water supply are based on the knowledge of the action of liquids under all conditions to which they may be subjected. Thus, the civil engineer, equipped with the theory which underlies all his work, is ready to apply that theory to the problems he is called upon to solve, be they as widely different as the erection of a huge bridge and the building of a reservoir.

The first essentials in any engineering project are (1) a reliable survey plan on which is shown every detail of the natural and artificial features of the area, or, in other words, " topography," and (2) a set of drawings known as " sections " which illustrate the changes in level of the ground and the depths of rivers or of the sea near the shore-line. These vitally necessary plans and sections are drawn from the data obtained by the so-called " fieldwork " of surveying and levelling.

We are fortunate, in the British Isles, in having available a complete set of excellent maps drawn to sufficiently large scales to be useful in scheming the preliminary general arrangement for many kinds of civil engineering works, such as new arterial roads and water-supply and sewerage projects, but before definite proposals and estimates can be produced it becomes necessary to have plans of an even larger scale. Thus, the largest map obtainable for general use has a scale of about 25 inches to 1 mile and a road with a width of 30 feet appears, on this scale, about an eighth of an inch wide, all the topographical details being shown to one twenty-five hundredth of their real size. But for the working drawings for, let us say, a new by-pass, the scale adopted would be fully 40 feet to 1 inch, in which case a 30-foot road would appear with a width of three-quarters of an inch.

There are still many parts of the world which have not yet been accurately surveyed at all, and the work involved in obtaining the map of an entire country is somewhat different in character to that required for preparing large-scale plans of the comparatively limited area covered by some such engineering scheme as a by-pass road. In the former case, for example, the curvature of the surface of the earth must be allowed for, whereas in the latter case, the earth is treated as a flat plane, so far as the plan is concerned, although the local undulations are, of course, shown on the sectional drawings.

THE SURVEYOR'S FIRST STEP: MEASUREMENT OF LENGTHS

THE surveyor's implements for measuring lengths are tapes and chains. The former are made of thin steel for accurate work and of linen, interwoven with very fine wire, for rough-and-ready work. Linen tapes change in length according to the humidity of the atmosphere, they easily stretch and are frequently several inches wrong in a length of 100 feet—the recognised length of the largest tapes, 66 and 50 feet being other common sizes. Chains are constructed of straight sections of steel wire, about an eighth of an inch thick, turned round at the ends into small loops and connected together by steel rings. A brass handle is fitted to each of the terminal sections and the full length of the chain is taken to the outside of the handles. The usual length for engineering surveys is 100 feet, but a second chain, known as the Gunter, is also used to a certain extent and this has a length of 66 feet. In either case, the chain consists of one hundred sections, each one foot long in the engineer's chain, and in the Gunter chain, ·66 of a foot, or nearly 8 inches long.

The Gunter chain provides an interesting example of the lengthy survival of old ideas. Gunter, a land surveyor, invented his chain several centuries ago and it is to him that we owe the lineal measurements of the " chain " and the " link," the former being one-eightieth of a mile, or a tenth of a furlong, and the " link " being one-hundredth part of a " chain." Chains are marked at 10 foot or 10 link intervals by pointed brass tags, the number of points indicating the distance. Thus, both 10 and 90 feet are represented by a tag with one point, 20 and 80 by two points, 30 and 70 by three points and 40 and 60 by four points. The 50-foot mark at the centre of the chain is a special round tag. This peculiar arrangement renders the chain reversible, end for end.

THE FIRST ESSENTIAL ACCURACY IN STARTING A SURVEY

THE highest degree of accuracy in lineal measuring is called for in determining the length of the " base line " used in surveying a very large area. This line may be several miles long—that used for finding the difference in the geographical positions of the Royal Observatories at Greenwich and Paris, for instance, ran from Hounslow to Hampton, in Middlesex, and was 5 miles long. Its measurement took five months to accomplish, in the year 1784, when that part of West Middlesex was a vast open space.

The accuracy of the whole survey depends upon the precision of the base measurement and the work, nowadays, is usually carried out with an Invar [1] tape or wire, since this material changes in length only very slightly with changes of temperature. The tape or wire is strained over supports and allowed to hang freely in between, and a calculated allowance is made both for the small amount of stretch due to the pull and for the shortening caused by the sag. Any metal measuring instrument, strictly speaking, gives its standard length only at one particular temperature, the standard figure usually recognised being 62 degrees Fahrenheit. If it is used at temperatures different from this, in such accurate work as base measurement, a correction has to be applied. When every possible precaution is taken and the proceedings stopped in unfavourable weather, it is estimated that the accuracy can be as high as 1 part in half-a-million, that is, the error would be only 1 inch in 8 miles.

MEASURING ANGLES IN UNITS TOO SMALL TO SEE

ONLY very small surveys can be carried out entirely by the use of lineal measurements and angular measurements become essential in all other cases. For this purpose the surveyor uses a " theodolite," [2] an apparatus consisting of a short telescope, with a vertical circular plate fastened to one side, mounted on a support attached to a pair of hori-

[1] See p. 71.   [2] For full description see p. 35.

zontal circular plates, which fit one over the other and are both capable of free rotation. The whole instrument screws on to the head of a tripod stand so that it is brought to a convenient height for taking observations through the telescope. Both the vertical and horizontal circles are graduated in degrees and fractions of a degree to enable angles to be read in both vertical and horizontal planes.

Angles are measured in degrees, minutes of arc and seconds of arc, and instruments intended for ordinary everyday use will give a reading to the nearest 20 or 30 seconds. Some idea of this accuracy may be obtained by imagining a circle, of any diameter, divided into 360 equal parts by lines radiating from the centre. The angles enclosed between each of the lines will be 1 degree. Next divide each of the angles between the radiating lines into 60 equal parts. The invisibly small angles produced by this sub-division will each be 1 minute. By a further sub-division of each of these angles into thirds we get angles of 20 seconds each, or by splitting each minute into halves we get angles of 30 seconds. Such fine readings could not be obtained, of course, by direct visual means from a graduated circle in the same manner that one can read inches on a foot-rule, but a simple device is adopted which is well known in other spheres of engineering, namely the " vernier."

ADAPTING THE RULER TO FINER MEASUREMENT

THE vernier consists of a short graduated scale which slides over a second scale, the edges being adjacent, and the latter, which may be termed the " main scale," may be graduated in any required units—possibly inches and tenths, if the scale is an ordinary straight one, or in degrees and half-degrees if it is circular, like those on a theodolite.

The short sliding scale, called the " vernier scale," is so graduated, however, that any given number of divisions on it, say " n," are equal in length to " $n-1$ " divisions on the main scale.

Thus, for purposes of demonstration, we may imagine a main scale graduated in inches and a vernier scale graduated so that 10 divisions equal in length 9 on the lower scale. When these two scales are placed together so that their zero marks coincide, we get the arrangement shown at the top of Fig. 1. It will be noticed that corresponding graduations

B   2

get more and more out of step and it is evident that each division on the vernier scale is nine-tenths of an inch wide. Thus, the two lines marked " 1 " are separated by one-tenth of an inch, those marked " 2 " by two-tenths, those marked " 3 " by three-tenths, and so on, until the two marked " 10 " are separated by a full inch.

Suppose, now, that the upper scale is slid along until it arrives at some position such as that shown in the lower part of Fig. 1. The length of travel is obviously 5 inches plus the distance XY and the latter could be guessed, by eye, to be about seven-eighths of an inch, but the upper scale enables the exact measurement to be read off. If we run along

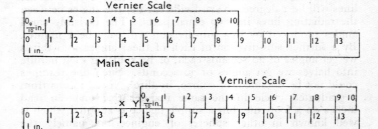

1. How the vernier scale aids accurate measurement. The coincidence of 9 on the vernier scale with a division on the main scale shows that XY is ·9 inches.

the upper scale it will be noticed that all the graduations are out of step with those of the lower scale with one—and only one—exception—that of the " 9," which falls exactly in line with the " 13." Now working backwards, from right to left, it will be apparent that the successive graduations are out of step by amounts increasing steadily by a tenth of an inch every time.

Thus " 8 " and " 12 " are separated by one-tenth, " 7 " and " 11 " by two-tenths, " 6 " and " 10 " by three-tenths and so on, until we discover that the " 0 " and the " 5 " are nine-tenths apart, i.e. the number of tenths here is the same as the number of the only graduation on the upper scale in which perfect alignment occurs with a graduation on the lower scale. Hence the distance XY is ·9 of an inch, or the reading of the combined scales at this particular setting is 4·9. We have been enabled, therefore, to obtain a reading to a tenth of an inch, although the main scale divisions were not finer than single inches.

This is the working principle of the vernier, but in practice, of course, such coarse graduations as inches would not be used. By having our main scale divided into tenths of inches, however, and using a suitable vernier scale, we could read to hundredths.

THE SURVEYOR'S FIRST ASSISTANT : THE ACCURATE THEODOLITE

TURNING again to the theodolite, its main constructional features must now be considered, in order that the application of the vernier method of reading may be explained.

Fig. 2 is a diagrammatic sketch of an instrument denuded of all superfluous details. The telescope, 6 to 8 inches long, is mounted at the apex of a triangular frame resembling the letter " A," in such a way that it can tilt up or down about a horizontal axis. The " A " frame is attached rigidly to a circular plate, known as the upper plate, of from 4 to 6 inches in diameter, and this plate has, on its underside, a central tapering, or conical, projection, R, which is an extremely accurate fit in a corresponding conical hole in the cylindrical portion, S, formed on the underside of a second circular plate, known as the lower plate and fitted immediately below the first. The lower plate has another tapering projection, V, which fits precisely in a tapered hole in the underframe, T, and the latter is supported by three radiating arms, X, each one of which has an adjustable levelling screw, L, threaded through it at its outer end. These screws have ball ends which fit into sockets in the base-plate, Y, attached to the tripod stand.

The two plates form a vital part of the instrument. They should rotate independently, but in close contact, and with perfect smoothness. They have bevelled edges, to which are attached finely graduated silver scales, the upper plate carrying two short vernier scales at diametrically opposite positions on its circumference and the lower plate having a continuously graduated circle right round. The divisions on the latter may be degrees and halves, or degrees and thirds, and the verniers are suitably divided to give the further extent of accuracy down to half minutes or twenty seconds.

Clamps are provided for locking the upper plate to the

lower and for locking the lower plate to the underframe of the instrument, so that three possible settings are obtainable :

(1) The lower plate may be locked so that it will not rotate and the upper plate may be clamped to the lower. The instrument will then be held stationary.

(2) The lower plate may be kept locked to the underframe, but the upper may be released, so that it will rotate freely over the lower.

(3) The upper and lower plates may be clamped together and the lower one freed from the underframe. The two plates will then rotate together.

THE FINEST SIGHTING-LINE—A SPIDER'S WEB !

SPIRIT levels are attached to the upper plate, so that the instrument may be levelled up by the screws, L, and the telescope is fitted with a " diaphragm " at the eye-piece end, nearest to the observer, which carries the so-called " cross hairs." Actually " cross-hairs" are never hairs, but are, somewhat surprisingly, more often spider's webs. This material has been found to provide the finest possible sighting line, combined with adequate strength. It must be remembered that the eye-piece of the telescope acts as a powerful magnifier and the finest silk thread, or similar fibre, when viewed through it would appear to have an extremely rough and ragged edge. The diaphragm, if of the web type, consists merely of a brass ring with the webs stretched across it and cemented on with shellac.

Another form of diaphragm consists of a similar ring fitted with a thin glass plate on which very fine sighting lines are etched. A favourite arrangement of lines is shown in Fig. 2 and consists of two verticals, placed close together, and three equidistant horizontals. The former are used for sighting on to a distant marking rod, the familiar type with white, black and red bands being employed for distances up to 3,000 or 4,000 feet, although longer sights may be taken if the background is suitable. The three horizontal lines are known as the " stadia hairs " and are used for determining distances by sighting on to a graduated staff.

MEASURING LENGTHS BY OBSERVING HEIGHTS

THE principle of this method of obtaining lengths without actually measuring them out on the ground depends upon the fact that the lines of sight passing through the two outer

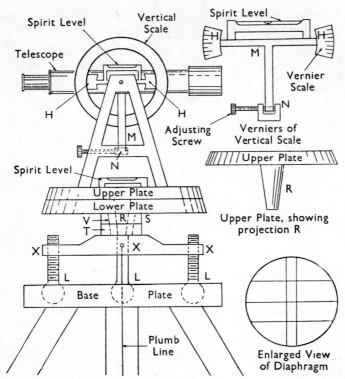

2. *The theodolite, which the surveyor uses for the accurate measurement of angles. Special parts are shown in greater detail on the right. The telescope is from 6 to 8 inches long ; the two plates rotate independently, but in close contact.*

horizontal cross-hairs diverge more and more as they travel farther and farther from the instrument, and thus they cut off greater and greater lengths on the graduated staff when viewed through the telescope, in the manner indicated in Fig. 3.

The theodolite also has a vertical circle (Fig. 2) attached rigidly to the side of the telescope, so that when the latter is tilted up or down, the circle moves round with it. Two short vernier scales, HH, are mounted on the upper arms of a

T-piece, M, so that they are in close contact with the vertical circle and the centre arm of the T-piece is carried down to a clip, N, attached to the " A " frame. An adjusting screw is provided in conjunction with this clip, and a spirit-level is fitted to the upper arm, so that the verniers may be set horizontally.

Exactly in the centre of the underside of the instrument is a hook to which a plumb-line is attached for setting up exactly over any given point or " station." Stations are often marked on the ground by wooden pegs about an inch square and a foot long, driven in firmly and having a

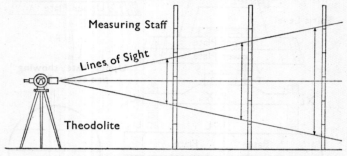

3. By sighting lengths on a graduated staff with the theo-dolite, the surveyor is able to find the distance of the staff without measuring it on the ground.

small nail driven into the top to provide an exact reference mark.

Instruments intended for the highest possible degree of accuracy will read to a single second, and a circle would have to be divided into 1,296,000 parts to produce angles of this size at the centre. These super-accurate instruments are exactly the same as the vernier type in general principles and design, except that the horizontal plates are usually larger, 8- and 10-inch diameters being common, and the verniers are replaced by micrometers.

A SCREW WHICH MEASURES TO ONE THOUSANDTH OF AN INCH

THE general idea of the micrometer may be best explained by picturing a screw, with a very fine and accurately cut thread, working in a nut. The end of the screw is fitted with a disc, and a fixed pointer is mounted in close contact with its rim, by some such device as that shown in Fig. 4. One complete revolution of the disc will move the screw forward in the nut by a distance equal to the screw's pitch, i.e. the spacing apart of its threads. Suppose, for instance, that the pitch is a fortieth of an inch, then one complete turn of the disc will move the end of the screw that distance. But if the rim of the disc is divided into twenty - five equal parts, and we move it by only one division, the end

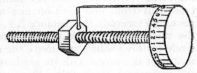

4. The principle of the micrometer, which measures $1/1000$ th inch.

of the screw will move by only one twenty-fifth of a fortieth of an inch, or by one thousandth of an inch. Here, then, is a method of measuring accurately a dimension far too small to be visible on an ordinary scale or foot-rule.

The application of this device to the theodolite may, perhaps, be understood from Fig. 5, where A represents the

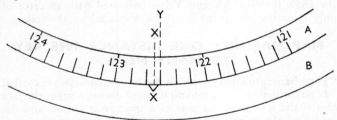

5. How an angle is registered by the notch X in the lower plate B of the theodolite. The distance XY on the upper plate A is measured accurately by a micrometer.

upper plate of the instrument and B the lower. In the case of micrometer instruments, the upper plate is continuously graduated round the entire circle and the lower plate is plain except for two small notches, cut at diametrically opposite points on the rim. X is one of these notches and provides the reference mark for taking a reading. In the diagram, the numerals represent degrees and each degree will be seen to be sub-divided into 6 parts, so that each short graduation represents 10 minutes.

At the setting shown, the notch is reading 122 degrees

30 minutes plus the small additional portion XY. Now just above each of the notches, an appliance is fitted known as a " micrometer eye-piece," comprising a tiny microscope and a movable cross-hair, the travel of which is regulated by a screw, provided with a graduated disc similar to that already described. One complete revolution of this disc carries the cross-hair from one division line on the upper plate to the next. To ascertain the distance XY, therefore, we look through the microscope (which renders the fine graduations on the circle plainly visible) and move the cross-hair from X to Y by means of the screw with its graduated disc, and the extent of the movement is given by the number of divisions through which the disc is turned.

The need for the very high degree of accuracy associated with theodolite work may be appreciated when it is remembered that the lines of sight may be several miles long and a small error in reading the angle between two such lines will result in quite a considerable difference in the real and apparent positions of the distant points. Thus, suppose X, Y, Z are three surveying stations, and that YZ is 1 mile long. If the angle between XY and YZ is measured with an error of only 1 minute, the point Z will be displaced by 18 inches.

MAP MAKING : ONE DISTANCE THE KEY TO MANY MORE

THE basic principle on which the largest surveys are carried out is that of " triangulation " and depends upon the fact that if the length of one side of a triangle is known and the angles of the figure are measured, the lengths of the other sides may be calculated. Thus, if we know the length of AB, in Fig. 6, and all the angles of the triangle ABC, the lengths of AC and BC can be calculated. If we next measure the angles of the triangle CDB, we can calculate its remaining two sides from the length of BC and this process may be continued indefinitely, being extended across a continent, if need be, and the distances between all the points can be determined, although no actual lineal measurements are made beyond the length AB. This would be the " base-line " and a suitable area of country would be chosen, fairly flat and free from obstructions, to facilitate its accurate measurement.

In practice, a second, or " check " base would be measured at some distance from the first and its calculated length, derived from the angular measurements, would be compared with the actual length. This method of triangulation enables a survey to be carried across the sea, within the limits of visibility, and one such triangle was carried across from Britain to Ireland, thus linking the surveys of the two countries, one length running from Wicklow to Pembroke, a distance of 107 miles.

Triangles on this scale, however, cannot be treated as plane figures with straight sides, but are really " spherical triangles," the sides of which follow the curvature of the earth, but the fundamental principle is the same. A survey based on spherical triangles is classified as " geodetic."

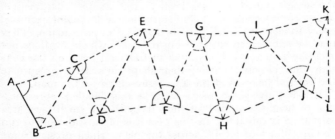

6. " Triangulation " : how the surveyor maps out an area by measuring the base line AB and a succession of angles at A, B, C, D, etc.

The large main triangulation is sub-divided into smaller triangles, which, in turn, are again sub-divided until we at length get to the small surveys needed to obtain the positions of houses, roads, railways, rivers and other topographical objects.

THE UPS AND DOWNS OF MAP-MAKING

BY the methods described, it is possible to construct a map of considerable detail, but so far no account has been taken of the changes of level in the ground. The constructed map represents a plan of the ground reduced to one level. For most practical purposes, however, this is useless. In civil life the portrayal of relief is of value for numerous purposes, from such mundane things as drains to denoting panoramas likely to attract the tourist.

The road and railway engineers are deeply interested in the matter of gradients. The modern road designer does not share the magnificent disregard for relief that was characteristic of his Roman predecessor, but has to compromise between gradients and directness, while the railway engineer, in the British Isles at least, is fettered by the fact that gradients steeper than one in a hundred, or preferably one in two hundred, will raise his running costs above the economic limit. Hence a map, if it is to be of any practical value, must show vertical distance as well as horizontal.

In order to make a thorough representation of the relief of the land, it is necessary to construct a complete series of contour lines. These are lines drawn on the map to represent imaginary lines in the field linking up all places which are of the same height above sea level or the assumed datum line. These are interpolated at convenient intervals, as, for example, every 10 feet for a small plan, or 100 feet for large maps. They may be supplemented by " Form lines," which are lines not accurately surveyed but drawn in freehand between the contour lines, closely following their shape, in order to accentuate the vertical features of the area represented on the map.

It is not always necessary to make this detailed representation of height, especially if the survey is of a small local area or if time is valuable. In this case it is often sufficient to run certain " lines of level " across the plan, which present some idea of the general slope of the land for purposes of drainage, etc. The simplest method is by the surveyor's "Dumpy " level and staff.

A typical example of a " Dumpy " level is illustrated in Fig. 7. This is much simpler in construction than the theodolite and consists of a telescope, which may be 10 to 18 inches in length, carrying a long spirit-level on the top, and mounted, through the medium of an accurately fitted spigot and socket bearing, upon a three- or four-armed frame. The latter is fitted with levelling screws, S, resting upon a plate attached to the tripod stand on which the instrument is placed when in use. The telescope can turn freely round and round in its bearing, but cannot tilt up and down in the same way as a theodolite, although slight tilting is, of course, produced if the levelling screws at the base are rotated and these are adjusted with great care until the spirit-level indicates that the telescope is horizontal, no matter to what position it may be turned.

A diaphragm, similar to that used in a theodolite, is fitted to the telescope at the eye-piece end, and observations

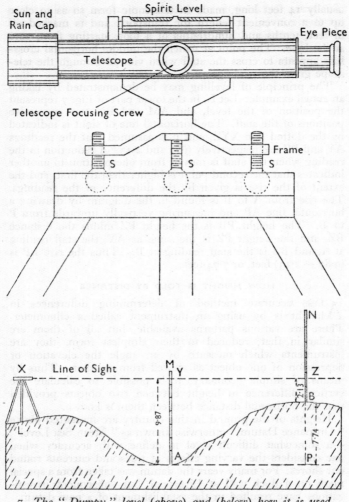

Sun and
Rain Cap

Spirit Level

Eye Piece

Telescope

Telescope Focusing Screw

Frame

S   S   S

N

X   Line of Sight   M   Y   Z

B

2·13

9·87

7·74

L   A   P

7. *The " Dumpy " level (above) and (below) how it is used
to sight ground levels by means of a graduated staff.*

are taken to a specially graduated staff held at the points
where the levels of the ground are required.   The staff is

usually 14 feet long, made in telescopic form so as to close up to a convenient length for transport, and is marked off in feet, tenths and hundredths of a foot, starting from zero at the base. The point at which the middle horizontal cross-hair appears to cross the staff when viewed through the telescope gives the reading.

The principle of levelling may be demonstrated by taking an actual example. Let L, in the lower part of Fig. 7 represent the position of the level, and AM and BN two successive positions of the staff. The horizontal line of sight is indicated by the dotted line XYZ, and it is assumed that the readings AY and BZ are respectively 9·87 and 2·13. A reduction in the reading when the staff is moved from one position to another indicates that the second point is higher than the first, and the extent of the rise is given by the difference of the readings. The rise from A to B is found in the diagram by drawing a horizontal line AP and measuring vertically upwards from P to B. The height PB is the height PZ minus the distance BZ, and the height PZ is the same as AY, the staff reading at A, and BZ is the staff reading at B. Thus the rise BP is (9·87 — 2·13) feet, or 7·74 feet.

HOW HEIGHT IS TOLD BY DISTANCE

A LESS accurate method of determining differences in height is by using an instrument called a clinometer. There are various patterns available, but all of them are similar in that, reduced to their simplest form, they are instruments which measure by an angle the elevation or depression of one object as viewed from another. Thus by means of simple geometry, it is possible to calculate the vertical difference in height between two objects provided that the horizontal distance between them is known.

Heights of the ground in this country are measured above " Ordnance Datum," otherwise known as " Mean Sea Level " —a somewhat difficult level to define with accuracy when one considers the varying effects of tides and currents round our shores. For many years the datum was taken from a special mark on a dock wall at Liverpool, but subsequent investigations have resulted in the establishment of a new datum.

The Ordnance surveyors have placed their official marks or " broad arrows " on large numbers of buildings, bridges, mile-stones, gate-posts and other objects in every part of the country, and these marks are cut into the brickwork, stone and timber and the location of each one is clearly defined on the large-scale Ordnance maps, namely those of either the 25 or 6 inch scales (25 or 6 inches to 1 mile). They are known as " Bench Marks " and are indicated on the maps by the letters " B.M." followed by a number. The latter is the height above sea-level of the short horizontal line which is always inscribed across the point, or top, of the arrow-shaped mark.

FINDING THE TRUE NORTH : THE ECCENTRICITIES OF THE MAGNETIC COMPASS

MAP-MAKING involves an accurate knowledge of the direction of north. The common implement for finding this direction is, of course, the magnetic compass but this does not show the true or geographical north—it points to magnetic north, being influenced by the north and south magnetic poles, which do not occupy the same positions as the north and south terrestrial or geographical poles. It is possible to apply a correction to the reading of the compass in order to find the true north, but this will not give a sufficient degree of precision for a geodetic survey. The difference in angle between the direction of magnetic north and the direction of any survey line is called the " magnetic bearing " of the line, and the angle between the magnetic north direction and the true north is termed " magnetic declination."

The compass exhibits a very remarkable and puzzling behaviour if its indications are carefully watched over a long period of time and it has been found that the declination varies from year to year and even very slightly from day to day. Roughly 300 years ago the compass, in England, pointed approximately in the true north direction—in fact, for a short period it gave a correct indication. Then it gradually deviated westwards until in 1816 the declination reached the figure of 24 degrees. This was followed by a gradual decrease, year by year, and by 1932 the difference between true and magnetic north was only about 13 degrees to the west. A small decrease, amounting to a few minutes annually, is still going on. The rate of decrease, however, is not constant and the declination differs for different localities on the earth's surface—it is not quite the same in the west of England as it is in London, for instance.

The compass is also rendered unreliable by the presence of masses of iron, steel, or even iron ores, in its vicinity ; and although every theodolite is equipped with a magnetic needle, its reading would be considerably deflected if the instrument were set up close to a large steel bridge, for instance, and in practice it is only used to give a preliminary reference direction which will enable a north-point to be placed on the plan with an accuracy of a degree or so.

THE GUIDING POLE STAR

FOR accurate work, and in all geodetic surveys, it is necessary to fix the direction of true north by taking observations, with a theodolite, of selected stars, and from data thus obtained it is possible to compute the angle between any line of the survey and an imaginary line on the earth's surface, known as the " meridian," which passes through the end of the survey line and also through the north and south poles. The angle between the survey line and the meridian is called the " azimuth " of the line.

The location of the meridian, that is, the line which gives the true north direction at any particular point, is often carried out by observing a star called " Polaris." If the imaginary line forming the earth's axis is prolonged beyond the north pole far into space, Polaris appears to describe a small circle round and round this line. It may be recognised in the sky by first locating the well-known group of stars known as the " Plough," or otherwise, the " Great Bear." The two stars forming the front of the " plough " form one straight line, if their directions are prolonged, with the Pole Star, or, to give it the classical name, Polaris, and when the telescope of the theodolite is centred exactly on to this star it will be pointing very nearly in the meridian plane. The precise amount of the discrepancy brought about by the fact that Polaris is not exactly over the pole, but circles round it, is capable of exact computation and the direction of the meridian fixed accordingly.

SIXTY-NINE YEARS TO MAKE A MAP : THE ORDNANCE SURVEY

" ORDNANCE maps " are very well known to the general public, but apart from the fact that they are issued by a somewhat mysterious Government department, and are very excellent and reliable productions, little seems to be known of the lengthy proceedings and the vast amount of labour involved in the " fieldwork " which had to be carried out before these maps could be prepared.

The work was officially commenced in 1791, by a branch of the military service known as the " Honourable Board of Ordnance," since merged into the Royal Engineers, and the original object was the production of a map of Great Britain and Ireland to the scale of 1 inch to 1 mile, no really accurate maps being then available. The survey was worked on the triangulation principle, the lines of the triangles being run between prominent points such as the towers of cathedrals, mountain tops, and other sites from which lengthy views were obtainable, and one such station was established on the dome of St. Paul's, special scaffolding and staging being erected to form a stand for the theodolite.

Two base lines were used, the first being measured on the shores of Lough Foyle and the second on Salisbury Plain— a third was measured as a check in 1909, in the neighbourhood of Lossiemouth, and from this it was estimated that the whole survey was accurate to within one inch in a mile, or, roughly, one in sixty-thousand. The average length of the sides of the triangles was 35 miles and some of the sights were carried out at night, using powerful lamps as reference marks. The work took no less a period than 69 years to complete.

In 1824, a survey of Ireland was authorised for the purpose of producing a series of maps to the scale of 6 inches to 1 mile, and sixteen years later it was decided to extend this survey to England and Scotland as well. These were the first " large-scale " maps produced by the Ordnance Survey and they show the boundaries of every field and each individual house.

A TRIUMPH OF SKILL AND ACCURACY : THE 25-INCH MAP

IN 1863, however, work was put in hand for even larger scale maps—the " 25-inch " variety in which every detail of the topography is shown one-twenty-five-hundredth of its real size. Thus, if we have a stretch of road 2,500 feet long, this will appear on the map one foot long. A mile of road will measure 25·344 inches, hence the popular term " 25-inch " by which these maps are described. They are extremely useful to civil and municipal engineers, and local authorities, such as County and Borough Councils, invariably possess a complete set covering their own districts. The scale is so large, however, that it would require 50,000 sheets to show the whole of Great Britain. On the 6-inch scale, 15,000 sheets would be needed.

Unfortunately, building and road developments progress at a faster rate than the revision of the Ordnance maps, so that in some areas they are very much out-of-date, but, apart from this, their accuracy and general excellence place them in the very front rank of cartographical publications.

THE AIRMAN'S CAMERA : A LIMITED HELP

THE aerial photographs which form a common feature of daily newspaper illustrations and are frequently used in advertisements to show to the fullest advantage the extent of a manufacturer's works, would naturally seem to be of utility for the production of survey plans, and it would not be unnatural to ask, " Cannot air photography supersede all these other elaborate methods of survey ? " At first the idea seems possible, but the more the question is studied, the more it becomes obvious that air photography cannot, as developed at present, be more than an adjunct to other forms of survey, unless under exceptional circumstances.

There is for instance the question of interpretation ; most air photographs which are on sale are adequately labelled so that there is little difficulty in understanding the nature of the country represented in the photograph. Air photographs, as a whole, are not easy to interpret, and such features as quarries, mounds, haystacks, pits, etc., require an experienced eye to explain. This difficulty partly arises because the aerial photograph represents a perspective plan of the ground which is likely to become distorted unless the camera is kept truly horizontal. In practice it is extremely difficult to ensure that the camera plate is perfectly horizontal, although it is possible to reduce the tilt to a very small minimum.

Various other distortions are also likely to occur which require great technical skill to eliminate. Moreover, the process of elimination necessitates the taking of at least two photographs from different angles of the same piece of ground, thereby increasing overhead charges considerably. It also involves certain measurements of heights which have to be taken by the ordinary field surveyor. Thus aerial survey is actually dependent on field surveying for its results.

COST AS A BARRIER TO AIR SURVEY

AERIAL photography is expensive. Aeroplanes are sensitive to weather conditions, and if flying is to be safe, weather observation stations have to be established and reports sent out to the various ground stations from which the survey planes start. Fuel may be a problem, and in the more remote districts, where air survey is most needed, fuel stations have to be set up, often at great cost. Such things as these mean that the overhead charges for aerial survey are considerable before the actual cameras are bought and before the plane leaves for its first trip.

It is an ideal method where the area to be surveyed is large and speed is an important factor. Reconnaissance work can often be carried out successfully from the air, and save much expense and preliminary survey work in the field. Useful work has been done in Northern Canada in this way, where maps were required speedily for purposes of exploitation and where accuracy was not a potent factor.

GROUND CONTROL TO ENSURE ACCURACY

WHEN accuracy is essential, it is necessary to establish an extensive and precise ground control. This consists of surveying a number of " fixed points " in the field by the ordinary methods. In regions such as the mouth of the Irrawaddy, where the river enters the sea by a myriad small distributaries, air survey has proved invaluable. Even here, the Survey of India was not content to risk error, and a ground control was established by surveyors working under conditions which were not only unhealthy, but wellnigh impossible.

The Sudd region of the Southern Sudan provides an excellent example of an area which, until the introduction of aerial survey, defied ordinary methods of map-making. Here it is possible, by the aid of air photographs, with a limited ground control, to obtain a fairly accurate survey of the region, with its swampy streamlets and scattered native settlements. Again air survey has been used with considerable success where rivers have had to be mapped with a view to studying their hydrology, either for purposes of navigation or irrigation, as for example in the case of the Zambesi and Nile rivers in Africa.

FORESTS WHICH HIDE THE FACE OF THE EARTH

IT is not, however, possible for air survey to solve the problem of map-making in all complicated regions. For instance, the difficulties of theodolite work when mapping the forest-clad creeks of the Amazon basin are dismaying, and here the aeroplane might be suggested as a possible solution to such horrors, but unfortunately it is able to offer little help. The vegetation of the tropical forest is so dense that it virtually obliterates the characteristic features of the earth's crust, and a photograph from the air presents the impression of an indeterminate mass of vegetation with rivers, except for the main ones, practically non-existent, because they have been shrouded by the luxuriant growth of the trees.

Air survey, so far as it is developed at present, therefore forms a subsidiary branch to the methods of map-making already described, and is especially useful for filling in the detail of difficult and inaccessible regions. By reason of expense it is necessary to restrict its use, and it is necessary to develop it along the lines for which it is best suited. At present its value lies in the specialistic work of which it is capable.

One application which has been employed with success is to use ordinary aerial photographs, as a means of revealing, quickly and infallibly, the particular areas in which new development is not shown on the existing Ordnance maps. The points where unmapped topography occurs are then re-surveyed by normal ground methods and the new detail superimposed on the old plans. This is particularly useful when examining the possible routes for such engineering works as arterial roads, and certain large cities have also been re-surveyed by this method.

MAKING BOTH ENDS OF THE TUNNEL MEET

THE fact that tube railways, with many changes of direction, can be constructed from different starting points and invariably join perfectly within a small fraction of an inch, often gives rise to wonderment, and this kind of work is a good example of the great accuracy which can be obtained by careful surveying with instruments in perfect adjustment.

Tunnel work, like other engineering jobs, is based on a " centre-line " running symmetrically through the new construction in the direction of its length, widths and heights being measured from this centre-line as may be required. It will thus be obvious that the accurate location of this basic line is absolutely essential.

In any scheme involving underground work, a ground survey is made first, showing the usual features, but, in addition, the positions of deep foundations, sewers and other underground conduits must be ascertained and included on the plan, and sections must be drawn showing these features at their correct depths. The route of the tunnel can then be decided upon, avoiding any points which might be dangerously affected by underground workings in their immediate locality. The direction of the centre-line of the tunnel as it passes under each shaft is then found from the plan, in relationship to the lines and fixed points of the over-ground survey, and this direction has to be transferred to the required depth down every shaft so that excavations can be commenced in their correct position and proceed in the right way.

This is done by hanging two plumb-lines—usually fine wires—down the shaft, each being located exactly on the tunnel centre-line, and these are used as sighting wires. A theodolite is set up in the shaft in perfect alignment with the wires and further points on the centre-line are fixed by the instrument as the work proceeds, its telescope being clamped in the direction in which the tunnel is to run.

The drawback of this method, however, lies in the fact that the wires may only be a few feet apart, and it may be necessary to produce this very short length of sighting line a very considerable distance, so that a very slight error in setting the instrument in alignment with the wires may amount to a very large error if the line is continued for a mile. Hence the need for extreme care.

POINT TO POINT : PLANNING THE CURVED TUNNEL

CURVES connecting the straights are set out by first calculating the positions of the points at which the arc diverges from one straight and joins the other. These are known as the " tangent points " and they are located on their respective straights, or "tangents", by measuring off their calculated " chainages," or distances, from fixed points.

If one imagines a curve marked out by a series of posts, as in Fig. 8, placed at regular intervals, and one stands at the point where it swings away from the straight, it will, of course, be apparent that the lines joining the observer to successive posts will deviate by steadily increasing amounts. If the radius of the curve is known and also the angle between the two straights into which the curve is to be fitted, it is possible to calculate the extent of this deviation for a whole series of points spaced at equal lengths, usually 50 or 100 feet, round the curve. These points may be located and marked on the ground by placing a theodolite at the starting point of the curve and turning the telescope to the successive angles of deviation while the appropriate distances are measured off as chords. This method is used both for tunnel and surface work.

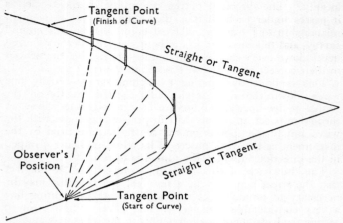

8. *How a curved path could be traced out on the ground by inserting a series of posts at regular intervals.*

WHAT THE ENGINEER DEMANDS OF MATERIALS

Most of us are endowed with an instinctive sense of proportion which enables us to judge whether a structure or appliance looks adequately strong ; and, in many cases, a design which " looks right " will prove eminently suitable for the particular purpose required. The principles of engineering, however, demand a much more thorough and exact investigation which must be carried out along two distinct, but parallel, lines : firstly, we must form an estimate of the loading which the structure may be expected to receive and deduce from this the stresses set up in its various parts, and secondly, we must have a precise knowledge of the constructional materials used.

We require, for instance, an exact idea of the stresses which will fracture the material when the loading is applied in various ways, and it is important to know whether any changes occur in the nature of the material when subjected to extremes of temperature or to long continued vibration.

The first part of the investigation is based largely on practical experience and mathematical principles, and the second part on the results of laboratory experiments, and the combination of practice, theory and research forms the threefold foundation of engineering science.

Between these three branches there is very close co-ordination, and methods of design are subject to continual modification to keep pace with the new facts which the laboratory workers are constantly bringing to light, but, nevertheless, there are certain branches of constructional work in which an element of doubt still exists, and a strict mathematical conception of practical conditions is not yet possible. Here, the engineer can proceed for part of the way along well-established lines where theory and practice are in harmony, but he ultimately reaches a point where his only guidance consists of rule-of-thumb methods based upon the successes and failures of previous designs.

It is very difficult, for instance, to arrive at an accurate figure for the pressure exerted by the mass of earth supported by the retaining walls so commonly seen in railway cuttings, and even more difficult to predict with certainty exactly how far up the wall that pressure will have its maximum effect.

The question of the stresses set up by heavy and fast-moving traffic in the surface and foundation of the modern highway is another problem which, as yet, is incapable of solution by direct mathematical methods.

The vast majority of structures, however, may be designed with precision on lines which will ensure adequate strength combined with the utmost economy in material, thus confirming the truth of the old statement that " an engineer is a man who can do for a shilling what the ordinary man could do for half a crown."

A TWO-TON LOAD ON A SQUARE INCH OF METAL

HAVING decided upon the broad principles and main features in the design of a structure, the next step consists in determining the heaviest load it may reasonably be expected to bear, making due allowance for such contingencies as wind-pressure. The manner in which this external loading is distributed throughout the various component members of the structure is then ascertained, and the stress in each member is found by dividing the load on that member by the area of the material which is resisting the load. For instance, a locomotive and tender with a total weight of 100 tons may produce a load of 20 tons upon a particular member of a lattice girder bridge. If the area of the cross-section of the metal girder resisting this load is 10 square inches, the stress in that member is 20 tons divided by 10, or 2 tons per square inch. In considering the imposed stresses or the resisting strength of structural units it is always customary to think in terms of tons or pounds *per square inch*.

THE THREE FORMS OF STRESS WHICH MATERIALS UNDERGO

To proceed a stage farther, it is necessary to appreciate that stresses may be classified in three main categories : tensile, compressive, and shearing.

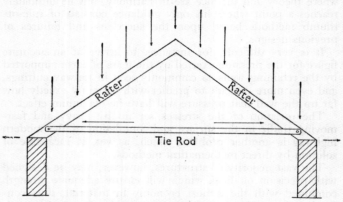

9. *A tie rod in a roof truss takes the tension due to the weight of the roof which tends to push the walls outwards.*

A tensile stress, or tension, is the type which occurs in a piece of string when a weight is suspended from it, or, to give another example, it is the type of stress set up in the tie-rod of a roof truss. Consider, first, a roof truss composed merely of two rafters, placed in contact at their upper ends and each resting on a supporting wall. The weight of the roof will tend to force the rafters apart at their lower ends and, if unchecked, might push the walls outwards, in the manner shown in Fig. 9. Suppose, now, that a horizontal tie-rod is added, connecting the lower ends of the rafters. The weight of the roof will still exert its original tendency to push the rafters downwards and outwards, but, in addition, it will have to tear apart the fibres of the tie-rod before any movement will occur. The tie-rod, subjected in this way to a pulling action at each end, is said to be *in tension* and the stress which is attempting to pull it apart is a *tensile* stress. Its magnitude will be a certain proportion of the weight of the roof divided by the area of the rod. A tensile stress is thus associated with a pull.

A compressive stress, on the other hand, is produced by a pushing action which tends to shorten or crush a structural unit. In the foregoing case of the triangulated roof-truss, the rafters are subjected to a compressive stress, or are *in compression* and it is obvious that certain materials, such as wire cables, may have considerable tensile strength, while their compressive strength, or resistance to pushing, is nil. For this reason, the tie-rod of a roof-truss is often a comparatively thin bar of circular section, while the rafters, which must stand compression without buckling, require stronger members of L or T shape.

A shearing stress, again, is of a different type from either tension or compression, and is best illustrated by considering the case of a rivet connecting two iron plates, as shown in Fig. 10.

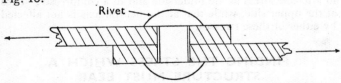

Rivet

10. When two plates held together by a rivet are pulled in opposite directions, the rivet suffers a " shearing stress "

If we imagine the plates to be pulled in opposite directions, movement is resisted by the rivet and there is a tendency for the latter to be sliced through at the point where the two plates are attempting to slide one over the other.

This slicing tendency is known as a *shearing stress* and it requires due consideration whenever rivets or bolts are used to connect structural units. The difference between shear and tension may be illustrated rather aptly by comparing the action of sharp and blunt scissors. The former will cut cleanly through a piece of cotton and the fracture is then due to a shearing stress, but the latter will break the cotton by tearing apart the fibres, resulting in a frayed end, and the fracture is due to a tensile stress.

THE STEEL BRIDGE BENDS

THE three types of stresses so far described are the so-called " simple stresses," but in actual practice a combination of types is frequently met with in one and the same structural unit. The commonest example is, perhaps, that of an ordinary beam, supporting the floor of a building or the " deck " of a bridge.

Under a load, such a beam will deflect, and it may be mentioned, at this juncture, that all structures, however solid and unyielding they may appear, actually deform very slightly when loads are placed upon them, returning to their original shape when the loading is released. The effect of such deformation upon a simple beam is to produce a downward curvature which slightly elongates the underside and slightly compresses the upper surface. Somewhere along the centre of the beam it would be possible to find a portion which is neither elongated nor compressed and an imaginary line passing through this area is termed the " neutral axis." The material of which the beam is composed is subjected to a tensile stress at the underside and to a compressive stress at the upper side, while that at the neutral axis is not affected by either of these stresses.

FINDING THE STRESS WHICH A STRUCTURE MUST BEAR

THE distribution of loading among the individual members of framed structures is usually determined by " graphical " methods, i.e. by a system of drawing in which both the structure frame and the loads upon it are represented by lines. A series of geometrical constructions are then carried out according to set rules and the loads on each individual member are finally represented to a predetermined scale by a further series of lines, and their magnitudes are scaled off the diagram exactly as one measures the distance between two towns on a map. Not only is the magnitude of the imposed stress derived in this way, but also its " sense," or, in other words we can tell whether it is tensile or compressive and we can design the member accordingly.

The required size of a tension member, measured through the material and expressed as its " cross-sectional area " is found by dividing the actual load which the member will have to support by the allowable working stress which the material will safely bear.   For compression members the question of buckling will have to be considered as well. Thus, we may discover, from our diagram, that a certain steel member will receive a compressive load of 30 tons.   Let us assume that its length is to be 8 feet.

If we take an allowable working stress of 8 tons per square inch, the cross-sectional area in square inches required to withstand the compression alone would be 30 divided by 8, or 3·75 square inches.   Now a T-section, 5 inches across the top and 3 inches deep, with metal $\frac{1}{2}$ inch thick, has a cross-sectional area of 3·766 square inches ; but a strut of this shape and size, with a length of 8 feet, would probably be unsafe from the point of view of buckling, and this possibility has to be investigated by a calculation based on one or other of several well-known formulæ.

Actually, these formulæ would indicate that the strut in question would bear roughly 50 tons before failing, but this only provides a factor of safety of well under 2, instead of the customary 4 and therefore a larger section would have to be adopted.   An angle-section, 8 feet long, with equal arms, 6 inches wide and metal $\frac{5}{8}$ inch thick, described as a " six by six by five-eights angle," will just buckle under a load of 130 tons, thus giving a factor of safety of slightly over 4, and this would be considered a suitable section for the member under consideration.

BENDING MOMENTS: THE MATHEMATICIAN LOOKS AT THE LEVER

IN dealing with beams we have to consider a somewhat intangible quantity called the " bending moment," obtained by multiplying a load by a length and expressed as so many "foot-pounds," " inch-tons," or " inch-pounds," according to the units in which we measure the load and the distance.

It is, in a way, a mathematical conception of leverage. Imagine, for example, that one pan of a pair of scales has a 10-pound weight on it.   This would be balanced by 10 pounds in the other pan, but if the scales, instead of having a symmetrical beam supported exactly in the centre, had a beam with unequal arms, the second 10-pound weight would no longer balance the first. If the portion of the beam on one side of the pivot were exactly three times as long as that on the other side and the 10-pound weight was suspended from the longer arm, it would require a 30-pound weight on the other side to effect balance.

Supposing that the arms were respectively 3 feet and 1 foot in length, as in Fig. 11, in mathematical language the " moment " of the 10-pound weight, about the pivot A, would be the product of the weight and the distance XA, or 30 foot-pounds. Similarly, the moment of the 30-pound weight is the product of the weight and the distance AY, again 30 foot-pounds, and since the moments are equal the system will balance because the moment, in this case, is merely an indication of the ability of one or other of the weights to swing the beam of the scales about its pivot.

THE CALCULATION BEHIND THE CHOICE OF A BEAM

APPLIED to structures, the simplest case is that of a cantilever (a common example of which is a bracket built into a wall) with a single load hanging from the projecting end. If the cantilever beam is 6 feet long and the load is a ton weight, the moment of this weight about the fixed end of the beam is 6×1 foot-tons, that is, 6 foot-tons. This particular type of moment is a measure of the ability of the weight to bend the beam and it is therefore called a " bending moment."

In actual practice, the bending moment varies from place to place along the length of a beam or a cantilever, but it is possible to calculate its value at any point for the most complicated systems of loading. The case of a beam supported freely at its ends and loaded uniformly throughout its length occurs quite often and here the bending moment is zero at the ends and increases according to a definite mathematical law until a maximum is reached at the centre of the span.

The change in the bending moment as one proceeds along the beam may be expressed graphically by means of a curve, or chart, obtained by calculating the moments at a large number of points, measuring these off vertically on squared paper against the corresponding distances along the beam measured horizontally and joining up the points so obtained to form a smooth curve. The curve for a uniformly loaded beam with its ends freely supported (that is, not rigidly built

in to a wall at each end) will always have the same characteristic
shape, shown in Fig. 11.

Having calculated the maximum bending moment, the
next proceeding is to determine what stresses this bending
moment will set up in the fibres of the beam at the extreme
positions on the top and bottom surfaces where conditions
are most severe. This is done by means of a formula involving
factors which depend upon the dimensions of the beam. We
therefore choose a beam of likely dimensions first and then
ascertain whether the maximum stress set up by the bending
moment is within the limit of the safe working stress.

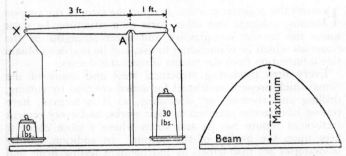

*11. Left : the balance illustrating " moments."   Right :
how the " bending moment " for a uniformly-loaded beam
reaches a maximum at its centre.*

HARD OUTSIDE, TOUGH INSIDE

THE constructional engineer is usually more interested in
the toughness of a material than in its hardness alone.
Toughness implies strength of interlocked fibres and the
ability to withstand tensile stresses, shocks, and the repeated
ebb and flow of intermittent loads. Structural steelwork,
such as bridge girders, must possess this quality—they must
be able to resist successfully the forces which attempt to pull
the metal apart when tension is applied, often with considerable suddenness, and they must be able to flex slightly under
a passing load and recover perfectly without any loss of fibre
strength.

Hardness, on the other hand, implies resistance to deformation or wear under concentrated local loading. It is often
only required as a surface quality, as will be apparent from

the " case hardening " of tools and other mechanical appliances, by which a hard, resistant skin is given to the metal to withstand intensive wear and tear. The interior of the metal may be much softer than the outer case-hardened skin and, indeed, is purposely left so, to avoid the risk of brittleness with which ultra-hardness is not uncommonly associated, and the result is a metal which is tough in the mass and extremely resistant to wear on its surface.

MEASURING THE STRENGTH OF MATERIALS

BEFORE the engineer can decide upon the sizes of the various beams, columns and other parts of a structure, he must know the tensile, compressive and shear strengths of the materials which he is intending to use, and he is able to obtain this information from the results of mechanical tests.

Every firm producing structural steel and many of the firms which prepare such steel for actual erection by cutting, drilling and riveting, or *fabricating*, as it is termed, have testing laboratories attached to their works, and every cement factory of repute has its test room where a close check is kept upon the quality of the output. In addition, similar laboratories are maintained by independent testing firms and well-equipped examples are to be found in all the principal engineering colleges.

As a further control upon the quality of recognised materials of constructions, such as steel and cement, there are the British Standard Specifications, drawn up and revised, from time to time, by the expert committees of the British Standards Institution, and any firm of standing which manufactures such materials will guarantee that its products conform to the appropriate specification.

In any civil engineering work of importance, samples of the steel, cement, and other constructional materials will be taken at frequent intervals and submitted to approved tests.

For steel, the tensile test is the most important. Tensile testing machines are constructed in many types and sizes and are classified according to the maximum load in tons which they are capable of applying to a specimen under test. The larger machines have a capacity of 100–300 tons and are usually driven electrically or hydraulically, while the smaller types, of 5 tons capacity, or less, are often worked by hand.

CHECKING THE WHOLE BY TESTING A PART

THE samples used for the tensile testing of steel are made in cylindrical form, the most common size being $4\frac{3}{4}$ inches in overall length and from $\frac{7}{8}$ inch to $1\frac{1}{8}$ inch in diameter at the ends where attachment is made to the testing machine. The central portion, for a length of $2\frac{1}{4}$ inches, is turned down to a diameter of exactly 0·564 inches, giving a cross-sectional area of $\frac{1}{4}$ square inch, and two marks are accurately inscribed on the cylinder, spaced precisely 2 inches apart. This is termed the *gauge length* and its significance will be appreciated later.

For purely structural steel, however, as distinct from those varieties used for such purposes as automobile and aircraft construction, test specimens of other forms are used. Thus, for structural steel plates, flat bars and rolled sections, a long, thin, rectangular sample is used, similar to that shown in Fig. 12, with a gauge length of 8 inches, a parallel portion containing the gauge length at least 9 inches long and, for thicknesses between $\frac{3}{8}$ and $\frac{7}{8}$ inches, the width of the narrow part is made 2 inches. For round bars, a cylindrical test piece is used in which the gauge length is 8 times the diameter and the parallel portion between the shouldered ends at least 9 times the diameter.

The working principle of a common type of testing machine may be represented in a simplified manner by the arrangement shown in Fig. 12. Imagine that one end of the test specimen is attached to the end of a large vertical screw, in such a way that the screw can rotate without turning the specimen. If the screw is rotated in a stationary nut it will travel either upwards or downwards according to the direction in which it is turned, and thus, upward or downward vertical movement will be imparted to the specimen.

Suppose, now, that the top end of the latter is attached to a long lever, pivoted at the point P, and that a sliding balance weight can be moved to and fro along the lever to maintain a correct balance, after the fashion of an ordinary steelyard. If the specimen is pulled downwards by the screw's rotation, the lever will tilt upwards at the end E and the weight must be slid outwards towards that end to preserve the condition of balance, and the greater the movement of the screw, the greater will be the pull on the specimen and the greater will be the distance which the weight must be moved.

In an actual machine, of course, there are many additional details, but the pull is applied to the specimen through the agency of a screw, either electrically or hand driven, and the amount of the pull, or load, expressed in tons or pounds, is indicated by the position of a balance weight on a graduated lever arm. In hydraulically driven machines, however, the pull is applied through the movement of a ram, or piston, which is propelled within its cylinder by intense water pressure.

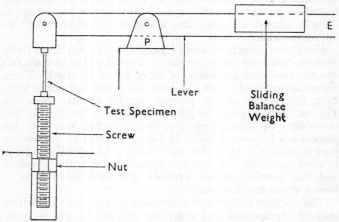

12. A machine used to test the effect of varied tensile stresses on a " test specimen " of steel or other metal.

NEARING THE BREAKING POINT : THE STEEL BEGINS TO STRETCH

As the test proceeds, the cylindrical steel specimen will extend slightly in length, but, if the loads are kept below a certain limit, it will return to its original length when the pull is released. During this portion of the test the steel is said to be *elastic* and the loading is described as being *within the elastic limit*. Furthermore, the amount of stretch within this limit is strictly proportional to the applied load—if the load is doubled, the extension will be doubled, and so on. If the pull is increased beyond the elastic limit, however, the specimen will stretch more and more in proportion to the load and will ultimately pull out into a tapering neck at the centre and then snap.

After the breaking load has been ascertained from the indicator on the machine, the specimen is removed, the two fractured pieces placed in close contact and the extended length between the gauge marks carefully measured, together with the reduced diameter at the point of fracture.

The amount of drawing out at the centre of the bar is an indication of the *ductility* of the metal and some degree of ductility is essential as an indication that the steel is not brittle. For this reason, engineers are not satisfied with a high tensile strength alone—a material might possess this property under a gradually applied load, but might snap without warning under a sudden stress. Such a material would show practically no ductility, or drawing out, before fracture and would only give a very slight extension on the original gauge length. For structural purposes, therefore, it is essential that the steel should give a certain minimum extension and reduction in diameter, in addition to an adequate tensile strength. The elongation is invariably stated as a percentage of the original gauge length, and the load at the point of fracture is divided by the original area of cross-section of the bar and gives the *ultimate tensile strength*, usually expressed in tons per square inch.

The *yield point*, just beyond the elastic limit, is also important, and is recognised by the occurrence of a perceptible extension, in a ductile metal, when the load reaches a certain magnitude.

Compression and shear tests are somewhat difficult to carry out with steel specimens, but the relationship between tensile, compressive and shear strengths is well established, and for ordinary structural steel, which will break under a tensile stress of about 30 tons per square inch, the ultimate compressive strength may be taken as 26 tons per square inch, and the ultimate shearing strength as 22 tons per square inch.

GETTING THE HARDNESS DOWN TO FIGURES

ALTHOUGH hardness is mainly important as a surface property, in the case of a homogeneous steel, or, in other words, a steel which has the same qualities throughout and has not merely been hardened by special treatment on its outer skin, there is a definite relationship between the degree of hardness and the tensile strength. A hardness test, in this case, is therefore of some utility as an indirect form of tensile test.

The most widely adopted method of determining the relative degree of hardness is by means of the Brinell test in which a small steel ball, approximately $\frac{3}{8}$ inch in diameter, and itself intensely hard, is pressed into the surface of the test sample under a load of nearly 3 tons. The Brinell machines are constructed to metric system dimensions, but the above are roughly the British equivalents. The diameter of the indentation formed in the specimen is accurately measured to the twentieth part of a millimetre (equivalent to two-thousandths of an inch) and a calculation is made in accordance with a special formula which gives the " Brinell Hardness Number " for the particular specimen. Naturally, the harder the material, the smaller will be the impression and the less its depth, but the Brinell formula is so devised that the hardness is *inversely* proportional to the diameter of the ball impression, and hence the harder the material, the higher the hardness number.

Common figures for comparatively soft structural steel, for instance, would fall within the range 120–150, whereas for a hard alloy steel, such as would be used for highly stressed motor-car parts, the Brinell number can easily reach 300. As a rough guide, the tensile strength, expressed in tons per square inch, may be taken as one-fifth of the Brinell number —thus, one-fifth of 150, the Brinell number, gives 30 tons per square inch, the normal tensile strength of the ordinary steel used in structural work.

The Brinell machine is compact and portable and a specially prepared test piece is not required, as it is for a tensile test —in fact the ball impression may be formed and measured on a large girder, or other structural member, even after the latter has been erected.

A second method of measuring the comparative hardness of a metal is by means of the Shore Scleroscope. This apparatus consists of a small diamond-pointed hammer, weighing $\frac{1}{12}$ ounce, which is allowed to fall on to the surface of the material from a fixed height. Actually it falls within a vertical glass tube which is graduated so that when the hammer rebounds, after striking the specimen, the height of rebound may be measured. A certain proportion of the energy of the hammer blow is absorbed by the material under test which, in consequence, is indented, but the remainder is returned to the hammer which thereupon rebounds to varying heights depending upon whether the sample is very hard, like steel, or very soft, like lead. The former will only absorb about 20 per cent of the blow and thus gives a small indentation and a high rebound, whereas the latter will absorb about 95%, resulting in a large indentation and a low rebound.

A HUMAN WEAKNESS IN METALS : FATIGUE

IT has long been realised that the breaking stress given by the ordinary tension test does not represent the true strength of the metal if the latter is repeatedly loaded, freed from load, and reloaded.   Under such treatment a piece of metal will ultimately fracture at a stress considerably lower than that given by a simple tensile test, and if the loading is not merely repeated, but, in addition, is *reversed*, alternating from tension to compression and back again, the metal will fracture at a stress even lower still.

This phenomenon is known as *fatigue* of the metal and is usually understood to be distinct from the somewhat similar deterioration produced by repeated impact blows, the term fatigue applying only to the weakening produced by repetition or reversal of stress, apart from impact.

The effect may, perhaps, be best understood by considering an actual example : A certain grade of structural steel had an ultimate tensile strength of 30 tons per square inch. When repeatedly stressed up to 25 tons per square inch and released from load, alternately, the material withstood about half-a-million repetitions of stress before fracturing.   When the stress was reduced to 23 tons per square inch the number of repetitions before fracture increased, in round numbers, to one million, and a reduction in stress intensity to 20 tons per square inch was accompanied by an increase in the number of repetitions to approximately four-and-a-half millions. The relation between two variable quantities such as the limiting stress and the number of repetitions producing fracture, may be represented by a *curve*, or *graph*, drawn on squared paper. Many such curves are, in reality, straight lines and give, from this characteristic, a simple relationship, or proportionality, between the two varying factors.   Other curves run down steeply, bend round, and then become practically level, approaching very near to, but never quite touching, a horizontal straight line. The results of plotting a chart, or graph, of the foregoing repeated load tests would be a curve of this type, as shown in Fig. 13.   The limiting range of stress, in each case, is measured vertically and the number of repetitions producing failure horizontally.

Many more graduations in the stress range than the three examples specifically mentioned would be necessary to obtain an accurate curve, and from a large number of experimental results it becomes possible to locate a whole series of points on the squared paper which may be blended into a smooth line. Each point is fixed in position by running vertically up the stress axis to any given limiting stress and then moving

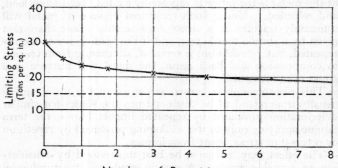

13. A curve showing how the tensile strength of a certain steel diminishes under repeated stresses, to a steady limit of 15 tons per square inch, below which any number of repetitions is possible without fracture.

horizontally across the paper to a point vertically above the corresponding number of repetitions which were required to fracture the specimen with that particular limiting stress.

The characteristic tailing-off of the graph will be noticed and it will be seen to be approaching a horizontal straight line passing through the stress value of 15 tons per square inch. It would be deduced from this that, provided the limiting stress never exceeded the above value, it could be applied, released, and re-applied an indefinite number of times, without producing a failure in the material.

SUDDEN CHANGES LOWER RESISTANCE

IT is a curious feature of fatigue that a less drastic effect is produced by merely *reducing* the load and then increasing it to its original value, than by releasing it entirely and then re-imposing it at its maximum. Thus, some tests on wrought iron revealed that if the load were merely allowed to fluctuate between maximum and half-load, the limiting stress, determined from a graph, was 21 tons per square inch, i.e. the loading could fluctuate between the two limits which stressed the metal to 21 and $10\frac{1}{2}$ tons per square inch respectively, without damage. If, however, the same metal were submitted to repeated loading, alternating with entire release, the limiting stress was only 15 tons per square inch, i.e. if the load fluctuation ranged between the value producing this stress and zero, again no damage would result.

The most severe treatment of all, however, is a complete reversal of stress, such as occurs if a beam is bent first downwards and then upwards, and, reverting to the wrought iron previously mentioned, the limiting stresses permissible under conditions of complete reversal were $7\frac{1}{2}$ tons per square inch tensile, alternating with a like intensity in compression.

Special allowance is made in structural and mechanical designs for members which are liable to receive reversed and fluctuating stresses, and this is usually accomplished either by adopting lower working stresses than those which are permissible with static, or steady, loading, or by multiplying the loads by a compensating factor. The effect is the same in both cases.

THE RAW MATERIALS OF CIVIL ENGINEERING

So far, in discussing materials, structural steel has been frequently mentioned. This is the commonly known *mild steel* which is used for bridges, steel-framed buildings, roof trusses and other structural purposes. It is obtainable in a large variety of sectional shapes, such as " rolled steel joists " which, in end view, resemble the letter I, and there are also L-shaped " angle irons " and T-shaped " tee irons," in addition to flat strips, rods, built-up plate girders, stanchions, or columns, and other units.

Mild steel possesses only a moderate tensile strength in comparison with special alloy steels, which will be dealt with later, but it is reasonably ductile and free from any brittleness which would render it dangerous if employed in structures where shock loading, or impact due to moving loads, is a factor to be considered, as it is in every railway and road bridge.

Moreover, mild steel is readily sawn through and drilled, and the building up and connecting together of complicated networks may therefore be accomplished easily. It is a reliable, standardised product and when supplied by a maker of repute may be relied upon to give an ultimate tensile strength of from 28 to 32 tons per square inch, in conjunction with a yield point of about 16 tons per square inch and an elongation of about 22 per cent on a gauge length of 2 inches. For this material the elastic limit occurs at about half the breaking stress—in other words, there will be no permanent elongation of a mild steel test specimen under a tensile stress of less than about 15 tons per square inch, but, in actual practice, care is taken to ensure that the loads are kept well within the elastic limit, and a common allowance for the working tensile stress is $7\frac{1}{2}$ tons. This is roughly half the stress which would cause a permanent distortion or one-quarter of the stress which would cause a fracture. In technical language, this provides a " Factor of Safety " of 4.

CAST IRON : A METAL TO WITHSTAND COMPRESSION

CAST iron, on the other hand, is a brittle metal and under a tensile test it will snap without showing any appreciable elongation or reduction of area at the fractured section. It will only support about 5 to 15 tons per square inch as a tensile stress, but the breaking stress in compression may be as much as 50 tons per square inch, although various grades, having different compositions, show very wide divergences in strength.

Cast iron is not used in structural work where tensile stresses are likely to be encountered, but it has the advantage that it is readily melted and casts well, and before the advent of mild steel as a structural material, it was used in the form of cast girders, examples of which may still be seen occasionally on old bridges which have not yet been re-built to conform better with modern practice.

It may be usefully employed to take compressive stresses, where no serious impact or shock loading is anticipated, and is, therefore, adopted for massive castings forming bed-plates and bearing-plates, and also for water and gas mains and sectional tanks. A fractured specimen of cast iron shows a crystalline, granular surface at the break which is quite unlike the tapering, silky-fibrous fracture of mild steel.

"WORKABLE" WROUGHT IRON, SOFT BUT TOUGH

WROUGHT iron is another metal which, like cast iron, has been largely superseded in structural engineering by mild steel. It is not brittle, however, but, on the other hand, is strongly fibrous and ductile. The process of manufacture from which its name is derived, involving much "working," squeezing and rolling, gives the metal its characteristic fibrous structure ; but it is a somewhat variable material and there is a wide range between the tensile strengths of good and bad samples. Even in the best qualities, however, it is rather less than that of mild steel, and 25 tons per square inch may be taken as a fair average value. Wrought iron possesses the valuable property of welding easily at the temperature of the ordinary blacksmith's fire—a much lower temperature than that required for welding steel, and it also offers a higher resistance to corrosion, but its uses in civil engineering practice are limited to a few special details such as ornamental ironwork (for which it is peculiarly suitable owing to its easy " workability ") and blacksmith's work in general.

All three metals, steel, cast iron, and wrought iron, have one feature in common—they consist essentially of the elements iron and carbon, with small quantities of other elements in addition. The proportion of the carbon present is, however, different in the three cases, mild steel having more carbon than wrought iron but less than cast iron. Average figures for the respective carbon contents are : ordinary mild or structural steel, about one-quarter or one-fifth of 1% ; cast iron, anything from 2 to 4% ; wrought iron, only about one-tenth of 1%.

ALLOY STEELS: AN ALLIANCE OF HARDNESS AND TOUGHNESS

IT is common knowledge that ordinary steel, if heated and cooled slowly in air, becomes softened, or *annealed*, but if heated and cooled suddenly in water or oil, it becomes hardened. It was discovered, however, as long ago as 1868, that the addition of another metal, tungsten, to a plain carbon steel resulted in an alloy which did not require this quenching in water or oil to produce a hardening effect, mere cooling in air being sufficient. In other words, this particular tungsten-steel was " self hardening " and, therefore, very advantageous for such purposes as tool making.

This was, probably, the earliest example of a special alloy steel, but further developments in the production of such materials took place in the eighties, when the beneficial results of adding two other metals—chromium and manganese—were realised, and it was found that intense hardness could be obtained without the disadvantage of brittleness. A steel, for instance, containing 2% of chromium and slightly less than 1% of carbon is immensely hard and tough, and is used for making rollers between which softer steels and other metals may be formed into various shapes. High quality steel balls and rollers for bearings are also made from chromium steel and possess a very considerable degree of both hardness and toughness, thus enabling them to resist abrasive, or grinding, wear and shock loading as well.

HOW CHROMIUM ADDS "STAINLESS" TO "STEEL"

MANY of the stainless steels, which are so much in vogue for domestic purposes, are chromium alloys,[1] from 12% to 20% of chromium giving a remarkable resistance to corrosion, but these steels were not discovered until nearly forty years after the original chromium steels. Though not extensively used in civil engineering practice, its permanently clean and bright appearance renders stainless steel a useful and attractive material for such details as entrance doors, handrails and beadings in railway stations, cinemas, and other large public buildings.

There is a small quantity of manganese in practically all steel, but when the quantity of this metal is increased from a mere trace to 12% or more, a special alloy steel results which, again, possesses to a very high degree that valuable combination of properties—hardness and toughness. Hence, manganese steel is used for a variety of purposes where great resistance to wear and tear is required. The immense nut-cracker jaws which crush huge lumps of granite into small fragments at stone quarries, the shovel scoops of steam-navvies which dig out hard, stony soil when a road or railway is to be cut through a hillside, and the tram rails at sharp curves and cross-overs where intense grinding wear is always in progress, are nearly always made of manganese steel.

Another metal which is largely used for producing an alloy steel is nickel. The advantage gained in this case is a marked improvement in tensile strength and elastic limit, in compari-

[1] See p. 251.

son with a plain steel having the same proportion of carbon, while, at the same time, there is no loss of ductility. For this reason, nickel steel is sometimes used instead of ordinary mild steel in very large bridges, where its superior strength enables the sizes of the structural members, and therefore the weight of the structure, to be reduced.

A NICKEL STEEL OF SPECIAL USE

ONE particular nickel steel, known as " Invar," has a curious property which may be mentioned in passing. This material possesses a high percentage of nickel and, unlike other metals, it only expands very slightly indeed when heated. An ordinary steel bar, for instance, would be elongated to such an extent that if we can imagine a continuous strip 1 mile long, its length would increase by about $\frac{3}{4}$ inch if the temperature rose as little as 1 degree Centigrade. A strip of Invar, however, of the same initial length would only increase its length by $\frac{1}{20}$ inch. For this reason, Invar is used for making measuring rods and tapes when great accuracy is required, as well as for a number of mechanical appliances, such as clock pendulums, in which a constant length is vitally important.

In addition to the alloys which contain iron, carbon and one other added metal, there are many complex alloys in which two or more added metals are introduced. Thus we have nickel-chrome steels,[1] so valuable for withstanding the rapidly alternating stresses, first tensile and then compressive, repeated again and again, at incredible speeds, in certain component parts of motor-car and aero-engines. Some of these nickel-chrome steels, after being heated and cooled in accordance with a carefully specified routine, known as *heat treatment*, may have an ultimate tensile strength as high as 100 tons per square inch.

CHANGING THE CHARACTER OF A METAL BY HEAT

THE process of heat treatment has a profound influence on the subsequent properties of the steel, and this is particularly true with an alloy. Thus, starting with one and the same material—a nickel-chrome steel, in this case—by varying the temperatures at which certain stages of the procedure are carried out, it is possible to obtain a graduated series of products, ranging from a very hard steel with an ultimate

[1] See p. 253.

tensile strength of 85 tons per square inch and an elongation of 10%, to a softer and more ductile steel having an ultimate strength of 55 tons per square inch and an elongation of 25%. This range of properties is obtained without any variation in the composition of the metal.

CONCRETE : THE BASIS OF MODERN BUILDING

THE vast majority of engineering structures involve the use of concrete in their foundations ; and an essential constituent of concrete is cement. The latter is frequently given the qualifying adjective " Portland," based upon a resemblance between hardened cement mortar and Portland stone, but there is no connection whatever between the locality and the material to which the name has become so firmly attached.

Cement is an artificial, or " synthetic," product, composed of two natural substances found in large quantities in many different areas—clay, and either chalk or limestone. The two former occur in convenient proximity at many points along the Thames estuary and in the Medway valley, while limestone is a common mineral of many of the northern counties, notably Derbyshire, and we therefore find cement works in such places as the Chatham district and at Hope, south of Sheffield. By a simple series of manufacturing processes, the two main constituents are blended into one uniform compound and finally a very fine powder is produced which, on mixing with a suitable amount of water, is first converted to a paste and ultimately sets to a hardness exceeding that of either of the ingredients.

If chalk is used, it is freed from any flints which it may contain when dug from the pit, and mixed into a thick, creamy " slurry " with the clay and added water. If limestone is used, it is ground into small fragments before mixing into a similar slurry. In either case, the latter is burnt, or " calcined," in a long horizontal cylinder, or " kiln," lined with fire-resisting material and kept slowly rotating, while intensely hot flames are projected into one end. The fuel employed is finely powdered coal, forced through nozzles by an air-blast, and in the most up-to-date works, the kilns are as much as 250 feet in length and 10 feet in diameter. The temperature in the hottest area is about 1,500 degrees Centigrade, and some idea of this intensity of heat may be realised by remembering that water boils at 100 degrees.

The product after burning is known as " clinker " and is then in the form of irregular lumps which are finally ground to the extremely fine powder with which we are familiar in the finished material. Cement of good quality is, indeed, so fine that about 95% of any given sample will pass through a sieve in which every square inch of surface has 180 meshes in one direction interwoven with 180 meshes in a direction at right angles.

FROM CEMENT TO MORTAR AND CONCRETE

CEMENT and water alone set to a hard material known as "neat cement," but it is more often mixed either with sand, in which case a *mortar* results, or with sand and fragments of stone, in which case *concrete* is formed. It is essential that the sand and stone should be perfectly clean—cleanliness, in this respect, meaning freedom from clay, organic matter, or dust : and care is also taken to keep to strict proportions in the mixture.

Thus, mortars are made in various degrees of " richness," as it is called, ranging from one part of sand to one part of cement, or a " one to one mix," down to six parts of sand to one of cement, or a " six to one mix." In inferior work, higher proportions of sand even than this are used, thus saving on the cost of the cement, but such poor mixes would not be tolerated in important engineering work.

Concrete may have such proportions as 3 parts of broken stone to 1½ parts of sand and 1 of cement, giving a rich mix, or 4 of stone, 2 of sand and 1 of cement for a good, ordinary mix. Very often, the proportions are stated by combining the quantity of sand and stone, and a " 6 to 1 concrete," for instance, would consist of 6 parts of broken stone and sand to 1 part of cement. The broken stone, or *coarse aggregate*, to use the technical expression, may consist of washed gravel, broken granite, fragments of hard limestone, or hard, well-burnt furnace clinker, and it is customary to specify the size of this material by stating two sieve dimensions, one of which the stone will pass, and the other on which it will be retained. For example, it may be stipulated that the stone must pass through a sieve having square holes ¾-inch across, while being retained upon a sieve with ¼-inch openings.

Another factor of importance in mixing concrete is the

E.   3* quantity of water added to the dry ingredients. If too little is used, a dry, crumbly mixture results which does not pack well into position, and, even if it hardens properly, will still be weak and porous. If, on the other hand, too much water is used, giving a so-called " sloppy " mix, much of the superfluous water will escape, after the concrete has been placed in position, and also during its handling, and will take with it a certain amount of cement. This is not only a waste, but it naturally weakens the concrete. The correct amount of water is judged by experience, and the general rule is to use the minimum quantity which will give a freely working mix, that is, one which can be easily shovelled, packed into place and rammed.

Great care must be taken of the concrete during its " curing " period, while the hardening process is taking place—it must be protected from hot sun and drying winds which would unduly hasten the hardening and produce cracks, and for this reason it is frequently covered with wet sacks or damp sand. It must also be protected, of course, from frost.

RAPID-HARDENING CEMENTS WHICH SPEED UP THE JOB

IN order to allow the hardening process to reach a reasonable stage of completion, concrete made with ordinary Portland cement is not usually allowed to receive any loading until from 21 to 28 days after mixing and placing in position. There are, however, rapid-hardening cements, which are modified forms of ordinary Portland, ground to an even finer powder, and these, in from 4 to 7 days, reach the same degree of hardness and strength which ordinary cement would need a month to acquire. By using these slightly more expensive rapid-hardening cements, therefore, the curing period may be reduced considerably, and in some cases, for instance, traffic is allowed to pass over new concrete used in road repairs after as short a time as twenty-four hours.

Aluminous cements, however, gain their strength even more quickly than the rapid-hardening varieties of Portland cement —a fact which is due to their different composition. These special cements, which are more costly than the ordinary type, are called aluminous because they contain a large proportion of alumina, which, in turn, is an essential component of clay and is, thus, a constituent, also, of Portland cement. There is, however, only 7% in the latter, as against 35% in a cement of the aluminous class, but this high percentage cannot be obtained by using clay as a raw material, a fact which necessitates the use of a mineral known as *bauxite*, composed principally of alumina.

An average aluminous cement becomes stronger in 1 day than ordinary Portland does in 100 days and considerably stronger in 8 hours than a rapid-hardening Portland in 24 hours.

UBIQUITOUS CONCRETE, THE ENGINEER'S MAID-OF-ALL-WORK

CONCRETE of everyday fair quality and made of normal Portland cement, after curing for a month, should require a stress of at least 1 ton per square inch to crush it, and much higher figures than this may be obtained with carefully prepared material. Unreinforced concrete, however, should only be used to take compressive loads, and makes an excellent foundation when well rammed into the excavated areas dug out for this purpose, but when reinforced with steel, in a manner which will be explained later, its sphere of utility is enormously increased, and it becomes an extremely valuable medium for the construction of bridges, large buildings, grain silos, water towers, retaining walls, dock walls and jetties, and almost every variety of engineering structure.

Concrete, usually lightly reinforced, is also largely used for making " pre-cast " units, such as fence posts, pillars, blocks of various types for building purposes, lamp-posts, guide-posts and similar items. These are manufactured by mass-production methods, allowed to mature, and sold when properly hardened off. Concrete pipes, in all sizes from 1 to 5 feet in diameter, are likewise turned out in vast numbers.

"SAFETY FIRST" IN BUILDING : TESTING THE CONCRETE

IN any extensive engineering work, such as a lengthy road contract, or a bridge, or large building, where concrete is being used, samples are repeatedly taken during the process of mixing, and are moulded into small cubes, usually of 6-inch side, or else into cylinders 6 inches in diameter and 1 foot in height, and these samples are matured under carefully controlled moist conditions for a definite period—usually 28 days, when using ordinary cement—and are then submitted to a crushing test. A hydraulic press forms a convenient testing machine for this purpose, although many tensile machines may be adapted to give compression tests, as well, if required.

The usual type of hydraulic press consists of a strong steel platform, mounted on a ram, or piston, which works up and down in a cylinder. Oil is pumped into this cylinder, either by hand or by mechanical means, and the pressure exerted on the underside of the ram causes it to rise. At a convenient height above the moving platform is a stationary platform, held rigidly to the foundations of the machine by massive bars, as shown diagrammatically in Fig. 14. If the test specimen is placed between the two platforms and the lower one raised,

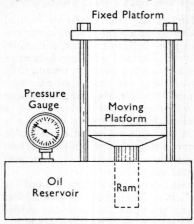

Fixed Platform

Pressure Gauge

Moving Platform

Oil Reservoir

Ram

a crushing action takes place and a gauge attached to the oil delivery pipe indicates the pressure which is being applied. The actual crushing stress on the sample is then calculated from the gauge reading.

14. The hydraulic press. When oil is pumped into the reservoir, the ram rises and exerts a crushing force between the two platforms.

The cement used in mixing the concrete is also submitted to periodical tests and, in this case, a tensile stress is applied to a sample moulded into the form of a figure 8. Cement mortars, containing a special "standard sand," in which the grains have a particular range of sizes, are tested, in addition to neat cement, and although mortars and concrete, in normal practice, are not called upon to withstand tensile stresses of any serious magnitude, the tensile test is the universally accepted criterion for the quality of the cement.

The test specimen, which is technically known as the British Standard Cement Briquette, is made of a special shape. The moulds are made of brass in two halves to facilitate the removal of the specimen, and the narrow neck between the two bulbous ends of the latter is 1 square inch in area.

The rounded ends are placed in suitably shaped curved grips and pulled apart in a specially designed testing machine. The same precautions as to curing under moist conditions are observed as for concrete, but instead of allowing an interval of 28 days to elapse before testing, the briquettes are tested after 3 and 7 days. After the latter period, a sample composed of neat cement should not break under a lower stress than 600 pounds per square inch, and one composed of 1 part of cement to 3 of standard sand should give a minimum tensile strength of 375 pounds per square inch.

A MATHEMATICAL MIXTURE : REINFORCED CONCRETE

CONCRETE and steel, totally incongruous as they appear to be, work perfectly well in double harness—they expand and contract by about the same amounts under the influence of rises and falls in temperature ; and the steel, which is used in the form of bars ranging from 2 inches down to $\frac{3}{16}$ inch in diameter, is protected from corrosion by the concrete in which it is embedded.

Ferro-concrete, or *reinforced concrete*, however, is not merely a steel framework encased in concrete—the matter is far more scientific and mathematical than that. It has been stated already that concrete is a satisfactory material when used to resist compression, and steel, of course, is an excellent material to resist tension. It may be remembered, also, that in the case of an ordinary beam, bending slightly under a load, we have tension on the underside and compression on the upper side, and this two-fold stressing is very commonly encountered.

In reinforced concrete, the stresses are shared between the two materials, the concrete taking the compression and the steel the tension, and this necessitates not only the correct proportioning of concrete to steel, but also the correct location of the steel bars so that they are placed where the tensile stresses occur.

Turning again to the case of a beam, when such a member is built into the surrounding parts of a structure, it no longer bends quite in the simple manner which has been described. True, for the major part of its length the underside will be curved downwards, producing a tensile stress on that side, but near to the supports, at the two ends, conditions are reversed and tension occurs on the upper side.

Steel must therefore be provided in the top part of the beam in the vicinity of the built-in ends, and a certain proportion of the bars which run, for the greater part of the span, along the lower side are bent up near the ends in order to take up the tensile stresses without allowing them to strain

the concrete. A section of a reinforced concrete beam, showing the bending up of the bars and also the manner in which
the ends are hooked to provide a good bond, is given in Fig. 15.

The usual working stress for the concrete is 600 pounds
per square inch compression, although in first-class work,
this allowance is increased to 750 pounds, while the working
tensile stress in the steel is usually taken as 16,000 pounds
per square inch, and, for the most economical design, the

*15. A section of a reinforced concrete beam showing how
the steel bars are bent to take the stresses most suitably and
hooked to give a good bond.*

proportions of steel and concrete are so adjusted that each
material is stressed as nearly as possible to these figures.

The predominant type of reinforcement consists of mild
steel bars, depending merely on surface friction and on the
hooked ends, for adequate adhesion to the concrete, but several
patented bars are obtainable which, by means of corrugations,
indentations, twisted strands, or some other device, form a
more effective " key " with the concrete than plain bars.

THE LIGHT-WEIGHT METALS: ALUMINIUM AND DURALUMIN[1]

THE same mineral, bauxite, which, in conjunction with
limestone, gives us the remarkable aluminous cements,
is also the source of the metal aluminium. Bauxite is, to all
intents and purposes, a rock composed of aluminium and
oxygen in chemical combination, and the removal of the
latter by an electrical refining process, leaves the metal which,
like cast iron, can be run, while molten, into moulds of convenient size, where it solidifies into short bars called *pigs*.
The tensile strength of the cast metal is only about 5 tons
per square inch, and its Brinell hardness number is about 25,
showing that it is comparatively soft.

It can, however, be rolled into sheets, which are produced
in large quantities from the cast pigs, and the rolling process,

[1] See also p. 246.

carried out with the metal first hot and then cold, reduces the ductility but increases the tensile strength. Sheets are rolled to three different classifications of hardness : " soft," " half-hard " and " hard " and the corresponding tensile strengths range from a minimum of 5 to a maximum of 12 tons per square inch, the latter being about the limiting value obtainable while still retaining an adequate degree of ductility and lack of brittleness.

Aluminium is also drawn into wire and, in this case, an even greater tensile strength is common, as much as 20 tons per square inch being a normal figure. It is also formed into tubes and pressed into all kinds of shapes, besides being " spun," or shaped by special tools while the sheet metal is spinning round in a lathe, and is, in short, very accommodating.

One interesting method of manipulation is known as " extrusion." In this mode of working a hot mass of the metal is placed in a cylinder, one end of which is closed by a plate having an orifice of any required shape, and a ram, fitting the cylinder very closely, is pushed into the other end. This forces the aluminium out through the orifice and the metal assumes exactly the same shape as the latter. In this way bars can be produced in a large variety of sections. These may be of simple form, such as round, square, or rectangular, or they may be L, I, T, or U bars, or more intricate in section. The tensile strength of extruded bars is from 5 to 6 tons per square inch.

On exposure to the atmosphere, aluminium quickly becomes oxidised and the film thus formed, though somewhat dulling the attractive, bright appearance of the metal, serves as a protective coating which checks any further corrosive action.

A WONDERFUL METAL FOR AIRCRAFT DESIGN

POSSIBLY the most striking and useful property of aluminium is its extreme lightness—it weighs only 162 pounds per cubic foot, as against 490 pounds per cubic foot for iron or steel or, in round numbers, it is only one-third the weight of the heavier metal and where a high tensile strength is not essential, it is, therefore, a very valuable material, and is of particular utility in automobile and aircraft construction, owing to its lightness.

If, however, a small quantity of copper is added to aluminium, together with minute amounts of the two metals magnesium and manganese, an alloy is obtained which possesses all the advantages of aluminium, but has, in addition, a tensile strength almost equal to that of mild steel. There are many alloys of this nature, varying slightly in composition, but the best known is " Duralumin " which consists, approximately, of 94·4% aluminium, 4% of copper and ·5% each of magnesium and manganese and ·6% of silicon.

This material may be *tempered*, that is, subjected to heat treatment, to give an ultimate tensile strength of 25 tons per square inch, while retaining sufficient ductility to show an elongation, after fracture, of about 15%. The Brinell hardness number is then about 100, indicating that Duralumin is rather softer than structural mild steel. Combining, as it does, lightness and strength, it is extensively used in aeroplanes, both for parts of the actual structure and for engine components.

Many aluminium alloys, like alloy steels, may be altered in their characteristics by tempering. Thus, the tensile strength of an alloy composed of 96% aluminium and 4% copper, may be roughly doubled by heating the ordinary soft metal for one hour at a temperature of 500 degrees Centigrade and then quenching in water. This added strength, however, is not acquired immediately after quenching, as it would be in the case of steel, but a gradual increase occurs and five days are required for the maximum to be reached.

Duralumin, in particular, is an alloy which exhibits this property of slowly gaining tensile strength—and hardness— by suitable tempering and another interesting fact is that, with this material, there is no loss of ductility after heat-treatment, but, sometimes, on the contrary, a gain. This, of course, is entirely different from the behaviour of most alloy steels, in which an increase in tensile strength by heat-treatment is usually accompanied by an increase in hardness, but a loss in ductility. It is interesting to note, furthermore, that if the heat-treated Duralumin is submitted to rolling, the tensile strength and hardness will be increased still more, but the ductility will now steadily diminish.

THE CIVIL ENGINEER FINDS A USE FOR DURALUMIN

ALTHOUGH the use of aluminium and its alloys is practically confined to mechanical, automobile and aeronautical engineering, one outstanding example of the utility of an aluminium alloy in the realm of civil engineering is worthy of note.

An old road bridge at Pittsburg, Pennsylvania, had become insufficiently strong for modern traffic, and strengthening the structure by replacing the old trusses with stronger ones was considered impossible. It was, therefore, decided to relieve the dead load on the bridge by removing the heavy steel floor and substituting in its place a lighter floor of aluminium alloy. This was successfully done in the autumn of 1933, the weight of the floor was reduced by 700 tons, and the bridge is now amply strong, not only for present-day requirements, but also for the future increases in traffic loading for many years to come. The work was accomplished in 24 days, at a cost of about £60,000, whereas complete reconstruction would have taken considerably longer and cost at least four times as much.

PLASTIC MATERIALS USED BY THE ROAD-MAKER

THE phenomenal increases in the volume, tonnage, and speed of road traffic have been accompanied by corresponding developments in highway engineering, and methods of construction are constantly being improved to withstand the ever-increasing stresses which the modern road is called upon to undergo. Road engineering is becoming an important and progressive sub-division of the civil engineering profession, just as railway engineering did in the forties of last century, and new materials are continually being tried under practical service conditions. Among those which have become more firmly established, so far, than any others are the so-called *bituminous* substances, which include tar, asphaltic bitumen, lake asphalt and rock asphalt.

Tar is produced, in a crude form, when coal is converted into gas, but before it is suitable for incorporation in a road surface, it requires to be refined by a process of distillation, in which the crude material is heated in a *still* and the vapours which are driven off subsequently reconverted into liquids by cooling in *condensers*. During the distilling process, the crude tar is not only freed from a large number of substances which would prove highly unsatisfactory and injurious on the road, but these same substances, which are of great utility in their appropriate spheres, are separated and collected.

They include, for instance, such things as creosote, for preserving timber, carbolic acid for making antiseptics, naphthalene, used for moth-balls and as a horticultural fumigant, and the very complex substances, with equally complex names, from which aniline dyes are produced.

The refined road tar, as the purified material is called, may be used for spraying the road surface, or it may be mixed, while hot, with heated fragments of stone or slag, in a mechanical mixer, so that each particle of the " aggregate " is uniformly coated, and the resulting product is then known as *tarmacadam*, or *tarmac* for short. This is spread on the road in a layer about 3 inches thick and rolled until firmly compacted by a steam-roller.

Just as tar is obtained as a residue from coal, so *asphaltic bitumen* is derived as a residual by-product from the refining of certain crude natural oils. Such oils are found principally in Texas, California, Mexico and Venezuela and, in addition to bitumen, they yield motor-spirit, fuel oil, and lubricating oil. Asphaltic bitumen is a black, sticky substance which somewhat resembles tar, but has a distinctly different smell and—to an expert—a difference in the " feel " of its stickiness. It is produced in widely varying degrees of hardness, but, when heated, it softens and ultimately liquefies.

THE MYSTERIOUS NATURAL "LAKES" OF PITCH

*L*AKE ASPHALT is a remarkable material derived from two main sources—the natural " pitch " lakes of Trinidad and Bermudez, the latter being on the Venezuelan mainland. The Trinidad lake is over 100 acres in extent and over 200 feet deep in places and consists of asphaltic bitumen in a natural form, very intimately mixed with finely divided mineral matter. Although termed a " lake ", the surface is sufficiently solid to allow temporary light railways to be laid down, on which " skips," or steel-bodied trucks, are pushed by hand.

The material is easily dug out and over 5 million tons have been removed without greatly lowering the general level, the holes which are dug out becoming filled up again in about 24 hours by the brownish-black semi-solid material which appears to rise from underground springs.

The Bermudez lake has ten times the area of the Trinidad lake, but is only about 10 feet deep and consists of practically pure bitumen, in contrast to the Trinidad material which contains about 60% of clay, very fine sand, and water.

Rock asphalt consists of limestone into which liquid natural bitumen has soaked, turning the grey colour of the stone into a brownish tint. The rock usually contains up to 10% of bitumen and is mined in the South of France, Switzerland, Sicily and a few other localities : none occurs in Great Britain. It is a hard material which may be pulverised to a fine powder and, if the latter is rammed by hot iron beaters, it solidifies and, under the repeated rolling action of traffic, it eventually becomes harder than the original native rock. It thus provides a unique form of road surface which actually improves under traffic.

HALF SOLID, HALF LIQUID : BITUMEN'S SPECIAL QUALITIES

THE term *bitumen*, as generally understood, is applied to semi-solid materials which, chemically, are classed as *hydrocarbons*—that is, they are composed of the two elements hydrogen and carbon, but in spite of the apparent simplicity which this statement seems to imply, their composition is of an extremely complex nature, the two elements being grouped and connected in the most intricate manner.

Bituminous substances, furthermore, possess the property of plasticity and this is best defined, perhaps, by stating that it is the ability to flow, by virtue of which an apparently solid piece of hard bitumen, if merely left to itself on a shelf, will gradually spread and ultimately droop down from the edge of the shelf, like an icicle. A plastic solid entirely lacks the property of elasticity which a piece of steel exhibits and which enables the latter to recover its original shape after the slight deformation produced by a load not greater than the elastic limit load.

It is true that the even surface of a quantity of bitumen enclosed in a vessel will recover its smoothness after an indentation has been made in it, but this recovery is due to plastic flow and not to elasticity. A bituminous " solid," in fact, is an intermediate type between a true solid, like steel, and a true liquid, like water. This plasticity is a valuable property from the point of view of the highway engineer, since it enables a road surface to be constructed which possesses a certain amount of resilience, or " give."

The asphaltic bitumens derived from natural oils and the refined lake asphalts are both used in a similar way for producing a road surfacing material—they are incorporated with sand and broken stone and a small quantity of some fine powder, such as cement, to act as a " filler," the whole process being carried out in a mechanical mixer while the materials are hot, and the mixed product, while still hot, is conveyed to the road and spread. It is, at this stage, a loosely packed material, but it quickly consolidates to a firm, impervious surface when steam-rolled. Asphalt is also used as a roofing material and as a " damp course " to prevent the ingress of water to basements.

A special type of oil-derivative bitumen, which readily liquefies when heated, is used for the surface treatment of roads, by spraying, in a similar manner to tar, and other types form the basis of bituminous paints.

SHOCK ABSORBING RUBBER, REDUCER OF NOISE

A MATERIAL which is coming more and more into the purview of research engineers is rubber, and some of its unique and interesting properties may be briefly mentioned. The source of rubber is the *latex*, or milky liquid, which exudes if a cut is made in the bark of the rubber tree. It is not, however, the sap of the tree, and the latter does not appear to be injured by the withdrawal of the latex. This milky liquid contains a proportion of watery material from which is easily removed a substance, which after drying, rolling and manipulating, is the familiar springy pure rubber. Most of the commercial products made from rubber contain a certain quantity of fine powder, added as a filler, giving solidity or body, and the colour of the filler often imparts to the finished material the grey and red colours which are so common.

Rubber is unique in its shock-absorbing powers and its resistance to abrasion—two most valuable properties in a material intended for road surfacing. Large slabs of rubber have been used as a paving material in special situations where quietness and lack of vibration are especially desirable, as for example, on the entrance roads to Euston and St. Pancras stations which pass beneath the respective hotels. Many types of rubber road blocks are in use, but, so far, only small experimental areas have been laid, one such trial area being in the Mersey Tunnel.

In practically every test of prolonged duration, rubber blocks have displayed an extraordinary resistance to surface wear, but they have the disadvantage of being excessively expensive by comparison with other well-established methods of construction. With a view to cheapening the cost, while still retaining, to some extent, the valuable properties inherent in rubber, experiments are in active progress in which latex or, alternatively, solid rubber, is mixed with other materials such as cement, tar, or asphaltic bitumen.

A remarkable compound of latex, cement and sand has been produced, for instance, which reveals properties quite unknown in ordinary cement mortars. When submitted to a drastic abrasion test, this rubber-cement shows no trace of wear, while ordinary concrete, or cement mortar, under similar treatment becomes seriously damaged. Such a material has distinct possibilities as a road surface.

THE DESIGN OF STEEL STRUCTURES

FROM the point of view of the civil engineer, steel and concrete are the two pre-eminent constructional materials, and either the one or the other or a combination of both is almost certain to form the basic framework of any large structure, even though it may seem, from its external appearance, to be built of brickwork or stone.

Considering, first, the design of steel-framed structures, however vast and complicated these may be, they are built up invariably from standard sections and, as already mentioned, the latter may be I-joists, channels, angles and other shapes, while, in addition, there are, of course, flat strips, round and square bars, and plates of various thicknesses.

Rolled steel sections, forming the fundamental units of the largest, as well as the smallest, steel-framed buildings and bridges, are produced almost entirely from mild steel, although the latest American practice in bridge design is tending towards the use, for large spans, of high-tensile alloy steels containing nickel, chromium and silicon, whilst a British alloy, known as " Chromador," which has an ultimate tensile strength of 37 to 43 tons per square inch, is available for structural purposes.

It is an interesting fact that improvements in the manufacture of many well-established and standardised materials have resulted in their qualities exceeding the requirements of the British Standard Specifications, and the latter have to be revised from time to time to keep abreast of manufacturing progress. Structural steel is a case in point and the higher limit of tensile stress for this material has been raised, in recent years, from 32 to 33 tons per square inch, and some designers now use a working stress of 8 tons per square inch instead of the more conservative value half-a-ton per square inch less.

Sheffield, the traditional centre of the steel industry, is not greatly interested in the particular form of mild steel used for structural sections, Middlesbrough and the Cleveland area being one of the principal manufacturing centres, although the West Riding possesses at least one large rolling mill which turns out structural material at Parkgate, near Rotherham.

The steel from the refining furnaces is cast into " ingots " —long rectangular pieces often weighing from 5 to 8 tons,

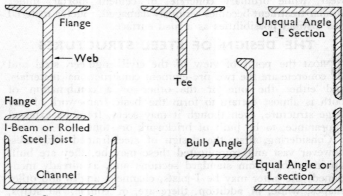

16. Some of the sections in which rolled steel beams are made

and these are re-heated to white heat and first pass through the " cogging mills," composed of large plain rolls which convert the ingots into the required shape for running through the section rolls. Thus a billet (as the ingot is known after rolling) may be too short and too thick for converting direct into a rolled joist, and the cogging mill squeezes this short, thick piece of metal into a much longer piece of the requisite cross-sectional area for the subsequent rolling in the section mill. Here the steel passes through a set of rolls which, according to their configuration and grooving, form I, T, L, or other sections, some of which are shown in Fig. 16. It will be noticed that these have rounded angles and that the beams and channels have slightly tapered flanges to facilitate the rolling process, since sharp angles and edges would have a tendency to jamb.[1]

---

[1] Refer to p. 241.

British Standard sections are made in a vast number of different shapes and dimensions. Thus, one series of I-beams alone consists of eighteen different sizes. The horizontal top and bottom portions of a section of this type are called the " flanges " and the vertical portion connecting them the " web." The largest size has an overall depth of 24 inches, a flange width of $7\frac{1}{2}$ inches, and a web thickness of about $\frac{1}{2}$ inch. A piece of this beam 1 foot long weighs 90 pounds. The smallest section in the series, by contrast, is only 3 inches deep, with a flange width of $1\frac{1}{2}$ inches and a web thickness of about an $\frac{1}{8}$ inch and a piece 1 foot long weighs 4 pounds. These particular sections are also known as " Rolled Steel Joists," commonly abbreviated to " R.S.J.'s."

Channels somewhat resemble an I-beam cut in half down the web, but the thickness of the former is greater than the web thickness of the corresponding beam. A channel of 3 inches depth and $1\frac{1}{2}$ inches flange width, for instance, has a web nearly a $\frac{1}{4}$ inch thick.

THE EFFICIENT "I" BEAM

THE reason for the adoption of the I section for steel beams may be appreciated by using an ordinary wooden ruler as a model bridge. If this is first held flat side uppermost quite an insignificant load will produce a large deflection at the centre of the span. If, however, the ruler is now held on edge, it will offer a considerable resistance to bending in a vertical plane, but will, of course, readily buckle sideways. Hence, a tall narrow rectangle forms a better beam shape than a wide flat one, but if a steel beam were made of solid rectangular section of sufficient thickness to be reasonably stiff sideways, an extremely heavy mass of metal would result.

Considering, once again, what happens when a simple beam bends, it will be recalled that the underside is stretched and the upper side compressed while somewhere near the centre there is a neutral axis which is neither elongated nor shortened. The most severe stressing, both tensile and compressive, occurs near the bottom and top surfaces of the beam, and the severity decreases as we approach the middle. In the " I " section the surplus material has been removed from the centre where the intensity of bending stress is relatively small, and concentrated instead at the top and bottom where it is most needed, thus effecting a saving in weight and also in valuable metal.

COMBINING THE GIRDERS TO GIVE GREATER STRENGTH

WHEN a certain limit of span, or severity of loading, is reached, even the largest rolled steel joists become inadequate, and built-up girders must be used. These still retain the characteristic " I " section, and are composed of separate flange and web plates united by angle-irons riveted into the corners, as shown in Fig. 17(*a*). When dealing with even larger spans and heavier loads, it may be necessary to use two separate web plates, riveted to double or triple flanges, as shown in Fig. 17(*b*) the arrangement being then known as a " box girder." It is very important, when designing a box

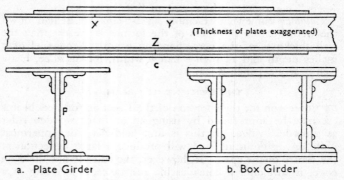

a. Plate Girder   b. Box Girder

17. How large girders are built up from standard units.

girder, to ensure that there is sufficient room inside to enable the interior to be painted from time to time. Additional flange plates are used as the centre of the span is approached, to take up the greater bending action which occurs there, and these extra plates often form convenient covers to overlap the joints in the plates beneath, as at X, Y and Z in Fig. 17(*c*).

Large plate and box girders require additional strengthening to provide sufficient rigidity, and this is accomplished by riveting vertical " stiffeners " to the web. These may be of angle- or T-section steel, and are sometimes brought round to the flanges and attached thereto, as shown at the left of Fig. 18, or a stronger form of stiffener may be adopted in which a vertical plate fitting tightly between the flanges is riveted at right angles to the web in the manner shown in the centre. Angle-irons are of great utility in making various connections, a typical joint between two girders using angle brackets being shown at the right of Fig. 18.

Although the mathematical details of design cannot be entered into here, it may be of interest to quote the generally accepted rule that the depth of a plate girder should never be less than one-twentieth of the span, the usual proportion being from one-tenth to one-twelfth. The width across the flanges may be from one-twentieth to one-fiftieth of the span and the minimum thickness of the plates used for the web and flanges is ⅜ inch.

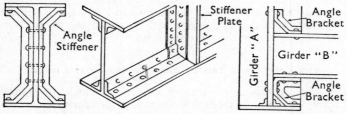

18. How girders are strengthened by angle stiffeners, stiffener plates and angle brackets.

SYMMETRY, BEAUTY AND STRENGTH : THE OPEN WEB GIRDER

IN bridge construction there is a limit to the span for which plate girders are suitable, and " open web " girders are then employed. They are also called " braced " or " lattice " girders, or, more simply, " trusses," and their adoption enables the metal to be disposed more efficiently and economically than in a plate girder, whilst their open character gives rise to far smaller stresses from wind pressure.

Certain distinctive types of truss are given the names of their originators—thus we have the " Warren " girder, composed of a top and bottom " boom " connected by inclined members, sloping either at 60 or 45 degrees to the horizontal and thus forming a series of equilateral or isosceles triangles, as shown in Fig. 19(*a*) and (*b*). Then, again, there is the " Whipple-Murphy " truss in which the top and bottom booms are connected both by inclined and vertical members as in Fig. 19(*c*) and (*d*).

More complicated systems of cross bracing are sometimes adopted. Thus a second Warren truss superimposed on the first, but placed upside down, gives us the lattice type shown in Fig. 19(e), where one set of members is shown full and the other in broken line. Trusses are arranged in pairs, side by side, and a railway track or roadway may be carried on supports attached either to the lower booms, as in Fig. 19(a) and (c), in which case the bridge is termed a through bridge, or to the upper booms, as in Fig. 19(b) and (d), in which case the bridge is termed a deck bridge.

A further development consists in making the upper boom curved, so that a greater depth of girder is obtained at the centre of the span and this gives a rather more graceful effect than is produced by a horizontal upper boom. Deck bridges are sometimes constructed with a curved lower boom, corresponding to a through bridge with a curved top boom, but the latter is by far the more usual type.

THE CANTILEVER TRUSS : BASIS OF THE FORTH BRIDGE

A SPECIAL design of trussed bridge of which there are several famous examples, including the world-renowned structure which spans the Firth of Forth, is worthy of mention. This is known as the " cantilever " type, and is a clever adaptation of balanced leverages.

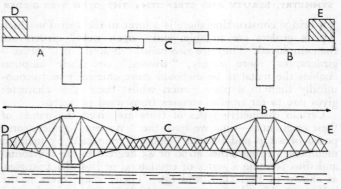

20. *The double cantilever in principle (above), and in practice (below) as part of the Forth Bridge.*

A cantilever is a beam which projects from a single support placed at one end, and a double cantilever consists of a pair of projecting arms having a common centre support. If two

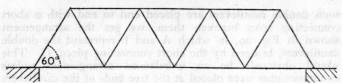

a. Warren girder in use for through bridge

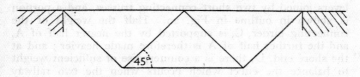

b. Warren girder in use for deck bridge

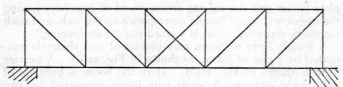

c Whipple Murphy truss for through bridge

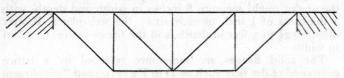

d. Deck bridge type Whipple Murphy truss

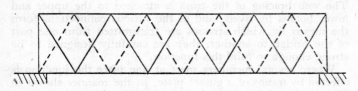

e. Lattice truss from two Warren trusses

19. VARIOUS TYPES OF BRIDGE TRUSSES.

such double cantilevers are placed end to end with a short connecting span between them, we get the arrangement shown in Fig. 20, in which A and B represent the double cantilevers, bridged by the short connecting piece, C. This would obviously be an unbalanced arrangement unless counterweights were placed at the free ends of the cantilevers D and E.

The Forth Bridge consists of three huge double cantilevers joined by two short connecting trusses, and a portion is shown in outline in Fig. 20. Half the weight of the connecting girder, C, is supported by the nearer half of A, and the further half of A is therefore made heavier ; and at the shore end, D, there is a counterpoise of sufficient weight to balance the effect which occurs when the two railway tracks on the girder C are occupied by trains.

In a truss, or open web girder, the main " booms " running across at the top and bottom, correspond to the flanges of a plate girder and the zig-zag arrangement of members joining the upper and lower booms corresponds to the web, and such members constitute what is termed the " web bracing."

A simple form of boom may consist of two channels connected by a pair of plates, as shown in Fig. 21(a). A heavier form is shown in Fig. 21(b). Here the boom is built up of four angle sections, A, each pair being connected by two plates, B, and top and bottom flanges, C. In a large bridge, the angles might measure 8 inches in width and depth, with a thickness of $\frac{7}{8}$ inch to each arm ; the web-plates, B, may often be $2\frac{1}{2}$ to 3 feet in depth, and the flange-plates, C, 5 feet in width.

The solid flanges are sometimes replaced by a lattice composed of flat bars such as D in Fig. 21(c) and " diaphragm plates," E, are inserted between the web-plates at intervals and connected thereto by small angles to give added stiffness. The web bracing of the truss is attached to the upper and lower booms by rivets, and as the various connections form the means by which stresses are transmitted from one part of the bridge to another, they are carefully designed to be strong enough to fulfil this function.

Where several members meet at one place the junction is effected by means of a gusset plate, in the manner shown in Fig. 21(d). Joints are also necessary at intervals in long members and these are made, as they are in plate girders, by using cover plates.

THE UNBENDING STRUT AND NON-STRETCHING TIE

THE individual units, according to whether they will have to stand tension or compression are classified as *ties* or *struts* respectively. A tie has to resist a pulling action, tending to tear it asunder from each end. A strut, on the other hand, has to resist a pushing action which is attempting both to crush it and to buckle it. Hence a tie need not necessarily be a stiff member which can only be buckled with

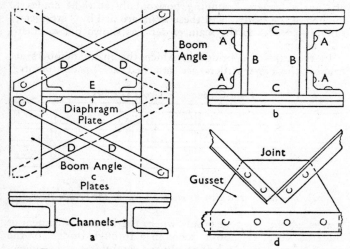

21. *Types of " boom " used to form the upper and lower edges of bridge trusses. In (d) is shown a method of joining several members by a gusset plate.*

difficulty—we have already seen that flexible cables will resist a tensile stress and, indeed, are employed for this purpose in suspension bridges—but a strut must possess lateral rigidity, so that it will preserve its true alignment without distorting under a compressive load.

For this reason, ties on steel bridges are often flat bars, but struts are invariably of more elaborate section. In a small truss they may be tees or angle sections, and in larger trusses they are built up of angles, tees, or channels connected by plates. It often happens that as a train or vehicle crosses a bridge, some of the members have to act first as ties and then as struts according to the position of the load ; and such units, of course, must be designed as struts, due allowance being made for the reversal of stress.

FROM NETWORK TO SOLID FLOOR

COMING next to the general arrangement of the various components, the main girders, whether of the plate, web or truss type, are generally connected by transverse beams, or " cross girders," running horizontally at right angles to the line of the bridge, and these again are tied by " stringers," running parallel to the main girders, as shown diagrammatically in Fig. 22.

In the case of a bridge in which the main members are trusses, the cross girders are attached at " panel points,"

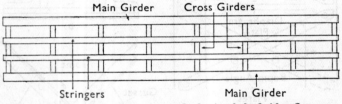

22. *The network which forms the basis of the bridge floor.*

that is, at the junction points where the bracing members of the truss meet the lower boom in a through bridge, or the upper boom in a deck bridge. In railway bridges the stringers are often called " rail bearers " and are designed to run immediately beneath the rails, thus giving support exactly where it is needed.

Over the stringers is placed the sheeting on which, in turn, the floor proper is constructed. The sheeting may be of curved steel plates, the two principal types being " cambered plates " which are supported along two edges and " buckled plates " which are supported on four edges, and in either case they are normally $\frac{1}{2}$ inch, or so, in thickness and are coated on their upper surface with a layer of asphalt, $\frac{3}{4}$ inch thick, as a preservative. The underside is usually exposed and may thus be painted.

Another very useful type of sheeting is " trough decking," shown in Fig. 23. This material, as rolled, somewhat resembles a trough with slanting sides and by riveting sections together, placing them alternately with the trough upwards and then downwards, a continuous floor is obtained in which every section, by virtue of its shape, actually forms an efficient beam. The troughing is made in several sizes, a medium type giving an overall depth, when riveted up, of about 6 inches, with a flange thickness, top and bottom, of ½ inch and the thickness of the slanting webs slightly more than a ¼ inch.

With cambered or buckled plates, stringers are always necessary and are usually spaced from 4 to 6 feet apart, but

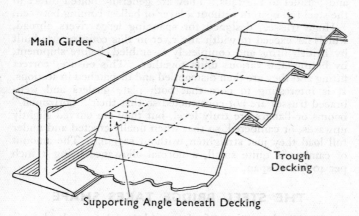

Main Girder

Trough Decking

Supporting Angle beneath Decking

23. How trough decking, which acts as a series of beams, can replace stringers and cross girders in a bridge floor.

trough decking can often be employed as a flooring without any additional support, in which case it is riveted direct to small angle brackets attached to the main girders, as shown in Fig. 23. The space above the decking of floor plates, in a highway bridge, is filled in with concrete to the required depth to bring the surfaces of the roadway and footpaths to the correct levels. The surface of the roadway is usually made of a material which will, to some extent, absorb the shocks and vibrations, due to the passing traffic. Wood-paving and asphalt are both suitable materials for this purpose. Tarmacadam, asphalt, or slab paving may be used for the footways.

EXTRA RAILS GUARD AGAINST DISASTER

IN the case of railway bridges, " ballast," generally composed of broken granite or hard slag of 2 to 3 inch size,[1] is interposed between the floor plates and the sleepers, and the latter carry both the running rails and also the " check " or " guard rails " which are invariably provided on a bridge to prevent the possibility of a derailment. Instead of the familiar sleepers placed at right angles to the track, longitudinal sleepers are sometimes used. These are long baulks of timber, about 10 inches square in section and run immediately beneath and parallel to the rails. They are generally bolted direct to the steel rail bearers without a layer of ballast coming between.

Huge trusses, designed for spanning large rivers abroad, which far exceed in width any river in this country, are built by British firms and completely assembled, before shipment, by bolting the various units together. This ensures correct fitting and they are then dismantled and dispatched in sections. It is interesting to note that both plate girders and web-braced trusses are not constructed so that their " horizontal " booms or flanges are truly level, but they are curved slightly upwards, or cambered, so that when finally erected and under full load they just straighten, without sagging. The amount of camber is quite small, a normal allowance being 1 inch per 40 feet of span.

THE STEEL BRIDGE TAKES SHAPE

THE actual erection of plate girder and truss bridges is accomplished by a variety of methods. A plate girder is invariably treated as a structural unit, even though it may be 100 feet or more in length and 10 feet deep. A girder of this size weighs roughly 50 tons and can be handled conveniently by two steam cranes of ordinary dimensions. The cross girders, stringers and flooring may either be riveted to the main girders direct, after the latter are in place, or conveniently sized sections of the bridge floor with its supporting members may be assembled first, dropped into position and then riveted to the main structure.

It frequently happens that a wide river is to be crossed by a bridge of several spans supported on a number of intermediate pillars or *piers*, as they are called. These are built

[1] See p. 73.

first, and should the water levels, currents, tides, and other natural conditions of the river be suitable, each span, consisting of its main girders and secondary members, may be erected complete on timber stagings built up on large " pontoons " or barges and supported by hydraulic jacks. (A jack capable of lifting 100 tons is quite a small and insignificant appliance, but it is a most useful implement to the civil engineer.) The barges are moored in a convenient position near the bridge site and when the erection is complete, they are floated into the correct position between the piers and the complete span lowered down into place.

ENGINEERING WIZARDRY : REPLACING A BRIDGE OVERNIGHT

THE amazing rapidity with which large railway bridges are renewed overnight becomes understandable when it is realised that the entire steelwork of the new bridge is usually erected first on a special staging mounted on rollers, close alongside the old structure. The new bearings are prepared in readiness, the old bridge, if of iron or steel, is demolished with great rapidity by means of oxy-acetylene flames which cut through metal as easily as a knife cuts butter, and when everything is ready, the new bridge is moved into position by jacks placed horizontally, or by wire hawsers pulled by winches or cranes. The rollers enable great weights to be moved with comparative ease.

In one notable example, an old steel railway bridge was recently replaced by a new truss bridge of over 100 feet span and weighing nearly 700 tons and the entire change over was accomplished within 24 hours.

REACHING OUT ACROSS THE WATER : THE STEEL ARCH

FOR both technical and economic reasons there is a limit to the span which can be covered by a single girder or truss, and it is often impossible to place intermediate piers in a river bed. When a span too wide for a single truss has to be bridged, a steel arch of open framework design is sometimes adopted. Possibly the best-known example is the immense structure with a span of 1650 feet across Sydney Harbour. The arched form is superior æsthetically to the truss bridge and the larger specimens have a very impressive appearance. The arch itself is sometimes carried high above the bridge floor, which is suspended beneath it by tension members, as in the Sydney Harbour bridge, and in other cases the arch is placed beneath the floor and supports it by means of columns, or compression members.

All arched structures, whether of steel, masonry, or concrete, transmit their loading in the form of a *thrust* or compression to their abutments [1] which must consequently have sufficient strength to take this stressing without movement. It will therefore be found that the abutments of arches are always very massive unless the structure is supported directly by non-yielding rock.

The method of constructing a large steel arch across a wide river is both ingenious and economically efficient, when, as frequently happens, it is impossible to build up any temporary support beneath the structure. The usual procedure is to build out the arch in two halves from the abutments, so that they form cantilevers until the moment of joining up at the centre. Cranes are used for lifting the steel sections, which are similar components to those used in trussed girder bridges, and these are lowered into position and riveted in place, one by one. This process is conveniently carried out by having a crane for lifting the steelwork mounted on each half of the arch and, in addition, two smaller cranes, each capable of lifting the first cranes when the latter are dismantled into suitably sized pieces.

The erection is continued up to the limit of reach of the larger cranes, which then lift the smaller cranes to a more forward position along the top of the arch. The latter, in turn, lift the first cranes forward, thus extending their working area, and the erection is continued. As the framework of the arch gradually extends, it is tied back by wire cables to strong supports on shore, until the two halves finally meet to form a self-supporting structure. The arch then provides the necessary support for the erection of the bridge floor.

HOW THE BEARINGS ALLOW FOR HEAT AND COLD

UNDER the influence of temperature changes large masses of steel naturally expand and contract, and allowance is made for this movement in bridges of any size by the inclusion in the design of some type of bearing which will permit relative motion to occur between the girders and the supports, thus relieving the structure from strain.

Large plate girders and trusses, for example, are often seated on rollers housed in a massive frame built into the

[1] See p. 102.

abutments, so that slight movement of the steelwork can be accommodated by rotation of the bearings. A bridge of 200 feet span, however, will change in length by less than 1 inch for a temperature change of 60 degrees Fahrenheit.

The rollers are made of cast steel and their surfaces and those of the plates with which they are in contact are very accurately machined. They may be from 3 to 6 inches in diameter and from 1 to 4 feet in length. Rockers are often used instead of cylindrical rollers, and these are specially shaped curved bars, also housed in a frame, and working freely in contact with one another.

In steel arch construction, freedom of movement is obtained by mounting the ends of the arch in very massive spherical bearings. In the new Wearmouth Bridge, Sunderland, for example, the lattice steel arch is attached at its lower ends to castings which carry spherical knuckles of nickel-chrome steel, and these knuckles rest in concave sockets built in to the bridge abutments. Both the knuckles and the sockets at their common bearing surfaces are, in reality, portions of a sphere which has a radius of no less than 5 feet, and this type of bearing gives excellent support while, at the same time, slight movement is possible between the ends of the arch ribs and the solid abutments.

The same effect is obtained by attaching the arch to the abutments by " pins." Thus, in the Tyne Bridge at New-castle, completed in 1928, the end of each steel arch rib is fitted with a casting having a groove running across it which forms one half of a cylinder, and a saddle bearing with an exactly similar groove forming the other half of the cylinder is attached to the abutment. Between the two there is a cylindrical pin, exactly fitting the grooves, its diameter being 1 foot and its length 8 feet 5 inches.

An arch constructed in this way with pins only at the abutment bearings is termed a " two-pinned arch," but it is common practice to make a flexible joint at the highest point, or crown, of the arch also, by using freely fitting pin bearings instead of riveting up the structure as one rigid framework. We thus obtain a " three-pinned arch," and the Wearmouth Bridge, Sunderland, is of this type, although, strictly speaking, the flexibility at the crown is not derived from a pin-joint, but from a ball-and-socket bearing similar in general design to that provided at the abutments, as already described.

In smaller bridges provision for expansion and contraction movements is sometimes made by merely allowing the girders to slide on their seatings at one abutment, the other end being fixed.

THE LIGHT AND GRACEFUL SUSPENSION BRIDGE

ANOTHER type of construction allowing a long span to be crossed without intermediate support is the suspension bridge. The span of the well-known example at Clifton, for instance, is 676 feet. The principal members in this type of structure are the suspension cables or chains from which the bridge floor is hung. These may be looked upon as inverted arches and just as the latter require strong abutments to take the thrust, so the cables of a suspension bridge require a strong anchorage to take their tension. In practice, they are usually carried over saddles on supporting towers and thence downwards to firm anchorages in the ground. Thus the cables of the Chelsea Bridge, London, are embedded on each side of the river in solid masses of masonry and concrete, 80 feet long, 45 feet thick and 40 feet deep.

A suspension bridge has a light and graceful appearance and is easily erected, since the cables, once in position, provide the means of support for carrying forward the construction of the floor by attaching the hanging suspension members and the decking piece by piece. In their simplest form, however, they lack rigidity and are not suitable for fast and heavy railway traffic, since dangerous vibrations would be set up, but when stiffened and braced by carrying the floor through on strong trussed girders hung from the cables, this disadvantage may be overcome.

Possibly the world's most outstanding example of a stiffened suspension bridge is the magnificent structure crossing the Hudson River at New York. This has the vast span of 3,500 feet between the cable towers, and has two decks, the upper one for road traffic, providing sufficient width for no less than eight lines of cars, in addition to two tramway tracks, while the lower can accommodate four railway tracks. The wire suspension cables, of which two pairs are employed, are each 36 inches in diameter and composed of more than 25,000 high tension steel wires.

Suspension chains, instead of cables, are frequently used and these are generally built up of a number of thin, flat bars provided with holes through which pins are passed, thus giving flexibility. In the Menai Bridge, built over 100 years ago by Thomas Telford, there are four main chains, each of which consists of four single chains placed one above

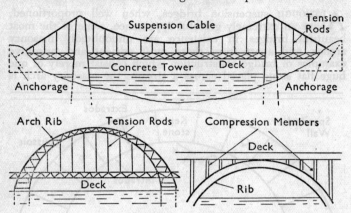

24. *Above : the main features of a suspension bridge. Below : two types of arched-rib bridges.*

the other. Each of the single chains consists of a number of long flat strips and a number of shorter flat strips pinned together alternately. The long sections are roughly 3 inches

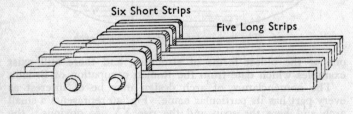

25. *How the chains of the Menai Suspension Bridge are built up of long and short metal strips used alternately.*

deep and 1 inch thick and the short pieces are about 8 inches deep and 1 inch thick. There are five of the former and six of the latter arranged side by side, in the manner shown in Fig. 25.

MASONRY ARCHES : THE BEAUTIFUL BRIDGES OF THE PAST

ALTHOUGH suspension bridges, when well proportioned, have an extremely graceful appearance, some of the most beautiful bridges in existence are undoubtedly masonry arches, and apart from those most ancient and primitive examples of bridge construction which consist merely of one huge flat stone placed across a stream, the masonry arch is

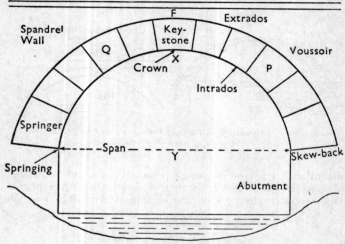

26. *The nomenclature of a masonry arch*

one of the oldest forms of structure, and there still exist examples which date from the Roman occupation of Britain.

The nomenclature of arch design may be of interest as every part has its particular name. Fig. 26 represents a small arch and here the span and the rise XY are obvious ; the springings and the crown lie on the inner surface, termed the soffit or intrados, while the outer surface is called the back or extrados. If the arch itself is constructed of individual stones, such as PQ, these are known as voussoirs, the lowest being the springers and the top centre one the key-stone, the depth of which is given by the dimension FX. The sloping beds on which the springers rest are the skew-backs. The

areas on either side of the extrados are called the spandrel
walls and the vertical supporting walls, the abutments.

Arches may be either circular arcs or elliptical, and in
the former case they are known as " segmental." Sometimes
a combination of circular arcs alone forms what is very nearly
a true elliptical arch, two being of equal radii, R in Fig. 27,
to give the arch shape at the springings, and a central arc of
larger radius, S, being blended in with the other two
to produce a flatter effect near the crown. Such an arch is
known as a " three centred " or " false elliptical " type.

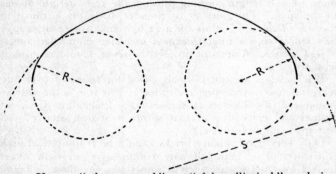

27. *How a " three-centred " or " false elliptical " arch is
built up from arcs of three circles.*

There are many masonry arches of 150 to 200 feet span—
those of London Bridge are 152 feet—and there are some
few examples even longer. Much of the design is based on
well-established rules, expressed by simple formulæ. Thus,
the depth of the keystone, according to one law, is obtained
by taking the square root of the radius of the arch at the
crown and multiplying it by a factor depending upon the
material of which the arch is to be constructed.

Suppose, for instance, that we have a span of 200 feet
and a rise of 40 feet (a very common proportion), the radius
at the crown in feet will then be very nearly 144, the square
root of which is 12. Assuming that the arch is to be built
in first-class stonework, the multiplying factor is ·36, giving
12 × ·36 feet or 4·32 feet for the depth of the keystone. For
a large span the arch ring would be gradually thickened from
the crown round to the springing.

The ratio of the rise to the span may vary between one-half, for a semi-circular arch, to one-eighth for a very flat arch, but one-third to one-fifth is the commonest proportion, the latter figure applying to the 152 foot arches of London Bridge already mentioned.

ARCHES BUILT OF BRICK : THE MAIDENHEAD BRIDGE

IN addition to cut stone arches, in which each voussoir has a slight taper narrowing towards the intrados to give a wedge action, arches are also constructed in concentric rings of brickwork, the bricks being placed on edge, with their greatest length running through the arch at right angles to the span. The number of rings is made proportional to the size of the arch—thus for a 12 foot span, three rings may be used, giving a total thickness inclusive of mortar joints, of $14\frac{1}{2}$ inches. A span of 40 feet, however, would require at least six rings.

Brick arches are not normally used for spans of over 100 feet, but one outstanding exception to this rule is the railway bridge over the Thames at Maidenhead, designed by the great Brunel and consisting of two elliptical arches, each of 128 feet span and 24 feet rise.

Only very good quality bricks should be employed in arch construction, and an ultimate compressive strength of at least 2 tons per square inch is sometimes specified—a figure roughly equivalent to that obtained with fair quality sandstone, but only about one quarter the crushing strength of good granite.

CALCULATION TO WHICH BEAUTY MUST CONFORM

BRICKWORK and masonry, though comparatively strong in compression, should never be submitted to tensile stresses, which would soon reveal their presence by the cracks they would inevitably produce. Now a brick or masonry arch transmits the loading in the form of a thrust which passes round the ring to the abutments. By a method of graphical construction it is possible to represent on a drawing the theoretical direction taken by the thrust in passing through the structure and this imaginary line, which, in all probability, gives a fair approximation to the conditions obtained in practice, is known as the " line of thrust."

The arch is first drawn out to a large scale and the arch-ring is divided circumferentially into three concentric strips, the central one being termed the "middle third." In order that the brickwork or masonry should nowhere be submitted to tension the line of thrust should keep within the confines of this central, or middle third, area, until it reaches the lowest portion of the arch ring whence it passes into the abutment. In preliminary designs, the line of thrust will sometimes pass not only beyond the middle third, but even outside the arch ring itself and the latter is then thickened, or redesigned in shape, until a satisfactory line of thrust is obtained and it is then assumed that there is no tension in the material.

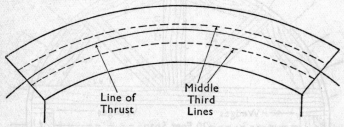

Line of Thrust

Middle Third Lines

28. In a masonry arch, the " line of thrust " due to the weight of the masonry should keep within the middle third (broken) lines to ensure safety.

A typical thrust diagram is shown in Fig. 28. It may be mentioned, however, that this particular graphical method probably errs on the safe side, as certain perfectly sound structures which have been in existence for many years should be unstable according to their line of thrust, but, nevertheless, the method is widely used and accepted.

BUILDING THE MASONRY ARCH : A FRAMEWORK OF TIMBERS

MASONRY or brick arch construction requires a timber centering to support the work while it is in progress. This consists of a number of curved timber ribs, carefully braced and strutted and boarded over so that a smooth surface is obtained exactly of the shape of the underside of the arch.

A typical example is shown in Fig. 29. The centering is supported at the correct level between the abutments or piers, which are constructed first, on a staging built of heavy timbers, the latter having to support the weight of the arch during the period of building. The arch is " turned," to use the technical term, starting from the springing on both sides and meeting at the centre.

When a sufficient time has elapsed to permit of the mortar setting, the centres are carefully lowered. This is accomplished in the following way : The centering is mounted either on double wedges or on blocks fitting into cylinders filled with sand, these devices being supported on the staging,

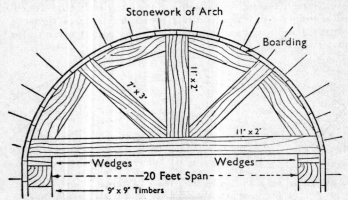

Stonework of Arch

Boarding

7" x 3"

11" x 2"

11" x 2"

Wedges   Wedges

20 Feet Span

9" x 9" Timbers

29. A timber centering for a small brick arch, showing the width and thicknesses of the timbers used.

and when the wedges are slackened or the sand run out from the cylinders, the centering gradually drops. In the case of stone arches with very thin mortar joints the centering may be lowered earlier than in brick arches in which the joints are far more numerous and thicker.

REINFORCED CONCRETE : A VERSATILE MODERN MEDIUM

REINFORCED concrete [1] may be adapted to an immense variety of structures and in bridge work alone it may be used, among others, for the following different types :

(1) Horizontal beams, supporting the floor, with or without cross beams. This corresponds to the ordinary girder type of steel bridge, and it is possible to construct an open-web braced girder in reinforced concrete, as well as in steel.

[1] See p. 77.

(2) Arches of the ordinary type exactly corresponding to brick or masonry arches.

(3) Arch ribs carrying the floor beneath.

(4) Arch ribs supporting the floor on columns, forming an "open spandrel arch."

The erection of reinforced concrete bridges involves two distinct modes of procedure : (1) " in situ " and (2) " pre-cast " work.

The first is the normal method for bridges of the beam and slab-floor type and for solid arches, and it consists of casting the structure in its permanent position, or " in situ," in a timber mould or, to use the technical term, " shuttering."

The second method has sometimes been adopted for bridges designed with arched ribs and consists of casting these, before erection, in timber moulds and lifting them into position on the bridge site later. Small units, especially those required in quantity such as balusters and coping pieces for parapets, are generally pre-cast in all cases, as it is easier to obtain good clean moulding from specially made separate metal moulds, than by attempting to form these rather intricate small details in built-up shuttering on the bridge itself.

FROM WOODEN MOULD TO CONCRETE BRIDGE

ONE disadvantage of reinforced concrete work is the necessity for moulds and shuttering, and for "in situ" work, the temporary timber casing must be sufficiently strong and rigid to hold its full complement of concrete and steel without distortion.

After the shuttering has been built, usually on a temporary timber staging and with smooth planed wood for the interior to give well cast surfaces to the concrete placed therein, the reinforcement is placed in position. This is built up of steel rods and connecting rods of smaller diameter looped to the main bars, threaded tightly together, and tied with wire to form a rigid framework. Much of this is assembled beforehand as self-contained units and is dropped into position in the shuttering, being held there in the correct position by wooden blocks and wedges.

The complete reinforcing element for a beam or column is generally dealt with in this way, but there is a great deal of subsequent connecting up of units within the shuttering, since the whole of the reinforcement must be efficiently tied together to form one interlocked system. Thus the steel rods in a column or beam must be connected to the network in the floor which the column or beam is supporting.

The reinforcement must also be sufficiently strong to permit of barrowfuls of concrete being run over it on planks, and when the steel has all been placed in position and the location of each bar carefully checked to a fraction of an inch, the concrete is packed thoroughly round the metal. It is then rammed into close contact with the interior of the shuttering so as to form a solid mass entirely free from unfilled spaces and with the reinforcement in precisely the correct position—a matter of vital importance in this type of construction.

In this class of work, where the concrete has to be pushed into small spaces and into the intricate steel network, it is made rather wetter than is allowable in large masses such as are encountered in foundation or road construction. The size of the aggregate is also limited to suit the spacing of the reinforcement.

In the erection of many large structures, the concrete, after being mixed in the familiar mechanical plant, is raised to a central tower, similar to that employed for the lofty crane which invariably overtops a big building in course of construction, and is discharged thence to various parts of the shuttering through radiating *shutes*, or troughs, placed at such an inclination that the concrete will flow down them.

BUILDING A MODERN CONCRETE BRIDGE

IT is now possible to consider in some detail the design of a typical highway bridge of medium size. The abutments would usually be of " mass concrete," that is, unreinforced concrete, containing larger aggregate and a lower cement content than that adopted for the concrete in the superstructure. When the abutments have been constructed up to the correct level, the shuttering for the beams and floor slab is erected.

The beams are rectangular in shape with bevelled corners to render the moulding easier, since it would be difficult to pack the concrete into sharp corners ; and assuming that we are dealing with a span of 50 feet, a normal size for the beams would be 5 feet in depth and 2 feet in width, the spacing between them being 9 feet, from the centre of one beam to the centre of the next.

Covering the beams would be a concrete slab about 10 inches thick, and both slab and beams would be completely reinforced. The main bars in the beams could be six in number, each 1½ inches in diameter, running longitudinally 2 inches from the bottom and bent up near the abutments and hooked round. The slab reinforcement could consist of 1 inch bars placed 2 inches above the base and bent upwards where the slab crosses the beams, and a second series of bars, known as " distribution " members, would be placed at right angles to the main slab reinforcement.

The upward bending of the beam and slab bars is carried out to a certain proportion of the bars only, leaving the remainder to run straight through, and a series of vertical rods called " stirrups " are run from the bottom of the beam and tied firmly into the slab reinforcement, thus uniting the two parts of the structure. The outer beams conveniently form the foundation for the parapets, which may be of the solid panel type, or the more artistic balustrade pattern. In either case reinforcing rods are brought up from the beam and taken well into the pillars, or piers, of the parapet so that the latter form an integral part of the structure.

After allowing a sufficient period to elapse for the setting of the concrete, the shuttering is removed, and any small faults in the moulded surfaces made good. Sometimes all exposed surfaces are rubbed down to improve the appearance, and there is a widespread tendency to conceal entirely the concrete with its rather ugly grey colour, and face all the exposed parts with brick or stone, so that the real constructional medium of the bridge is disguised.

Hampton Court Bridge, for instance, is a reinforced concrete structure, although its skilful facing hides the fact and it appears to be built of brick and stone. This was a special feature of the design and was introduced to provide a harmonious effect with the adjacent Palace.

WHAT THE BRIDGE MUST SUSTAIN : A FULL LOAD OF TRACTION ENGINES

MODERN highway bridges are designed to carry what is known as the Ministry of Transport Standard Loading, and this consists of very heavy trains of traction engines and trailers covering the entire bridge. Each train is composed of an engine weighing 20 tons and three trailers, each weighing 13 tons, and all these loads are increased by 50% to make due allowance for impact effect, so that the entire train produces a theoretical loading of nearly 90 tons. This very severe Standard Loading is intended to cover possible future developments in road transport, but, even so, large bridges which have been built in industrial areas, such as Glasgow and Newcastle-on-Tyne, have been designed to carry an added loading, over and above the standard, to allow for the exceptional local conditions, since extremely heavy weights are conveyed by road in these districts.

Thus, the Wearmouth Bridge, at Sunderland, was designed to carry a uniformly distributed loading of 1½ hundredweights per square foot over the whole deck, in addition to a single lorry carrying no less than 150 tons on only two axles.

Again, the King George V Bridge at Glasgow was constructed to carry two tram tracks, each fully occupied by trams, the weight of each loaded tram being 13 tons, a uniformly distributed load of 1 hundredweight per square foot over the rest of the carriageway and footpaths, and a single load of 120 tons carried on two axles only and drawn by five traction engines, weighing 15 tons each.

The weight of a large bridge, in itself, is considerable and must, of course, be allowed for in the design. The weight of the steel alone, for instance, in the arch and deck of the Tyne Bridge, Newcastle, is 4,000 tons.

ALLOWING FOR THE FORCE OF THE WIND

WIND pressure provides a further source of loading on all exposed structures, and its magnitude is rather a matter of empirical estimation. The usual allowance for the pressure exerted by a hurricane is 50 pounds per square foot, a figure adopted in the case of the Sunderland Bridge previously mentioned. The loading produced by a dense crowd of people may amount to as much as 150 pounds per square foot and this is a common allowance in designing the floors of large public buildings. Warehouse floors, however, may be subjected to nearly double this intensity.

Turning now to railway bridges, it is interesting to note, as a matter of comparison, that the large single loads, each carried only on two axles, allowed for in the Sunderland and Glasgow bridges as legitimate highway loads, roughly correspond to the weight of a modern " Pacific " locomotive. In the case of the railway engine, however, this loading is distributed over no less than 9 axles, assuming that the locomotive has a six-wheeled tender, providing a considerably lower intensity of load.

Railway engineers are able to form a very accurate idea of the loads imposed upon their bridges, unlike their colleagues, the highway engineers, who have not the same control of the vehicles which cross their structures and who can only take the Ministry of Transport Standard Loading as an approximate guide.

When the complicated question of impact is considered, however, both railway and road engineers are compelled to work largely on assumptions. The exact effects produced when a 400-ton train, headed by a locomotive weighing 150 tons, thunders on to a bridge at 80 miles an hour, are not precisely known and, in addition, there are the peculiar vibrations set up by the rapidly oscillating mechanism of the locomotive itself to be considered. The designer of highway bridges has his own problems in this connection, and finds it difficult to estimate the stresses set up by a heavy lorry running with damaged solid tyres or by a vehicle which rebounds from imperfections in the road surface.

CONCRETE OR STEEL : WHICH SHALL IT BE ?

MANY beautiful old stone bridges have been rebuilt in reinforced concrete and the new bridge has been faced with the old stones taken from the ancient structure, giving a very attractive appearance in keeping with the surroundings.

Reinforced concrete is thus a very adaptable material, and is often the most economical form of construction if good supplies of suitable aggregate are available in the immediate vicinity of the work so that the concrete can be cheaply made.

Much of the labour involved is comparatively unskilled, in contrast to the highly skilled workmanship required in steel erection. Many of the new bridges built in conjunction with road improvement schemes have been carried out in ferro-concrete from considerations of economy both in first cost and in subsequent maintenance, which should be negligible in comparison with a steel structure which requires incessant painting.

Steel bridges, however, remain the standard type for railway work, since they are better suited for withstanding the vibration and impact effects of fast and heavy trains and, as we have already seen, they are also capable of rapid erection when renewals are required with the minimum interference with traffic.

FIRST ESSENTIAL OF BUILDING :
THE FOUNDATIONS

WHENEVER it is possible to do so, foundations are carried down to a reliable stratum, such as hard rock, by open excavation, that is, by simply digging out a hole of the necessary dimensions, timbering the sides where required and filling in with concrete. It is often impossible, however, to reach sufficiently firm material within a reasonably shallow depth, and in this case " pile foundations " are often used.

Piles are long cylindrical, square, or octagonal pillars made of timber or reinforced concrete, which are driven into the ground by hammer blows. Another form of the same device is the *screw-pile*—an iron cylinder with a large screwing blade, somewhat resembling a propeller at the lower end, which causes the pile to penetrate downwards when rotated.

Timber piles are usually of pitch pine, this wood being obtainable in long straight lengths, 40 to 50 feet being common, with a cross-section as large as 14 inches square. The lower end is tapered and fits into a wrought-iron or steel shoe which is sharply pointed. Reinforced concrete piles are made in much the same lengths and cross-sections as timber piles, and are also fitted with pointed iron or steel shoes. They are usually cast in horizontal moulds and very carefully matured. For ordinary Portland cement, the maturing period may be from 1 to 3 months, but the use of rapid-hardening cement permits this lengthy interval to be reduced to 7 days, and piles made of aluminous cement have been driven successfully after only 60 hours.

A typical reinforced concrete pile may be 14 inches square, 35 to 40 feet long, and reinforced with four longitudinal rods, $1\frac{1}{8}$ inches in diameter bound round with stout wire. Where necessary, however, larger and longer piles may be used, 18 inch square section being sometimes employed, or octagonal with a width of 17 inches across the flats, and lengths as great as 75 feet. Piles of this size weigh 9 or 10 tons each and are largely adopted for foundation work along the foreshore of the Thames estuary.

DRIVING THE FOUNDATIONS INTO THE EARTH

BOTH timber and reinforced concrete piles are driven by mounting them in a *pile frame*—a tall timber erection consisting of stout uprights of rather greater height than the full length of the pile, and fitted with guides in which the latter can slide. The appliance is well stayed and adequate strength is very necessary, since pile-driving is a process involving a great deal of shock and vibration.

The pile is held vertically, but is quite free to move downwards when struck on the top surface. The hammer usually weighs 30 cwt. or 2 tons and may be one of three types :

(1) A freely falling hammer dropped from various heights, 5 feet being quite usual.

(2) A similar hammer dropped on the end of a wire cable instead of falling freely.

(3) A " steam-hammer," attached to a plunger rod which alternately raises and lowers it.

Vertical driving is usual in the majority of ordinary foundations for large buildings and bridge piers, but in the case of arch abutments where the thrust due to the loading is inclined, the bearing piles may be driven in at a suitable angle. This is done by using an inclined, or " raking " pile frame. It is often impossible to drive piles to a sufficient depth to ensure that they are actually resting on rock or some other very hard foundation, and unless some such material is reached, the piles derive their bearing power from the " skin friction " between their surfaces and that of the surrounding soil.

HOW FAR MAY THE PILE BE DRIVEN ?

DURING the process of driving, very careful observations are made of the distance moved by the pile after each blow, and driving is continued until the hammer produces only a certain small movement after a given number of impacts. The calculation of the bearing-power of piles is based largely on empirical formulæ, that is, formulæ which are not capable of strict mathematical proof, but which are founded on the result of experiment and practical experience. Very different results are given by different rules, and the matter is one in which conclusive facts are still lacking. The widely varying conditions met with in practice render definite rules very difficult of application, but the following examples quoted at random may serve to illustrate the general procedure:

At Neuilly Bridge, France, the pile hammer weighed 2,000 lb., the drop was 5 feet, and driving was continued until 16 blows produced a sinkage of only $\frac{1}{4}$ inch.

At certain foundations of the Ford Works, Dagenham, large piles were driven by a 6-ton hammer until 100 blows gave a *set*, or settlement of not more than 4 inches, the hammer fall being 3 feet 6 inches.

At the Colne Bridge, near Watford, on the modern by-pass road which skirts the north of the town, the piles for the abutment foundations were driven by a steam-hammer of 2 tons weight and 4 feet stroke, and the specified set to which driving had to be continued was 54 blows to 1 foot penetration.

The first blows usually produce considerable sinkage of the pile and, in normal circumstances, the amount of penetration gradually decreases until the stipulated set is reached, but it sometimes happens that the pile, after sinking steadily for a certain distance, suddenly enters a loose substratum and " runs away," giving many anxious moments to the engineers in charge.

The piles are spaced out to cover a sufficient area to carry the superstructure, whether it be a pier, an abutment, a wall, or tall factory chimney, but they are not usually placed closer than 3 or 4 feet apart. The tops are brought to the correct level, cross-beams are added and finally the mass concrete which forms the bulk of the foundation.

BUILDING ON A BOX OF SOIL

IT is sometimes possible to increase the bearing power of a loose soil, such as certain types of gravel or sand, by enclosing a sufficient area within a continuous boundary formed by piles set in actual contact. These are termed *sheet piles* and are rectangular in section, a normal size being 12 inches on the face and 6 inches on the edges where contact takes place. This sheeting prevents the spread of the loose material, and thus enables it to support a far greater weight than it would do otherwise.

In this connection some figures relating to the allowable loading on various soils may be of interest : Rocks vary greatly in compressive strength and the allowable loading may range from 10 tons per square foot for very hard rock down to as little as 2 tons per square foot for the softest varieties. Ballast, gravel and sharp sand, provided they are well drained, may carry from 1 to 5 tons per square foot. Clays are treacherous soils and their bearing power is greatly lessened by the presence of water, but 1 ton per square foot is usually considered safe.

There are certain types of soil, such as marshy silt and water-logged sands to which no safe bearing loads can be assigned, and these are unsuitable for open excavation foundations which depend upon subsoil resistance and some special type of foundation involving piles, or similar devices, would be adopted in such situations.

DIGGING DOWN TO ROCK BOTTOM : CAISSONS AND MONOLITHS

ANOTHER interesting type of foundation is the *caisson*, or *monolith*, and although the shapes and sizes of caissons may vary considerably, the most common type is the cylinder. Let us imagine, therefore, a cast-iron or steel cylinder, say 8 feet in diameter and the same in height, lined inside with a layer of brickwork and standing erect, with a sharp cutting edge round its base. If the soil is dug away from the inside edge, this large heavy cylinder will gradually sink and if the whole of the soil is removed from the inside as fast as the cylinder travels downwards, we shall finally arrive at the point when its top edge is flush with the outside ground. We shall thus have obtained a circular hole, 8 feet deep and about the same in diameter, with an outer lining of metal and an inner lining of brick. If a second cylinder were now placed on top of the first and bolted to it, the excavation and sinking could be repeated as before, the depth being increased as required.

In practice the excavated shaft would be carried through all the various unreliable and soft strata which might occur near the surface and continued until some hard, firm material, such as reliable rock, or even hard chalk or compact ballast, was reached. The cylinder automatically provides its own support to prevent the sides of the hole from caving in as the work proceeds, and when completed to the necessary depth, the opening may be filled in with concrete, thus forming a strong pillar which will transmit the weight of a structure down to the firm subsoil where it may be safely borne without fear of settlement.

Cylindrical caissons are from 6 to 20 feet in diameter, and rectangular and octagonal forms are also used. They are sometimes roofed over, and heavy weights, known as " kent-ledge," are placed on the top to assist the sinking. The excavation may either be carried out by hand, or, in the case of open cylinders, by " grabbing," a method in which a large steel scoop with two open jaws is lowered into the caisson by a crane and plunged into the soil. The jaws then close, retaining a scoopful of earth, which is raised and emptied on to a dump, or into wagons for removal.

DIGGING A FOUNDATION UNDER WATER

IN water-logged soils, or in cases where a caisson has to be sunk in a river bed to provide the foundation for the intermediate pier of a bridge, it is customary to use a closed type into which compressed air is pumped to keep out the water. The pressure is adjusted to suit the circumstances—it may be only slightly above the atmospheric pressure of 14 pounds per square inch, or it may be as much as 45 pounds per square inch above atmospheric pressure, resulting in a total pressure over 4 times as great as that in the outside air.

In the case of a compressed air caisson, it is not possible to pass directly into or out of the working chamber where the high pressure prevails, so that an intermediate chamber, called an *air-lock*, is interposed between the inner portion of the caisson and the outer air. This chamber is fitted with airtight doors, and, before entering from the outside, the pressure within is adjusted to be the same as the ordinary atmospheric pressure. Having entered, the air-lock pressure is gradually raised until it is the same as that in the working chamber, which can then be entered safely. On returning to the outside, the process is reversed, the air-lock pressure being gradually reduced until it is again equal to atmospheric, when the outer door may be opened.

THE CONVENIENT AND NOISELESS PRESSURE PILES

AMONG the many problems which confront the civil engineer, one of the commonest is encountered again and again when foundations are required in a poor subsoil where the situation is too cramped to permit of cylinder sinking or the erection of a pile frame, or where there are old and unstable buildings close by which might be shaken down if a pile-driver were allowed to work in the vicinity with its very marked vibration. One method of tackling this difficulty is by the use of *pressure piles*.

This process consists of boring a hole into the ground, with a diameter of roughly 1 foot, by means of a well-sinker's auger which is screwed down into the soil. This appliance has a sharp cutting edge and a hollow cylindrical shape, the excavated material being retained inside and subsequently removed when the auger is withdrawn from the hole. As the excavation proceeds, a steel lining is inserted, and the reach of the boring tool is extended, from time to time, by the addition of extra lengths of rod to the handle.

This work is carried out entirely by manual means, and as soon as the required depth has been obtained, a cap is screwed on to the top length of lining which is standing clear of the ground. A small pipe is passed through an opening in this cap, and pushed down to the bottom of the bore-hole. Compressed air is then blown in, and this drives out through the tube any subsoil water which may have collected in the hole. Concrete, mixed rather wet, is next dropped in, and the compressed air is again used. This exerts a pressure on the underside of the cap, and this upward push assists in the raising of the steel lining.

A convenient method of doing this is by means of a winch and pulley. The latter is hung from a tripod erection placed over the bore-hole, and a wire rope is threaded through, fastened to the top rim of the steel lining and carried to the winch. The turning of the winch handle exerts enough pull, in conjunction with the air-pressure inside the bore-hole, to lift the lining, and as soon as this is raised, the concrete at the bottom of the hole is, of course, in direct contact with the surrounding soil. The compressed air forces it out into any weak places and into any cracks, but great care is taken to ensure that the bottom of the steel lining is well below the top of the concrete. The process possesses the great advantages that a headroom of as little as 6 feet is sufficient, and that no vibration or noise is caused.

HOW WATER FLOWS IN PIPES AND CHANNELS

FOR scientific purposes, fluids include both liquids and gases, their behaviour being similar in many respects, although, naturally, there is a definite border line beyond which the similarity ceases. Both liquids and gases, for instance, when confined in a vessel, exert a pressure perpendicular to the surface of the vessel at every point. Thus, if the cylinder in Fig. 30 (left) were filled with liquid, the latter would support a piston, P, and a pressure would be exerted everywhere within the cylinder, perpendicular to the walls and of the same intensity as that exerted upwards against the underside of the

piston. Conditions are similar within the interior of a motor
or cycle tyre, an outward pressure being exerted by the compressed air in all directions, as indicated in Fig. 30 (centre),
which shows a cross-section of the tyre.

There is this important difference, however, between a
liquid and a gas—the liquid in the case of the cylinder and
piston could only be compressed by an extremely small
amount, no matter how heavily the piston were weighted,
whereas a gas can be compressed very considerably by the

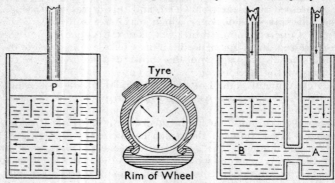

30. (*Left.*)   *How liquid enclosed in a cylinder presses
on the walls and supports a piston.* (*Centre.*)   *A section
of a tyre showing how the enclosed air presses on it in
all directions.* (*Right.*)   *The hydraulic jack, by means of
which a small pressure P supports a large weight W.*

application of sufficient pressure. The incompressibility of
water may be realised by supposing that the cylinder contained 1,000 gallons. To hold this quantity it would be 10
feet high, with a diameter of nearly 5 feet. If, now, the piston
were loaded with 2,380 tons, it would exert a pressure of 1
ton per square inch over the whole of its area, but water is
so very nearly incompressible that, even under this enormous
weight, the piston would sink by less than 1 inch.

LARGE FORCES FOR SMALL: THE HYDRAULIC JACK

THANKS to this high degree of incompressibility, water acts
as a very convenient medium for the transmission of
pressure, and this property is utilised in such devices as
hydraulic jacks and rams. The principle of these appliances

may be understood by imagining two cylinders and pistons of widely differing diameters, such as A and B in Fig. 30 (right), connected together at their bases. The " power " is, in practice, a small force, represented by P, acting on a small piston. This gives rise to a definite intensity of pressure, calculated by dividing the load on the piston by the area of its face.

Suppose, for instance, that the former is only 2 pounds and the latter 1 square foot. The pressure intensity will then be 2 pounds per square foot, and this will be transmitted through the water to every square foot of the piston W in the larger cylinder B. If the area of this second piston is 10 square feet, we shall thus get a total pressure of 2 × 10, or 20 pounds, exerted here and a 2 pound weight at P will therefore balance a 20 pound weight at W. In this way it is possible, with a hydraulic jack, to lift a very heavy weight with quite a small force.

PUTTING THE FLOW IN FIGURES : TWO IMPORTANT TERMS

THE civil engineer is constantly considering the flow of water in pipes or channels—even in the sphere of road construction, which, at first sight, does not appear to have any connection with the subject of hydraulics, the necessity for dealing with storm water brings us at once to the question —how large must the drain pipes be to carry the water away from the road in times of the heaviest rain, so that there shall be no risk of flooding ?

In calculations relating to flow in pipes or channels there are two fundamental technical terms which require explanation—one of these is the " Wetted Perimeter," and this is the total length of the cross-section of the pipe or channel which is in actual contact with the water. If a pipe is entirely full, the wetted perimeter is the whole circumference of the pipe, or if a rectangular channel of width 10 feet has a stream of water in it 2 feet deep, the wetted perimeter will be (2 + 10 + 2) feet, or 14 feet.

The second term is the " Hydraulic Mean Depth," and this is found by dividing the area of cross-section of the stream by the wetted perimeter. Thus, reverting to the case of the pipe running full, the cross-sectional area of the stream is, of course, the area of the circular pipe, which is obtained by multiplying the radius r by itself, and then multiplying the product by 3·14, i.e. 3·14 × r × r.

The wetted perimeter is the same as the circumference, and this is obtained by multiplying the radius by 2, and then by the same factor, 3·14, i.e. $2 \times 3·14 \times r$. Hence the hydraulic mean depth will be $\dfrac{3·14 \times r \times r}{2 \times 3·14 \times r}$ or $\dfrac{r}{2}$, i.e. half the radius, or one-quarter the diameter. Again, the channel has a stream area of 10×2 square feet, or 20 square feet. Its wetted perimeter is 14 feet. Hence its hydraulic mean depth is 20 divided by 14, or 1·4 feet. The hydraulic mean depth is always represented by the letter " m " in pipe and channel calculations.

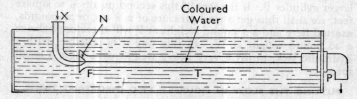

31. The apparatus used by Reynolds for studying the flow of water in pipes under various conditions.

REYNOLDS' HISTORIC EXPERIMENTS

THE study of the flow of water in pipes was investigated by Professor Osborne Reynolds in a very interesting and ingenious manner, and although the results of his experiments were published as long ago as 1884, they are still considered to be most valuable contributions to the subject of pipe flow.

One particular type of apparatus used by Reynolds is shown diagrammatically in Fig. 31 and consisted of a horizontal glass tube, T, immersed in a glass tank filled with water, and having at one end a funnel shaped inlet, F. A second tube, X, with a nozzle end, N, projected into the inlet funnel, and the tank had an outlet pipe, P, through which water could be run off. When the water in the tank was allowed to flow out, a stream was produced through the tube, T, and into this stream was projected a thread of coloured water from the pipe X, and through the nozzle N. The presence of this coloured thread enabled the conditions of flow within the glass tube to be examined, and even photographed, and it was found that at low velocities of flow the coloured stream was smooth and unbroken, but that at higher velocities it was turbulent and eddying.

MEASURING THE FRICTION BETWEEN WATER AND PIPE

WHENEVER water flows through a pipe there is naturally a frictional effect between the two, and from a large number of experimental results it has been deduced that the friction between the pipe and the flowing water is proportional to the square of the velocity, that is, if we double the speed of the stream, we increase the friction four times. The friction is also proportional to the wetted surface, and inversely proportional to the area of cross-section of the stream, the wetted surface being the product of the length of the pipe, and the wetted perimeter.

When one quantity is proportional to another, the relationship may be expressed, mathematically, by stating that the first quantity is equal to the second multiplied by a constant factor. To give a simple illustration, we may state that the quantity of petrol used by a car is proportional to the distance travelled. If we call the total quantity of petrol Q, and the distance travelled D miles, then Q is equal to D multiplied by a constant factor. In this case, the constant factor is, of course, the quantity of petrol consumed per mile.

But in the case of inverse relationships, the factor is divided instead of multiplied by the second quantity. Suppose, for instance, we state that the time, t, occupied by a journey is inversely proportional to the speed of travel, s. We may then write : $t = \dfrac{\text{A constant factor}}{s}$. Here the constant factor will be the distance travelled. Coming back to the question of pipe-friction and considering the relationships already given, we may call the velocity of the stream V, the wetted perimeter P, the length of the pipe L, and the area of cross-section of the stream A, and we may then summarise the facts by means of the following equation :

$$\text{Pipe friction} = \frac{\text{A constant factor} \times V^2 \times L \times P}{A}.$$

But the area of cross-section of the stream divided by the wetted perimeter, or $\dfrac{A}{P}$, is the quantity already described as the Hydraulic Mean Depth, and in the above equation we have $\dfrac{P}{A}$ instead of $\dfrac{A}{P}$, so that we can write :

$$\text{Pipe friction} = \text{A constant factor} \times \frac{V^2 \times L}{m}.$$

The constant factor depends upon the type and size of pipe and whether its interior is smooth or rough.

FINDING THE SPEED OF WATER IN A SLOPING PIPE

ANOTHER technical term used in pipe calculations is the "Hydraulic Gradient." Suppose a long pipe AB, in Fig. 32, has a downward slope from A to B, with a stream of water flowing through it and completely filling the pipe, and suppose vertical glass tubes, C and D, were inserted at A and B. The water would rise to a certain height in each, but

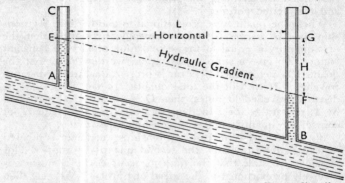

32. Showing the meaning of the term "hydraulic gradient" applied to a pipe line AB.

would be lower in the pipe D than in the pipe C, owing to friction losses. If the heights to which the water rises are E and F respectively, a line joining E to F would be the "Hydraulic Gradient," or "Virtual Slope" of the pipe. Imagine a line EG drawn through the water-level in the first tube—the drop in level between the water columns in the two tubes will then be represented by the height GF. If we call this amount "H," and the distance between the tubes "L," the value of the hydraulic gradient expressed numerically is "H" divided by "L," just as the gradient of a hill is measured by dividing the vertical rise by the horizontal length. The fraction $\frac{H}{L}$ is always represented in hydraulic calculations by the letter "i," and the velocity of flow is given by multiplying the hydraulic gradient by the hydraulic mean depth, taking the square-root of the product and multiplying it by a constant factor. The latter, again, depends upon the type and condition of the pipe.

In mathematical symbols, this statement is written :

$$v \text{, the velocity of flow} = \text{a constant, } c, \times \sqrt{mi}.$$

The value of c for new cast-iron pipes may range from 95 to 152, and for old cast-iron pipes from 63 to 118.

It is rather an interesting fact that a pipe does not discharge the maximum amount of water when it is completely full, but both mathematical theory and practical experience show that it actually gives the greatest flow when it is running with roughly 95% of its full cross-sectional area, the increased velocity in this case more than compensating for the slight reduction in the area of the stream.

GAUGING THE FLOW OF WATER IN CHANNELS

IN the case of a stream of water flowing in an open channel, or in a pipe which is not running full, the water has what is termed a " free surface," and the hydraulic gradient then coincides with the quadrant of the latter and this, in turn, will be practically the same as the slope of the channel or pipe. The same rules and formulæ still hold good, however, and as a rough and ready approximate rule, the constant factor " c " in the formula $v = c\sqrt{mi}$, for giving the average velocity in channels and streams, may be taken as 95.

It is often necessary to obtain some idea of the quantity of water flowing in a stream or river. This information is essential, for example, if a certain proportion of the water is to be diverted into reservoirs for water-supply purposes, in the way that a part of the Thames is drawn off into storage by the Metropolitan Water Board. It is also required, as preliminary data, if a scheme is under consideration for using the water to drive turbines for the generation of electricity.

The measurement of the flow is sometimes carried out by constructing a weir or " rectangular notch " across the stream. This resembles a dam which is not high enough to hold back the water, but merely provides a uniform opening through which the stream can flow. Straight approach walls are built alongside the banks on the upstream side, to regulate the flow before the notch is reached, and if the head of water over the sill is accurately measured and the width of the notch is known, we have sufficient data to calculate the amount of water passing over in a given time.

For small streams, a triangular, or " V " notch is sometimes used. The surface velocity of a stream or river is obtained by finding the time taken by floats—usually small
discs of wood—to travel on the surface of the stream from one
point to another a known distance away, but this method will
not provide a complete knowledge of the flow and requires
to be supplemented by a " gauging " by means of a current
meter.

APPLYING A SPEEDOMETER TO THE RIVER

INFORMATION of the surface flow alone is of but little use if
an accurate estimate is to be made of the quantity of water
passing a certain point on a river in a certain time, and we
require to know the velocity of the water at many different
depths and at the edges of the river as well as in mid-stream.
For this purpose, a current meter is used. These are of several
types, but one in common use consists of a heavy weight,
shaped rather like a fish, which is submerged in the water,
either on a cable or on a long rod. A small propeller is fitted
at one end of the apparatus and this is driven round by the
movement of the water—the faster the stream, the faster it
will rotate. Its speed is accurately indicated by a simple
electrical method—after a given number of revolutions, say
every 10, an electrical contact is made and a bell rings, and
by timing the intervals between the rings by means of a stop-
watch, the number of revolutions of the propeller per minute
may be easily calculated.

Each individual instrument is specially calibrated by
drawing it at known speeds through still water contained
in a long channel, so that the speed of flow is known which
will produce any given speed of rotation of the propeller.
By placing the current meter at the requisite points, we
can measure the speed of the current at a large number of
different positions across a river from shore to shore and
also at a large number of different depths, and from this
data it is possible to get a very accurate idea of the total quantity
of water passing the site chosen for the current meter measurements.

Different parts of a river flow past a given point at different
speeds—the water at the centre of the stream travels faster
than that at the sides and the maximum speed does not occur
at the surface, but at some distance below it, often at about
one-third of the total depth.

SETTING THE RIVER TO WORK FOR MAN

THE charter of the Institution of Civil Engineers defines the work of its members as " the art of directing the great sources of power in Nature for the use and convenience of man," and no more appropriate example of such work could be found than that provided by the hydro-electric schemes which convert the energy of streams, rivers, and waterfalls into the electrical energy which gives us lighting, heating, and motive-power.

In spite of the fact that it has been estimated that nearly half a million horse-power could be generated from the rivers and streams of England, coal is still our pre-eminent source of power. In Sweden and Switzerland, which are not so favourably situated as England from the point of view of coal supply, there are ample waterfalls, and it is not surprising, therefore, that hydro-electric schemes are adopted to a far greater extent in these two countries than in our own.

The power available from moving water depends upon two main factors—the quantity and the head. The available quantity is often very difficult to estimate with precision. The " catchment area " which is to provide the necessary water is first chosen, and this is usually a valley high up among mountains or hills, where moisture-laden winds from the sea will yield a heavy rainfall.

CIRCUMVENTING THE SEASONS : RIVERS AND DAMS

GENERALLY the rain collects in rivers or streams which run off from the valley, but the quantity flowing is almost certain to vary greatly at different times of the year—it is quite usual in Scottish rivers, for instance, to find that the flow in times of flood is from 250 to 500 times the dry-weather volume. Fluctuation of this magnitude would obviously be impossible to deal with in a hydro-electric scheme, steady conditions of flow being an essential factor, and storage accommodation is therefore provided to collect the heavy rains of the wet periods, this provision not only preventing floods, but also enabling the smaller flows of the dry seasons to be supplemented, thus balancing the supply.

It sometimes happens that natural lakes are ready to hand to form convenient reservoirs, but if not, storage areas are frequently formed by constructing dams across the rivers at suitable sites, such as the points where they pass through narrow gorges, thus converting dry valleys into artificial lakes.

The natural flow of water from a valley is rarely dammed up entirely, however, and a certain amount is usually allowed to take its normal course to meet the claims of the various authorities and individuals who have rights in connection with the river and who depend upon it, in one way or another, for the supply of water.

The storage reservoir is connected with the power-house by a pipe-line, or tunnel, or sometimes both, as in the case of the Lochaber hydro-electric scheme, in Inverness-shire, which supplies electricity to the British Aluminium Company's works and is designed for an ultimate output of 120,000 horse-power. The generating station, in this case, is connected with natural reservoirs by means of a tunnel, 15 miles long, drilled through the solid rock beneath the shoulders of Ben Nevis, with a final length of steel pipe-line, rather more than half-a-mile long. The generating plant is invariably situated at a much lower level than the reservoir to provide an adequate working head.

AVAILABLE POWER IN THEORY AND PRACTICE

IN speaking of the "head of water," a distinction should be made between the "gross," or total, head and the "nett," or effective, head. The former is measured by the vertical distance between the level of the water-surface at the source of supply and the point of admission to the turbines, or other machinery. Thus, if AB, in Fig. 33, represents the reservoir, connected by the pipe-line CD with the power plant, the gross head is obtained by imagining a horizontal line FE drawn at the level of the water-surface in the reservoir and a vertical line DE drawn from the centre of the pipe at its outlet to meet this horizontal at the point E. The height DE is then the gross head and gives an idea of the total available energy in the water, but a certain proportion will be used up in overcoming the friction in the pipe-line and in the various valves and screens which form an essential part of the pipe-line equipment, so that if a long vertical glass tube were inserted near the outlet D, the water would not rise to the full height DE, but to a somewhat lower level which would be the nett, or effective, head, actually remaining at the point of entry to the turbines.

The gross head at Lochaber is 800 feet.

THE GIGANTIC POWER OF MOVING WATER

A CUBIC foot of water weighs nearly $62\frac{1}{4}$ pounds and if we can visualise an enormous torrent like the Niagara Falls, it is not difficult to realise that the sheer weight of this moving water represents a stupendous force. To take a very much smaller example, let us consider the case of a pipe-line consisting only of a single tube, 1 foot in diameter, connecting a power-house with a reservoir 1 mile distant, and with a gross head of 500 feet. The water will emerge with a velocity of about 14 feet per second (or about 10 miles per hour), the quantity of flow being about 11 cubic feet per second, or

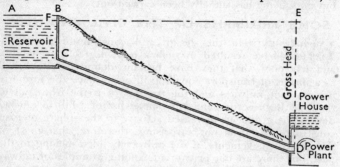

33. *The meaning of "gross head" applied to a hydro-electric installation served by a reservoir.*

19 tons of water per minute and the theoretical horse-power available from this stream of water is 650.

Even a small stream, running gently along at the very usual mean velocity of 3 feet per second would give roughly a half horse-power if allowed to push against the vanes of a water-wheel, assuming that these vanes are 5 feet broad, with a submerged depth of 1 foot. The efficiency of a water-wheel of this primitive type would be so low, however, that not more than half this horse-power would be actually utilised. Turbines, on the other hand, have a very high overall efficiency, 80 to 85% being common figures.

TAMING THE TIDES: AN UNDEVELOPED POSSIBILITY

IN many estuaries the incoming tides rise to a considerable height above the level of low-water. In the Thames, for instance, at Tilbury, the difference in height between low and high water may be as much as 23 feet and in the funnel-shaped estuary of the Severn as much as 40 feet. If a storage area of sufficient capacity could be provided, adjacent to the estuary, with a dam across its entrance of such a height that a proportion of the high level tidal flow would pass over, the contents of the reservoir would be replenished at every high tide, and by an adjustment of the outflow from the reservoir to the power station it would be possible to maintain a suitable minimum head and thus secure a definite power output.   This is a fascinating possibility and suggestions have been made repeatedly that tidal power should be utilised, but no scheme has actually been carried out.

SOME TRIUMPHS OF THE CIVIL ENGINEER

IMPROVEMENTS in the design and construction of motor vehicles have resulted in such a high degree of reliability and efficiency that they have become definitely established as a means of transport equalling in importance the formerly pre-eminent railways and the transfer of traffic from rail to road has been accompanied by somewhat of a lull in railway development and an increased activity in the sphere of road construction.   It is not surprising, therefore, that most of the great achievements of the railway builders belong to the past, but there are one or two outstanding examples of railway construction of comparatively recent times which are sufficiently noteworthy to be placed on record.

There is always something peculiarly triumphant in carrying a railway across, or through, a mighty range of mountains, and the Andes, which form such a formidable barrier between the east and west coasts of South America, would appear to offer an absolutely impregnable obstacle to the most courageous railway engineer and yet they have been conquered and the steel track of the Transandine Railway runs between the two loftiest peaks of the entire range which go towering up to heights of over 22,000 feet above sea-level. This line connects Argentine with Chile and its highest point is in the 2 mile long Summit Tunnel, 2000 feet beneath the Uspallata Pass which lies between the two mountains already mentioned and is, itself, at an altitude of some 12,500 feet above the sea.

The Transandine Railway forms a connecting link between Buenos Aires, on the Atlantic, and Valparaiso, on the Pacific, but, unfortunately, through running is not possible owing to the change of gauge, the railways from the ocean coasts to the junctions with the Transandine line at Mendoza (651 miles from Buenos Aires) and Santa Rosa de los Andes (89 miles from Valparaiso) being of 5 feet 6 inches gauge, while the intervening 155 miles of the Transandine Railway itself were built to the metre gauge, slightly over 3 feet in width, owing to the great difficulties in construction.

CLIMBING THE MOUNTAINS BY RACK-RAIL AND TUNNEL

RAILWAYS located in mountainous country may be built in two ways : they may be ordinary " adhesion " lines, having the normal familiar permanent-way, in which case the tractive power of the locomotive is entirely transmitted through the adhesion of the driving-wheels upon the smooth rails, or, alternatively, a " rack-rail " may be employed, placed between the two ordinary rails, and having teeth which engage with the pinion-wheels of a specially designed locomotive so that the latter is actually geared to the track and transmits its power through the interlocking of the teeth.

Adhesion lines give perfectly satisfactory results on surprisingly steep gradients, 1 in 25 being not uncommon abroad, although an incline of this steepness would be considered impossible on a British main line intended for express passenger traffic. In mountainous country, however, it is not always feasible to keep down to this gradient, even, without climbing in zig-zags and spirals, just as the mountain roads are designed as a series of straights, rising at easy slopes along the mountain sides and connected by hair-pin corners. The latter, of course, are not practicable in railway work, much larger curves being necessary, and it is interesting to note that this spiral construction is often carried out in mountain tunnels, the St. Gothard being a " corkscrew " tunnel of this type, although few travellers realise it.

The zig-zag and spiral method of climbing naturally involves a greater length of line than the more direct route possible with a " rack " line, as the latter is able to tackle the gradients in bolder fashion and this principle has been adopted on the more difficult sections of the Transandine Railway, where there are gradients as steep as 1 in $12\frac{1}{2}$. This is equivalent in road practice to a very moderate climb, which any modern car should be able to ascend easily at 30 miles per hour, in top gear, but to the railway engineer it is a very severe grade.

E.

BUILDING A RAILWAY ON PRECIPICE WALLS

THE difficulties encountered during the construction of the Transandine line were many and varied. Much of the route is in the snow region where snowslides, avalanches, and drifts 30 feet deep are of frequent occurrence—then for 85 miles the line follows the Mendoza River, a raging torrent running in a narrow gorge the sides of which are sheer precipices of solid rock. In these forbidding walls a narrow ledge had first to be dynamited to form a track for mules, on the backs of which everything needed for the preliminary part of the construction had to be conveyed. The route for the line itself had also to be blasted out of the precipitous mountain sides and in thirty-five separate places tunnelled through the rock masses towering above.

Matters were not assisted by the occasional earthquakes which are common in this part of South America, but fortunately the line has, so far, escaped serious damage from this cause. Snow, ice, and terrific winds hampered the work, just as they interfere with the traffic now that the line is completed and " snow-sheds " have had to be erected at many places to enclose the line partially and keep snow-slides and avalanches clear of the track. Temperatures well below freezing-point in the winter have necessitated the construction of deep frost-proof water-tanks for locomotive supplies, and weather conditions have, on occasion, been so severe that traffic has been stopped completely, as it was for six consecutive months in 1914 when blizzards were continuous and the snow-fall aggregated 19 feet, with drifts considerably deeper.

The constructional work was subject to repeated interruptions through lack of capital and was not finally completed until 23 years had elapsed from the date of its commencement, but the triumphant conclusion was at last achieved, making it possible to travel from Buenos Aires to Valparaiso by a rail journey of less than 1,000 miles, instead of having to make sea-voyages of more than three times the distance through the Straits of Magellan or round Cape Horn.

A TRIUMPH OF MODERN BRIDGE BUILDING

THE importance of road transport is again reflected in the fact that most of the outstanding examples of modern bridge construction are either highway bridges, pure and simple, or, if carrying rail traffic, are also provided with carriageways for road vehicles. The famous Sydney Bridge, arched so gracefully across the world's most beautiful harbour, about 4½ miles from its entrance, is a dual bridge for road and rail, and although eclipsed by one or two rivals in the matter of span, is a masterpiece of British design and construction.

One of the ruling factors in its planning was the necessity for providing adequate headroom to permit of the passage underneath of the largest ocean liners, and there is a clearance of no less than 170 feet below the central 600 feet of the main span. Two natural features at the site were favourable—the subsoil is rock, thus rendering the foundation work comparatively simple, and the river banks rise steeply, thus enabling the approach spans to be arranged without severe gradients, in spite of the liberal headroom beneath the bridge floor.

In general design the bridge consists of a steel arch, hinged at the abutments, with the deck slung beneath from hangers for the major part of the span and supported directly on the arch trusses in the region of the " springing." The arch has a clear span of 1,650 feet and is very gracefully curved, the upper chord rising to a height of 440 feet above waterlevel.

At each end are massive pylons, built of reinforced concrete faced with granite and rising to a height of 285 feet above the water, and the approaches, graded easily at 1 in 40 and 1 in 39, are carried on latticed trusses, supported on granite piers, the total length of the entire bridge, approaches included, being very nearly three-quarters of a mile.

The arch is composed of two trusses, placed side by side, about 100 feet apart, and each consisting of 28 braced panels of the " N " type, the diagonals changing in direction at the crown, in the manner shown in the outline diagram, Fig. 34.

Some idea of the size of the structure may be obtained from the fact that the depth of the arch-truss at the abutments is 188 feet, diminishing to 60 feet at the crown. The deck extends outside the trusses on each side, the area between the steel arches having a central roadway 57 feet wide, with a railway track of the standard 4 feet 8½ inches gauge running on both sides of this central carriageway, while the portion of the deck outside the trusses carries a second railway track on each side, together with a 10-foot pathway for pedestrians on the extreme outer edges.

CREEPING OUT ACROSS THE RIVER: HOW THE SYDNEY BRIDGE WAS BUILT

VERY briefly, the method of construction was as follows: The approach spans were erected on temporary timber stagings, the pylons were built up to the level of the bridge deck and the foundations were prepared for the four hinged bearings of the arch, each consisting of a pin $14\frac{1}{2}$ inches in diameter and 13 feet 8 inches long. The lower chord members adjacent to the bearing pins were then assembled and the four end panels erected, a temporary support of steelwork being used underneath.

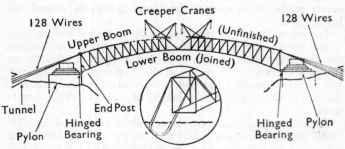

34. *Sydney Harbour Bridge in construction, showing* (inset) *how the wire ropes holding the arch form a loop anchored in a tunnel bored in the solid rock.*

The next process was to attach 128 wire ropes to the top end of the vertical member, or "end post" of one panel on each side of the bridge, immediately adjacent to the pylons. These ropes were brought down at an angle of roughly 45 degrees, as indicated in Fig. 34, and led into a tunnel bored in the solid sandstone. This tunnel passed beneath the approach spans and curved completely round so that the wires could be brought back to the end post of the other truss, forming a loop, anchored in the solid rock, and thus affording an immensely strong support to hold back the arch which was gradually built out from each abutment, as a cantilever. It may be remembered that an exactly similar procedure, apart from the underground anchorage, was adopted in the Tyne Bridge, Newcastle, previously mentioned.

A " creeper " crane on each half of the arch was used for lifting the sections of steel from the river and placing them in position for riveting. These cranes gradually worked their way along the upper chords of the trusses, spanning across from one truss to the other, and each consisted of a self-propelling under-carriage on which were mounted a main crane capable of lifting 120 tons and several smaller auxiliary cranes. At last the two creeper cranes had each run out to the crowns of their respective half-arches and, in this position, were 800 feet outwards from the abutments and 400 odd feet above the water-level—they each weighed 600 tons and there were 19,000 tons of steel in each half-arch and practically all this weight was being held by the anchor ropes.

TWO WEEKS TO TRAVEL FORTY FEET

THE end posts had been purposely tilted backwards on the hinged bearings to allow for the stretch in the wires, and also to ensure that there should be a gap of 40 feet in the two halves of the arch at the crown previous to the very delicate process of joining up. Each of the 128 wire ropes was then slackened very slightly, in turn, and the 40-foot gap diminished by one twentieth of an inch at a time until, after two weeks of this slow approach, the lower chords of the two halves met and took their bearing on a pin, 8 inches in diameter, inserted temporarily to receive the thrust.

By skilful adjustment, the top chord was next made to take its fair share of the loading, hydraulic jacks being used to exert a straining action between the two halves of the arch, and accurately machined steel slabs were finally inserted and bolted up to make the permanent closure. The deck was then proceeded with, the creeper cranes being still employed on the top of the arch for lifting the hangers and deck material and thus the great bridge was completed. The cost was approximately four-and-a-quarter million pounds, about 51,000 tons of steel were used and the bridge was opened eight years after the contract was signed.

A MODERN HIGHWAY UNDER THE MERSEY

THE work of the civil engineer presents great contrasts— on one job he may be high in the air, spanning a river by some lofty bridge, and next he may be deep down below the water, boring a tunnel through which road or railway traffic may take its swift and easy passage. The demands of modern transport call for more and more facilities to speed it on its way and time-wasting ferries can no longer be tolerated on busy routes, but in the estuaries leading to great ports the water traffic must also be considered and sufficient headroom for lofty masts and a free channel unobstructed by bridge piers must be provided for the in-coming and out-going craft. The problem may be solved either by an elevated arch of vast span, as at Sydney, or by an immense suspension bridge, as at New York, or by a tunnel, as at Liverpool, where the great 44-foot tube beneath the Mersey provides a splendid modern artery for road traffic between that city and Birkenhead.

The Mersey Tunnel is remarkable for its large diameter— it is very much bigger than the London tubes, for example— and it has, for the most part, a carriageway width of 36 feet providing four traffic lanes, and is slightly over 2 miles long. In addition to entrances and exits for through traffic, it has branches for dock traffic forming bifurcated arms at each end.

TUNNELLING BY "CUTTING SHIELD" UNDER THE RIVER

THE tunnel was constructed by means of a cutting shield, rather like that used for the London tubes and, very crudely, this consists of a shallow cylindrical steel frame of slightly larger diameter than the tunnel itself, placed with its axis horizontal and having a cutting edge on its front circumference. It is forced slowly forward into the soil by means of a number of hydraulic rams, or jacks, and the earth is excavated from the interior as the work proceeds. The shield is closely followed up by the tunnel lining, formed of cast-iron segments, and the area between the back of the lining and the surrounding soil is filled with a cement-sand "grout," forced in under pressure.

The roadway in the Mersey Tunnel is really a platform at the level of the horizontal diameter, supported by two longitudinal walls, as shown in Fig. 35. The upper half of the tunnel thus forms a semi-circular arch above the roadway, while underneath there is a large central cavity with two smaller ones on each side.

KERB VENTILATION AND A CAST-IRON ROADWAY

THE two outer cavities beneath the roadway form air-ducts and fresh air is pumped into them from six ventilating stations whose huge fans deliver $2\frac{1}{4}$ million cubic feet per minute. This fresh air passes into the tunnel through narrow slots in the kerb-faces of the footways which line the carriageway on both sides and the vitiated air is drawn out by suction fans from the roof of the tunnel, so that a current of moving air is always passing upwards from the road level and carrying with it the exhaust fumes from the traffic.

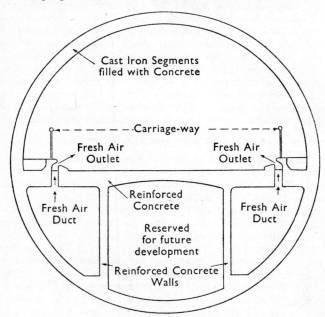

35. A section through the Mersey Tunnel.

The most elaborate signalling and fire equipment has been adopted to deal with any emergency, and should a vehicle be too high to pass safely through, it will automatically intercept a beam of light placed at every entrance and, in so doing, will cause interference with a photo-electric cell, with the result that a warning bell rings and illuminated signs light up to check the driver.

This wonderful engineering feat has taken 9 years to complete, and the magnitude of the task will be realised when one learns that 270,000 tons of concrete were used and that the total weight of the cast-iron segments forming the tunnel lining was 82,000 tons and a million bolts were needed to connect them together. Another amazing fact is that 580 miles of electric cable have been used to supply the 2,000 odd lamps.

Two of the most ultra-modern forms of road-surface have been used—cast-iron blocks for the majority of the area, with a short length of rubber blocks at the point where the tunnel crosses the Mersey Railway, the rubber being used here to absorb any vibration which might cause damage to the railway tunnels beneath.

A strange coincidence in figures provides a rather striking reflection on the magnitude of such herculean efforts as the Sydney Bridge and the Mersey Tunnel—traffic passes over the former at a height of 170 feet above the water-level, while the latter, at its deepest part, is 170 feet below the river.

THE ENGINEER AND THE TRAFFIC PROBLEMS

Less spectacular than a great bridge or tunnel, the modern arterial roads are, nevertheless, invaluable national possessions—"time is money," particularly in the world of commercial transport, and when it is borne in mind that many of the busy by-passes carry about 10,000 goods vehicles per day, if each traffic unit only saves 5 minutes through the avoidance of a lengthy crawl through a congested area, the aggregate saving is 833 hours. It is interesting to note that the road engineer is following the example of the railway engineer by segregating the traffic into " up " and " down " one-way tracks.

The Western Avenue, a main artery from London to Buckinghamshire and the Midlands, is, in part, a multi-track road. For several miles there are separate one-way roads for eastbound and westbound traffic, cyclists are accommodated on their own one-way concrete tracks, and there are footpaths in addition. Each of the carriage roads is 27 feet wide, taking three lines of vehicles, and there is a 14-foot central island between them. Building developments are kept well back and given access by special " service " roads running parallel to the main thoroughfare.

A diagrammatic section of the latter, showing the six rights of way for the various road users, is given in Fig. 36. An ultra-modern road of this type is, naturally, expensive and the cost of this particular length of the Western Avenue is £60,000 per mile.

An excellent example of the picturesque rural type of arterial road is the Guildford and Godalming By-pass, which is just over 9 miles long and passes through some of the most charming Surrey countryside—parkland strips have been reserved alongside this road for considerable lengths in the more rustic parts and left in their natural state, ribbon development being prohibited in these areas. The verges and embankments are planted with trees and shrubs and even the bridges have been made to tone in with the surroundings

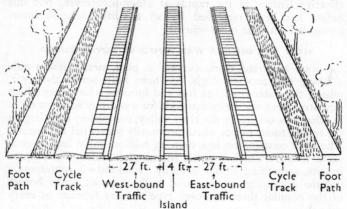

| Foot Path | Cycle Track | 27 ft. West-bound Traffic | 4 ft. Island | 27 ft. East-bound Traffic | Cycle Track | Foot Path |

36. Part of the multi-track Western Avenue, a main outlet from London to the Midlands.

by facing the parapets, wing-walls and abutments with the beautifully tinted Bargate stone which is quarried locally.

To ensure that no gradient should be steeper than 1 in 25 very heavy excavations and embankments were necessary in this undulating Downland country, the huge total of 700,000 tons of material being dug out of the elevated parts and banked up in the low-lying sections and 70,000 tons of sand and shingle and 14,000 tons of cement were used in making the concrete for the carriageway. The work was in progress for about 5 years and the cost was roughly £374,000.

HARNESSING POWER AND MAKING GEOGRAPHY

WATER as an obstacle to transport is overcome by some such bold method as a Sydney Bridge or a Mersey Tunnel—water, rushing forward with enormous tonnage, is held up and diverted into ordered channels and its energy converted into electricity by some such scheme as the Dneiprostroi plant in Soviet Russia, which may well be taken as the outstanding example of a gigantic hydro-electric enterprise. It has an output of 810,000 horse-power and utilises the flow of the Dneiper. This is the third largest river in Europe and would have been a navigable waterway of great importance, connecting lands of considerable agricultural and mineral wealth with the Black Sea, but for the very effective barrier of the rapids at Dneipropetrovsk, but this defect has been remedied by an auxiliary scheme interconnected with the main scheme.

HOW THE DNEIPER WAS TAMED BY SOVIET RUSSIA

A HUGE concrete dam, curved in plan, nearly half-a-mile long and 200 feet high, has been built across the river, raising the water-level 120 feet and forming a large lake which now stretches over the countryside for a width of some 10 miles in what was originally the river valley, completely submerging the tempestuous rapids which previously prevented navigation. The dam contains no less than 43 million cubic feet of concrete, a figure which is rather meaningless unless we compare it with something which is easily visualised—it represents a volume equivalent to the solid bulk of about 2,000 houses of the popular three-bedroom type so very familiar in every suburb.

The river passes through 46 openings near the top of the dam, the 46 cascades roaring through the gaps in the curved concrete wall forming a most impressive spectacle. The high-level water upstream of the dam is connected with the low-level downstream water by a triple lock, each compartment having a length of 400 feet and a width of 60 feet, thus enabling vessels from the Black Sea to pass through to the upper reaches of the river.

IMPROVING THE SCENERY AND ALTERING THE MAP

T HE geography of our own country has also been altered in places by the formation of artificial lakes, and those who have visited the beautiful Elan Valley, on the western borders of Radnorshire, will agree that here, at least, the engineer has added to the beauties of Nature. Three dams have been constructed in this valley at three different levels, forming great reservoirs for the water-supply of the city of

Birmingham. The rainfall is heavy in this Welsh upland valley and water is constantly flowing from the upper reservoir and pouring over the dams in beautiful cascades, thus aerating the water before it passes into the 80-mile pipe line to the midland metropolis.

Water-supply and hydro-electric schemes give us these silvery lakes which so greatly enhance the mountain scenery in which they are often located, but on the eastern side of England, in the neighbourhood of the Wash, the map has been more drastically altered by actually extending the coast-line seawards. A great deal of this area was inundated until, by the efforts of the engineer, the sea was banked out, the water led into dykes and drains and pumped, day and night, into rivers like the Nene and the Ouse which in many places flow between great banks at higher levels than the surrounding fields and roads. The land thus re-claimed is some of the most fertile in the whole country, making these gains in England's area all the more valuable.

These few examples of the varied activities of the civil engineer may serve to throw a little light on his constant rivalry with natural obstacles—high mountains and wide estuaries which have hampered transport for countless centuries are vanquished by his subtle artifices ; he conjures brilliant light, smokeless heat and clean power from waterfalls and rivers and has even the temerity to defy the encroaching waves and turn salt swamps into fertile market gardens.

RECOMMENDED READING

FOR those who wish to inquire further into the subject of surveying there is an excellent book upon the subject by Middleton and Chadwick, published in two volumes by Messrs. Spon. The first volume deals with plane surveying, i.e. the kind of work which is not of sufficient magnitude to necessitate the consideration of the earth's spherical shape, and it includes a most interesting chapter on the history of surveying from very early times.

The application of astronomy to surveying is described in detail in *Astronomy for Surveyors* by Rice-Oxley and Shearer (Methuen). There is a good series of small books dealing with the manufacture and properties of various engineering materials published by Messrs. Pitman under the general title of *The Common Commodities and Industries Series*. Separate volumes, by recognised authorities, deal with Concrete and Reinforced Concrete, Iron and Steel, Rubber, and Stones and Quarries. The mathematical principles involved in civil engineering design, so far as steel bridges, roof trusses and hydraulics are concerned, are treated in an excellent manner in the well-known textbook *Applied Mechanics* by Professor D. A. Low (Longmans). A welcome feature of this book is the clearness of the innumerable diagrams, but it is not easy reading for anyone lacking a good mathematical foundation.

Those who are particularly interested in hydraulics will find that the book on this subject by Lewitt, published by Messrs. Pitman, covers the field in a comprehensive manner, but here again, a good grounding in mathematics is necessary if the book is to be thoroughly understood. Well-illustrated descriptions of many outstanding triumphs of civil engineering will be found in *Engineering Wonders of the World*, and the whole science of up-to-date highway engineering is dealt with in a most interesting manner in *Modern Road Construction* by Bradley and Hancock.

PUTTING NATURE TO WORK: THE SCIENCE OF MACHINES

by N. H. Pitts, B.Sc.(Eng.)

IT is a truism to say that to-day we live in an age of Machines. The more we succeed in getting the machine to work for us, the more we find for it to do. Ultimately, this " work " is all physical work, which is being performed in countless factories and workshops throughout the world. It is in these that " wild nature " is enslaved, and made to exert its enormous energy for man. Machines cannot literally do the work themselves. No motor-car can run by itself—it must be filled with petrol first. The petrol provides the energy required for movement—the motor-car is merely the instrument by which that energy is applied to the desired end. So it is with all machines, in every case they are but devices for canalising energy. They cannot provide it, they are only there to utilise it.

No man has yet succeeded in creating energy. It is the fact of extracting energy from Nature that engages his ingenuity. If manual power had to run every machine the Machine Age as we know it could never have even begun. But man has at his hand an enormous supply of natural energy. Machines are but the tools with which nature sets to work. The earth contains vast stores of hidden energy, and it is in the adaptation of this colossal energy to his own ends that man becomes more and more adept.

The history of mechanical engineering is the story of continual development, the inventions of new methods and improvement of old for the seizing of this natural energy, taming, transforming and finally applying it for the service of man. Mechanics, or the science of machines, is directly responsible for this task. The civil engineer, electrician, chemist and physicist must all collaborate, and without their assistance and the benefit of their knowledge, the mechanical engineer to-day would be seriously crippled. But it is his special domain to design and build the machines which will harness the latent energy of the earth, and devote it to the service of humanity.

141

It is difficult to define energy. It is something as intangible, as hard to describe as to explain the nature of colour to a man born blind. The human body is a store of energy—the vital " something " which enables one to move, to do work and walk about. With it—life ; without it—death. So with the world. Energy is around us in every form—the earth abounds in it, the very air vibrates with it. Energy is to the world what life is to the human body.

" Energy can neither be created nor destroyed." This is one of the first rules of science, and on it is based the existence of mechanical engineering. It is perhaps at first sight open to considerable argument. " What then," one might ask, " has happened to all this energy, this power that we are consuming every day of our lives—where has it gone ? Why are miners constantly bringing coal from the earth, oil wells gushing forth millions of gallons of oil, and why this concern for the future supplies of these commodities ? Surely if energy cannot be destroyed, our present supply is enough, there is no need to increase it. Moreover, what is the use of trying to do so, if it cannot be created ? "

The explanation lies in the fact that energy is an elusive thing ; it cannot be caught and killed—it will always escape in some other form. Heat, motion, force, chemical energy, falling weights, electricity, all are forms of energy, and all are mutually interchangeable. If it is " used up " in one form, it will be found that it has only been turned into another. It can be traced through any number of manifestations, but at the end it still exists, divided and distributed perhaps in many ways, but its total amount unchanged.

THE GOLFER'S BREAKFAST ENERGY : WHERE DOES IT GO?

As an example of the way in which energy is transferred but not destroyed, take for instance the mighty effort which a golfer spends in propelling his small white ball through the air. He himself has derived this energy from food which has given oxygen and vitamins to his body and enabled him to swing the golf club. The swinging club strikes the ball and transfers to this the energy which previously the club possessed by virtue of its motion. After impact the ball itself possesses it, also in the form of motion. Slowly however its speed is reduced, it falls to the ground, bounces, rolls and stops. Where now is the energy of the golfer's breakfast ?

Actually it has been given up to the air through which the

ball travels. Air always resists motion, as anyone who has put his hand out of an express train will realise. It retards the movement of the ball largely by the effect of friction of the air against its surface, just as a child sliding on the ice is eventually stopped by the friction between ice and shoes. Further, if a gymnast slides down a rope, clasping it too tightly with his hands, they will be burnt and blistered by heat. In this example lies the explanation, work done against friction reappears in the form of heat. (To realise this, one has only to consider the earliest form of fire-lighting—the generation of so much heat by merely rubbing two sticks together, that they burst into flame.) The friction between air and golf ball is exactly the same, and reappears as heat. Thus the energy of movement gradually leaves the ball, and is transformed into energy of heat in the surrounding air. Actually, of course, the volume of air is so vast, that its temperature is raised only an infinitesimal amount by the small amount of heat generated in this way.

Energy which has been given up to the air as heat in this manner is said to have been " dissipated "—that is to say, it is no longer available for the performance of useful work. It is in this way that most of the power produced in the power stations of the world finally takes its leave of man. It may pass through innumerable changes and transformations first, in some of which it might seem that it really had disappeared for ever. Nevertheless it is still there, though possessed by another system of bodies and in a different form, and in the end it is " dissipated " in this manner—but never destroyed.

THE MANY FORMS WHICH ENERGY CAN TAKE

IN the example of the golfer just described, we have seen how energy has changed its form, been given up by one body to another, and finally been surrendered to the atmosphere. In the human body, the chemical energy contained in food is transformed into warmth and the potential " mechanical " energy which enables the golfer to swing his club. In so doing, this energy is transferred from him to his club, and again from this to the golf ball, and eventually to the air. In this succession of events it has changed its form from chemical energy to heat and mechanical energy, from that to the energy of motion of the club and ball, and ultimately back to heat. Secondly it has been transferred in the process of being given up by the food to the human body, and thence to the golf club, the ball, and finally air.

This is merely an instance of the factors which govern all processes in which energy is utilised. In the power station, as with the golfer, energy is continuously changing its form and its location. Nothing else can be done with it. In the power station, however, " raw " energy on a large scale is being altered and transferred from one " mechanism " to another, and everything is done to control these changes as much as possible in the directions required.

The food on which these power stations thrive is only one form of energy—fuel. Whether it be coal, or oil, the energy is already there ; this is not the first stage in its life. Fuel is a compact form of energy and is supplied as such all ready for man's use. We know that energy cannot be created or destroyed—but we do not know the ultimate origin of the supply already in existence. We can trace it back to a certain extent however. We know that it does not spring from this earth. For our supply of this vital power, we must look far away—millions of miles across the unknown space.

THE DEBT WE OWE TO THE SUN

THE Sun-Worshippers of ancient times expressed homage to the object which they vaguely felt to be the " Giver of Life "—the beneficent deity which raised their crops and whose rays brought health and life to the human beings on earth. Little though they understood its action, how right they were !

And, great though the advance of science and the ingenuity of the engineer may be, how entirely dependent we still are on the sun to-day ! It is the great originator and producer of practically all power supplies, and to it indirectly we are indebted for our electricity, motor cars, ships, railways and everything in this mechanical age which depends on power supply.

From time immemorial, ages before man existed, the sun has poured forth a small share of its tremendous energy to the earth. It is continually radiating heat and energy through space. Only a fraction has reached the earth, and of this only a fraction has been utilised, accumulating in the earth until those vast stores of coal and oil, which have supplied the driving force for all our so-called " Power-Stations " and power production plant, have been amassed and buried under the ground.

HOW TIME AND THE EARTH HAVE STORED THE SUN'S ENERGY

UNDER the power of the sun's rays, the green colouring matter of plant-leaves has the power of causing chemical combination between the plant and carbon dioxide in the air. How the vital changes involved are brought about is not known, only the results of these changes. In the past, masses of vegetation were probably covered over with a layer of damp earthy material and cut off from light and air. In this way, rotting was prevented, and slow decay over hundreds of thousands of years has transformed the dead vegetable, and probably animal, matter into huge layers of coal and oil. During this period, however, the energy which the plants and trees had absorbed from the sun has not been lost; it is still present as chemical energy.

It is this chemical energy which all fuels possess and which enables them to burn—whether it is vegetable life which died ages ago, such as coal and oil, or whether it is living plant life like wood or peat. In each case, it is the sun's rays which have caused either the growth of the latter, or the decay of the former. Thus stores of energy have been laid up which can later be liberated and used by man. In this way a small part of the sun's energy has been retained ; it has been changed in form and now lies dormant in coal and oil deposits, forests and peat-bogs. Our first and greatest source of energy is that produced by the combustion of these fuels and the resultant liberation of their latent energy in the form of heat.

The second most important form of energy is that of water power. Here again the sun is the source of energy. The evaporation of seas and lakes by its heat, the formation of clouds and subsequent rain is well known. Rain falling on mountains and hills forms rivers and streams which flow down to their lowest level, the sea. Enormous quantities of water are thus set in motion by the sun, and these rivers and water-falls possess tremendous energy. Some of this power is utilised in hydro-electric power stations and transformed into electricity which can be distributed over the land.

Other possible sources of power are those held by the wind and the tides. Considerable research and experiments have been done with a view to obtaining power on a large scale from windmills or " wind-motors." Also, day in and day out, enormous energy is called into play by the motion of the tides, and if only this could be successfully tapped, the world would be independent of its diminishing stores of coal and oil.

In passing, it may be of interest to note that successful attempts have also been made to utilise the internal heat of the earth itself. In the extinct volcanic regions of Tuscany, natural steam springs issue from the earth. At Lardarello a power station has been erected in which 5,000 KW. are generated by turbines operating on this natural steam. Volcanic regions of this nature exist in several parts of the world, and geological research is being done with this object in view.

HOW WE "SWITCH ON THE SUN" WHEN THE SUN GOES DOWN

WHETHER it be in coal mine, oil well, or river, there is the energy retained by the earth, and that is how man finds it. It is now for him to adapt it and utilise it for his own ends. These are the forms available, and from them springs all our mechanical civilisation of to-day.

The electric lamp shining in one's room owes its light solely to the sun. It may seem perhaps a long way, but actually, as we switch on the light, we are giving just another form to energy which reached the earth from the sun hundreds of thousands of years ago. Our electricity comes from a power station miles away, where it is produced from an electric generator. This is rotated by a steam turbine which in its turn is driven by steam generated in boilers by the heat from a furnace of burning coal. It is as coal that we first find this energy, but ages ago this coal was vegetable life, living in the sunshine. The sun's rays warmed it and gave it life, until its gradual decay under the surface of the earth turned it into the familiar " black diamonds."

So it is with all the power we use, whether generated from coal, oil or water, it goes through many forms, but it all has a common origin, the sun. Water turbines, steam engines, or internal combustion engines using oil and petrol—all derive their energy from this source, and we are entirely dependent on it.

Only if man succeeded in unlocking the atomic energy of the rocks and generating light, heat and power by " atomic energy " engines and machinery, might human life be possible if the sun cooled and its supply of energy ceased.

MAN'S SMALL PART IN THE VAST CYCLE OF ENERGY

ONLY a fraction of the sun's energy is locked up as fuel or water power, the rest has been radiated through space. The portion that has remained on the earth is however mostly in a convenient form and comparatively easily freed. Coal, for instance, contains energy in a compact and organised form —chemical energy which is all given up as heat when the coal is burnt. This heat represents the first stage in the process by which the natural energy is directed to do work.

From this point, as the energy goes from furnace to steam, from steam to engine or electric generator and finally to the machines of the factory and workshop, it becomes less easy to keep complete control over it. From the original compact form of chemical energy, it is split up, converted and transferred in many ways. The difficulty lies not so much in converting it in this way, as in retaining it all and preventing its escape. Throughout the process, "leaks" of energy take place. Constantly it is striving to escape, and despite all efforts to stop these "leaks," complete success is impossible. Consequently not all the original energy of the coal actually reaches the machines where power is used. Only a portion of it actually does useful work—the rest has been lost on the way.

These leaks are many and varied, but usually the final result is the same. Whether through radiation, friction, or otherwise, some energy is constantly escaping to the atmosphere in the form of heat. All that which does not reach the machines is dissipated in this way.

To return to the golfer, the ball never receives quite as much energy as he puts into the club. At every change in form, and whenever energy is transferred from one body to another, a little is lost on the way. Perhaps not lost, but all these small leaks are given up to the atmosphere and are then beyond our control.

Ultimately, however, all energy reaches the same end. Whenever power is used, in industry or otherwise, it is finally transformed into heat, frictional or otherwise, and is given up to the air. All the energy that is taken from the earth eventually reaches the atmosphere once more and is radiated from earth into space, disappearing into unknown regions of the universe. The majority of the sun's energy is radiated through space without this intermediate period on the earth. That which does remain however is relatively soon dissipated by man, and all our power houses, hydro-electric schemes, etc., represent but a transitory stage of the sun's rays in this path through the universe.

THE ENGINEER'S TASK : PUTTING ENERGY TO WORK

IT is the duty of the mechanical engineer to make best use of this " pause " in the path of energy. He it is who must utilise the natural resources of power obtainable in the earth. He must extract as much of the available energy as is possible, and it must be done cheaply and easily. The energy must be guided through various stages and different forms, and he must see that as little as possible is lost to the atmosphere in the process. Then having tamed it and harnessed it to machines in which it can be usefully applied—he must devise means for making efficient use of it. A steam engine cannot make bridges or shoes by itself, it can only produce power which can then be turned to these purposes.

The mechanical engineer must invent the necessary machines by which this can be done. Thirdly and of equal importance, he must not only think of ways of producing and utilising power, but he must be able to put his ideas into concrete form. In other words, he must actually design and make machines which will perform these duties, and which will be strong enough and safe enough to fulfil them without unreasonable fear of breakdown or endangering of human life. In short, the field of mechanical engineering is the " Science of Machines."

FROM STORED ENERGY TO MECHANICAL POWER

AS will now be understood, the " production of power " is in reality no such thing. It is a process for adapting energy in the form provided by nature, and converting it into a supply of power of a nature readily useable for driving machinery, generating electricity, etc. A " power station " is therefore really an " energy conversion " station. The characteristics of each power plant and its prime movers (or engines) depend on the form in which energy is available, and the nature of the work to be done and the power required.

The two chief sources of natural power existing in the world are of course combustible fuels and water power. All power production of any importance falls into either of these two classes. Very different machinery is required for each kind of power plant, although there are superficial points of resemblance between, for example, steam and water turbines. The principles underlying their operation, however, are so different that it is essential to treat them separately. The two types are : *combustion* or *heat-engines* whose power is derived from the heat evolved during the combustion of a fuel, and *hydraulic* or *water-engines* driven directly by water power.

PRESSURE AND TEMPERATURE : HOW A GAS CAN DO WORK

HEAT engines deal essentially with high temperature gases, as distinct from the ordinary cold water which is the working medium in hydraulic machinery. These gases are the media by which heat is turned into the " mechanical " energy of moving machinery, which in its turn supplies power to meet the various requirements.

Unlike solids and liquids, a gas can have any volume. It may be compressed into a smaller volume at a higher pressure, whilst a fall in its pressure will cause it to expand and take up a larger volume. When the handle of a bicycle pump is pushed in, air inside is compressed into a smaller volume at a pressure greater than that in the tyre, so that the valve opens and the air is pumped in. On the other hand if high pressure air were introduced into the pump from an external source the reverse would happen ; it would expand and push the pump handle out. In doing so it would exert the same force on the handle as before was required to push it in and compress the air. Again, if a gas is heated and raised to a higher temperature it will expand ; or if it is in a confined space and is not free to do so, its pressure will rise instead.

It is on these peculiar characteristics of gases that the results of heating depends. A supply of gas of some kind at a high pressure (and temperature) is introduced into the engine. There it is free to expand to a larger volume and a lower temperature, but to do so it must " force its way " out just as the compressed air would push out the handle in a reversed bicycle pump. In its expansion it sets the moving parts of the engine in motion.

The conversion of the latent energy of a fuel into mechanical motion is achieved by burning the fuel, and either using the gaseous products of combustion themselves as the expanding medium, or using their heat to raise some other gas to the required pressure and temperature. More will be said later of the difference between these two methods, but it

will be as well at this stage to explain the significance of
" Combustion."

GETTING UP THE PRESSURE BY BURNING FUEL

FUELS may be either solid, liquid or gaseous, and there
are several forms of each.   The chief requirements are
cheapness, availability, ease of handling and application, and
the evolution of a large amount of heat when burnt.   In
actual practice those used almost universally are coal, petrol
and oil, and " gas " (which may be of several kinds).

All these consist mainly of some substance (chiefly carbon
or " hydro-carbons ") which " burns."   In other words,
under certain circumstances, it will combine with the oxygen
of the air to form certain gases, giving off great heat in the
process.   This is purely a chemical reaction, and in it the
chemical energy of the fuel is transformed into heat possessed
by the gaseous products of combustion.   Some means are
usually necessary to start the process (just as matches, paper,
etc., are required to light a fire), but once started it will continue of its own accord.

It should be noted, however, that fuels cannot burn by
themselves—oxygen (or air) must be present for the chemical
reaction involved to take place.   If a lighted match were
introduced into a gasometer containing gas alone, and no
air or oxygen—the match would be extinguished.   Gas explosions can only take place when a mixture of gas and air
is ignited.   Instantaneous combustion, then, causes such a
rapid increase in pressure that an " explosion " occurs.   The
controlled supply of air for combustion is for this reason an
important point, as on this depends the extent of the action.
Incomplete combustion means that some fuel escapes unburnt or only partially so, and its energy is thus wasted.

During combustion the fuel is changed into gases at a
very high temperature, and at a high or low pressure as required.   As previously stated, the engine is operated by the
expansion of gases from a higher to a lower pressure.   The
heat available in the hot gases of combustion must therefore
be used to charge the engine with a gas at the necessary
pressure.   This may be done in two ways.   The heat may be
used to convert water into high-pressure steam, which is
then admitted to the engine, where it expands and does work.
Or a mixture of air and the fuel itself may be introduced
directly into the engine and there burnt.   Owing to the heat

evolved and the confined space, the resulting gases are raised not only to a high temperature but also to a high pressure. They are therefore capable of doing work themselves in the same way as the high-pressure steam in the first case. The first class—" External-Combustion Engines "—includes all steam engines and steam turbines ; the second—" Internal-Combustion Engines "—includes all gas, oil and petrol engines.

FROM STEAM PRESSURE TO MOTION

EVERY schoolboy has heard the story—probably untrue—of how James Watt, idly watching a kettle boiling on the fire one afternoon was suddenly inspired with the idea of using the energy of steam to drive an engine. This anecdote, though apocryphal, really indicates the fundamental principle of the steam-engine (with the exception of the turbine) and from this principle in turn has sprung the universally used internal-combustion engine of to-day. The day of the historic steam-engine, with its great cylinders and pistons and its connecting rods whirling majestically through the air, may be on the wane, but without these herculean machines the comparatively small and compact turbine and internal-combustion engines could never have developed.

Let us see what the " boiling kettle " has become to-day and how in a steam-power plant, the heat from fuel, in conjunction with water, is turned to the service of mankind. In Fig. 37 is a diagrammatic view showing the simplest " cycle of operation " of a steam-power plant. First we have the boiler where the heat from burning fuel turns water into high-pressure steam. This then passes to the steam engine, and by its expansion down to a lower pressure rotates the engine shaft from which the power is taken. After leaving the engine, the steam is not wasted but passes to a " condenser " where it is condensed into the form of water once more. From there it is pumped back into the boiler and used again, being continually turned into steam, used in the engine, and condensed into water again. The various stages of this cycle of operations will be considered in turn.

THE KETTLE BEGINS TO GROW : BOILERS

THE simplest form of boiler is a plain cylindrical " shell " containing water, supported over a furnace. The heat from the burning fuel underneath turns some of the water into steam which is then led away in a pipe to the engine. As, however, it is necessary, not merely to burn fuel and turn water into steam, but to burn as little fuel and obtain as much steam as possible, this simple form of boiler is little used except for such purposes as heating buildings, etc., as it is very wasteful of fuel. However, the principle remains the same and the problem of the boiler designer is to ensure the most effective transfer of heat from the furnace gases to the water. And though in practice far more complicated than the above simple type of boiler, the various types in use are

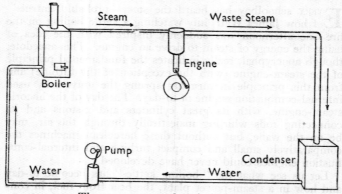

37. The steam-power plant in its simplest form

only developments, improvements, even inversions, of that form. Boilers may be divided into three general classes: Flue boilers, Fire-tube boilers, Water-tube boilers.

Heat must pass from furnace or " flue " gases to the water, through the intervening steel casing, or shell. In order to facilitate this passage of heat, therefore, the area (or " heating surface ") over which the gases are in contact with the water container must be made as large as possible, and so the " flue boiler " was introduced. In this, after the gases had passed from the furnace round the bottom of the boiler, they were not allowed to escape as in the simple boiler first described, but were now led back through a steel tube, a " flue " passing right through the middle of the water in the cylinder, and more heat was extracted from them by this means.

From this developed the internally-fired boiler, in which the central flue was made large enough to contain the furnace itself, the gases passing down the flue, and being led back along the outside of the shell. In the Cornish boiler the fire is placed in the mouth of the flue, down which the hot gases sweep, heating the water in the shell on their way, and returning round the outside of the shell through passages in the surrounding brickwork. It will be appreciated that a far greater heating surface is provided by this means, and therefore a greater amount of heat from the fuel is employed in turning water into steam, instead of escaping up the chimney. Flue boilers may have one or two flues.

A FURTHER REFINEMENT: THE FIRE-TUBE BOILER

IN order still further to increase the heating area, the one or two flues of the flue boiler were next replaced by a large number of small tubes by which the gases passed from end to end of the boiler, this being known as the " fire-tube "

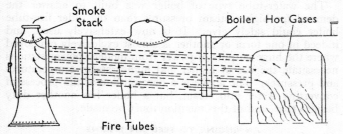

38. The essentials of the " fire-tube " locomotive boiler

boiler. These may be made in a variety of ways, either internally or externally fired, and either vertical or horizontal. One of the most common forms of fire-tube boiler is the locomotive boiler, of which a view is given in Fig. 38.

Here the hot gases pass from the fire, through the boiler and out of the chimney. The fire-tube boiler is also very largely used in ships, though it is gradually being replaced by the water-tube boiler.

INVERTING THE PROCESS FOR SAFETY: THE WATER-TUBE BOILER

FIRE-TUBE boilers are easily made, and quite cheap, but they have disadvantages, particularly with the very high pressure steam now used. An explosion would be disastrous, owing to the single large water and steam space. Largely for this reason, all boilers used in large power installations are of the " water-tube " type. In this boiler the water circulates through small tubes, round the outside of which pass the furnace gases. As its name implies, it is an inversion of the fire-tube boiler, and, while the large heating surface is still obtainable, it possesses greater strength to resist high pressures, and the bursting of one small water tube would not be nearly so disastrous as if the whole shell of a fire-tube boiler were to burst.

Usually the main quantity of water and steam are contained in one or more horizontal cylindrical drums, and the water passes from these drums, through the tubes placed in the path of the furnace gases, and back into the drum, some being converted into steam on the way. The furnace gases are made to pursue a winding path, to ensure that as much heat as possible is used in converting water into steam.

The water-tube type of boiler was built to answer the demand for higher steam pressures than the older fire-tube boiler could safely give. It is now extensively used, and indeed in one form or another is almost exclusively employed where the huge outputs of power from modern power stations necessitate the use of higher and higher steam temperatures and pressures. The above is a bare outline of the process of converting water into steam, but a boiler has another duty besides that, and of this mention must be made.

AN ENGINE TO FEED AN ENGINE

IF the water in the boiler were merely converted into steam at a low temperature, on reaching the engine the steam would have cooled a little, and during expansion would cool still further, until eventually the engine would probably contain quite a large quantity of water which had condensed from the steam due to this cooling. This would be a most undesirable feature.

To avoid it, and in order to get as much useful work from the steam as possible, the latter is taken through a " superheater " before it leaves the boiler on its way to the engine. This consists of a few tubes, placed in the very hottest part of the flue gases, through which the steam passes and receives its final quantity of heat from the furnace and is raised to a still higher temperature. From the superheater it passes to the engine, where it is now able to do its work more efficiently and satisfactorily.

Water is continually leaving the boiler in the form of steam, and of course more water, known as "feed water," must be introduced into the boiler to make up for this. This feed water is steam that has passed through the engine and been converted into water again in the condenser, whence it is extracted, and must be introduced once more into the boiler, and this against the very high pressure of the steam and water inside. This may be done by means of a device known as an "injector." Here the force of a jet of steam at high pressure is used to open a valve and force the feed water into the boiler. In all large boiler installations, however, a special "feed pump" is necessary to pump the water in against the pressure inside the boiler. This is driven by a small steam engine operated by steam from the main steam supply pipe.

THE "ROBOT" STOKER WHICH FEEDS THE FURNACE

EQUALLY as important as the steam side of the boiler operation, and calling for as much careful control and attention, is the maintenance of the furnace. If the boiler is fired with coal, this may be in the form of small "slack," and is kept in large conical shaped bunkers up in the boiler-house roof. Coal shutes bring it from the bunkers to the furnace entrance, and a ceaselessly moving grate carries it into the roaring fire inside. This grate is in the form of an endless chain which carries the coal through the furnace until it is all burnt away. The ash is then discharged down the back, and the grate bends down and returns underneath. By this means, stoking of the fires is purely mechanical, and the coal is untouched by hand throughout. Hand stoking, at any rate for the large boilers required in power stations, has been a thing of the past for many years.

Other forms of fuel than slack coal may be used, such as oil, or "pulverised" coal. Oil is sprayed into the furnace, together with a regulated amount of air, and the mixture of vaporised oil and air ignite and burn spontaneously. Pulverised coal, that is to say, coal which has been crushed to very fine pieces, is fed into the furnace in a somewhat similar way.

As mentioned before, it is most essential that the fuel in the furnace be supplied with an adequate quantity of air. The fuel must also be made to burn very rapidly, so that water may be quickly converted into steam. The effect of blowing a domestic fire with bellows is well known, and the same effect is made use of in the great fires of boilers—a " draught " is essential for the satisfactory and rapid burning of the fuel. This may be natural draught, obtained in exactly the same way as that from the chimney of a fire in one's room ; but for large boilers it must be increased artificially and air is either blown through the furnace through the grate, or a draught is created by sucking the flue gases and air out of the furnace by means of external fans or a combination of both.

HOW STEAM IS PUT TO WORK

FROM the mechanically-stoked furnace, with its artificial draught, most of the available energy in the fuel has been successfully transferred to the steam passing from the boiler and superheater. It is now necessary to use this steam to drive the engine, whose power may be used for generating electricity, or any other purpose. Steam is made to do its task in two ways. It may be used to push a piston to and fro in a cylinder, and since the motion of the piston is backwards and forwards in a straight line, this is known as a " reciprocating steam engine." (The term " steam engine " has come to be used to denote this type of engine only.) Or it may be used to drive a " steam turbine." This is a more recent invention than the steam engine, and the latter will be dealt with first. It may be noted, however, that in each case the ultimate object is to use the energy of the steam to rotate a shaft, and from this the power is finally taken.

The energy of the steam is turned into work by allowing it to expand, and so move the engine. Let us see how this is done in the steam engine. This itself consists essentially of :

THE CYLINDER.—The chamber in which the steam expands.

THE PISTON AND PISTON ROD.—The piston is pushed to and fro in the cylinder by the expanding steam. Attached to it is a rod (projecting through a hole in the cylinder end) known as the piston rod.

THE CRANKSHAFT.—The revolving shaft from which the power is taken.

THE CONNECTING ROD.—A rigid link, which connects the crankshaft to the piston rod. By this means the " to and

High Pressure Steam

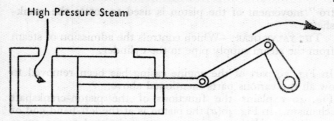

a. High pressure steam enters the cylinder

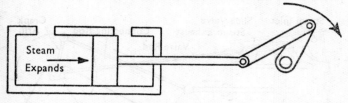

Steam
Expands

b. The piston is driven to the right

High Pressure Steam

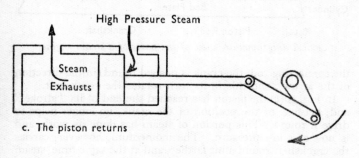

Steam
Exhausts

c. The piston returns

Steam
Expands

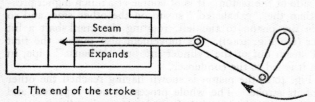

d. The end of the stroke

40. THE PISTON STROKE IN A STEAM ENGINE

fro " movement of the piston is used to rotate the crank-shaft.

THE VALVE GEAR.—Which controls the admission of steam from the steam supply pipe to the cylinder.

In Fig. 39 part of the engine casing has been removed to show all the various parts mentioned above.

Fig. 40 explains the functions of the piston-crankshaft mechanism. In Fig. 40(a) the piston is at the left-hand end of the cylinder. High-pressure steam is admitted to the space shown, and as it can only increase its volume by pushing the piston to the right, it does so. At the same time, by means of

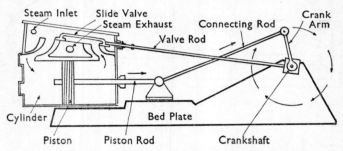

39. *A diagrammatic view of the parts of a steam engine*

the connecting rod, the crank is pushed round (in the direction of the arrow), and this in its turn rotates the crankshaft.

In Fig. 40(b) the piston has reached the end of its " stroke " and, because of the position of the crank, no longer helps to drive it round. This portion of steam has done its work, and is now at a low pressure. The momentum, however, carries the crankshaft round a bit farther, and at the same time, steam is admitted to the cylinder again, but this time to the right-hand side of the piston. It is of course at a much higher pressure than the " exhausted " steam on the other side, and so pushes the piston to the left, rotating the crankshaft a bit farther (see Fig. 40(c)). Its movement also pushes the first lot of steam out of the cylinder into an " exhaust " pipe, in which it is led to the condenser.

In Fig. 40(d) the piston is shown having reached the other end of its stroke. The whole process is now repeated, and by this means the crankshaft is kept continually rotating.

Now let us examine the action of the engine, outlined briefly above, in a little more detail.

THE STEAM ENGINE EXAMINED

FIG. 41 shows the cylinder of Fig. 39 but greatly enlarged. On top of the cylinder is a box-like structure called the "steam chest." The steam from the boilers is admitted into this by the inlet pipe. The steam valve slides to and fro, alternately covering and uncovering the openings A and B, through which the steam may enter either end of the cylinder. The valve, called a "slide valve," by virtue of its motion, is shown admitting the steam through the opening A to the left-

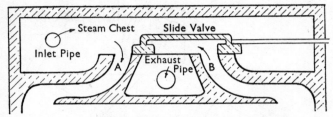

41. An enlarged view of the steam chest, showing how the slide valve works.

hand side of the piston (as in Fig. 40(*a*)). At the same time, the expanded, low-pressure steam on the right-hand side is free to escape through the opening B, as it is pushed out of the cylinder by the piston moving to the right. Now it does not go back into the steam chest of course, but escapes into the exhaust pipe.

The manner in which the valve gear controls the engine will now be understood. First it moves to the right and opens the opening A, admitting new steam to the cylinder. It then moves partly to the left, closing the cylinder while the steam expands and pushes the piston on its stroke. When the steam has been expanded right down to low pressure, the piston stops and begins to return. By this time, the valve has travelled right over to the left, and the old steam is pushed out of the cylinder, back through the opening A and out into the exhaust pipe. This happens exactly as is shown taking place at A in the drawing, except that the valve is now at the left-hand end of its stroke instead of the right.

It will be seen that the movement of the valve is similar to that of the piston. Actually it is driven from the crankshaft through the " valve rod," in almost the same way as that in which the piston, through the connecting rod, rotates the crankshaft, but the procedure is reversed. The movement of the valve may be altered, and by this means, the amount of work done by the steam at each stroke is regulated to meet the demand for power. It can also control the speed of the engine and its direction, reversing being effected by

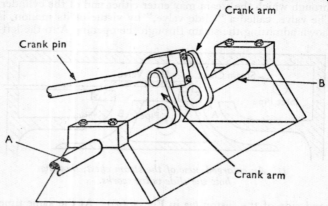

42. A simple form of crankshaft, showing its bearings and the connections by crank arm and crank pin to the piston.

a simple adjustment to the valve movement. The valve is made to regulate the engine in this way by means of the " valve gear," a rather complicated mechanism.

Fig. 42 shows a simple form of crankshaft. The round ends A and B rotate in bearings mounted on the engine bedplate, and the connecting rod is joined to the " crank pin." The valve-driving mechanism is not shown, but it is mounted on an extension of the crankshaft. On one end of the latter also is fixed the pulley or coupling for transferring the power of the engine to other machinery.

A PART TO CONTROL THE WHOLE: VALVE GEAR

VALVES, valve-gear and the control of the steam supplied to the cylinders are a very important feature of the steam engine. Slide valves of the type described, and piston valves (which are really only cylindrical slide valves) must have a reciprocating motion, corresponding to that of the main piston. A valve rod takes the place of the piston rod, and this is given a reciprocating motion from the crankshaft. There are various methods of achieving this, but for all practical purposes it may be considered as a reversal of the piston, connecting-rod, crank process, that is, a small auxiliary crank on the main shaft driving the valve rod through a connecting rod.

The valve is not open to the cylinder during the whole of the "working stroke" of the piston. High-pressure steam is admitted during the first part, the supply is then "cut off," and the steam enclosed in the cylinder now expands and completes the stroke. In the same way, the passage to the exhaust pipe is closed by the valve before the end of the exhaust stroke, the steam then trapped in the cylinder being compressed by the piston and acting as a "cushion" to bring it smoothly to rest. There are thus four functions which the valve must perform in each "cycle." It must open to allow steam to enter ("admission"); it must close again after the first part of the stroke ("cut-off"); it must open the path to the exhaust pipe ("release"); and it must close it again before the end of the return stroke ("compression").

In Fig. 43(a) the valve is shown at its central position, and it travels an equal distance each side of this. Consider for the moment only the left-hand end of the cylinder. The position of the valve at the four main points of its stroke are shown in Fig. 43, the arrows indicating the direction of its motion at each moment. In Fig. 43(b), for instance, it is on the point of opening and admitting steam to the cylinder. As steam takes a certain time (though very short) to pass through the various passages into the cylinder, the valve must be already open as the piston reaches the end of its exhaust stroke. By this means the full force of the steam acts on the piston right at the beginning of the stroke. The amount of this preliminary opening is known as the "lead."

In practice, it is usually arranged that the valve moves more than half of its total left to right travel before the piston begins its stroke. In a similar way for all the other functions, the valve must be well ahead of the piston. For this reason the angle between the relative positions of the main crank and the auxiliary valve crank or the crankshaft is known as the "angular advance."

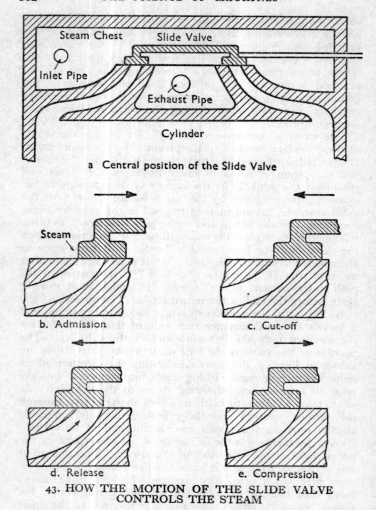

a Central position of the Slide Valve

Steam

b. Admission   c. Cut-off

d. Release   e. Compression

43. HOW THE MOTION OF THE SLIDE VALVE
CONTROLS THE STEAM

There are two necessary adjustments which must be made
to the performance of the valve. Many steam engines, notably
locomotive and marine type, frequently need reversing. In
this case, all the operations must be reversed. Secondly, the

power required from the engine is subject to many variations, and the quantity of steam admitted to the cylinder must be reduced for smaller powers by arranging for an earlier " cut-off " point to suit. This may be done by reducing the stroke of the valve and increasing the " angular advance." Therefore two valve cranks are really needed, one for forward motion and the other for reverse. Moreover, each must be adjustable in such a manner that various " cut-off " points may be obtained for different loads. In actual practice " valve-cranks " are not used, as the crankshaft construction would be far too complicated. Many arrangements are in use for giving the valve its motion, but in each case their action is fundamentally that of the two cranks described above. For all practical purposes the valve movement may be considered to be derived in this way.

THE STEPHENSON LINK MOTION

THE valve gear invented by Stephenson is shown diagrammatically in Fig. 44. It is one of the oldest forms, and has been very widely used for locomotives. Two " cranks " A and B, one for forward and one for reverse, are attached to the crankshaft in positions relative to the main crank as shown in Fig. 44(1). A is connected through the rod C to a curved link F, B being similarly connected. The end of the valve rod is joined to F, which, however, is free to slide up and down. It is lifted or lowered by a hand lever in the driver's cab, operating the mechanism G.

The operation of this gear is shown in the two lower figures. For forward motion the link F is lowered. The valve rod now derives practically all its motion from the " forward crank " A. B swings idly to and fro on the lower end of F without affecting the movement of the valve to any appreciable extent. Thus for any position of the valve rod on the upper half of F, the valve is actuated chiefly by the crank A, and the locomotive moves in a forward direction. Similarly, any position on the lower half will give backward movement.

The positions shown in the centre and at the bottom are known as " full forward " and " full backward gear " respectively. In each case the cut-off takes place at the latest point, and the cylinder receives its maximum quantity of steam. By setting the link F in any intermediate position, the valve is given a movement such as would be obtained by a shorter " crank " (giving a shorter valve stroke) with a greater angle of advance. This, as mentioned previously, has the effect of producing an earlier " cut-off " and a correspondingly smaller admission of steam. This mechanism therefore not only enables the engine to be reversed, but also serves to adjust the power of the engine to the demand at any condition of running.

One drawback to the Stephenson link motion is that the amount of " lead " varies with the position of the gear. However, its simplicity, and quite good steam distribution, resulted in its extensive use, although to-day more complicated mechanisms are generally employed.

SETTING THE STEAM TO WORK IN STAGES

THE simple form of steam engine just described is not, however, suitable for producing a large output of power as it stands. The greater the power required, obviously the more steam will be necessary. The cylinder may be made large enough to take this steam at a high pressure, when it is compressed into a small volume ; but what will happen when the steam has expanded and increased in volume ? The single cylinder of this engine will now have to be of an enormous size, which, if for no other reason than the great cost of manufacture, is undesirable, and other means must be found.

One way of decreasing the size of cylinder necessary is to stop the expansion of the steam before it has reached its final volume. While still at a medium pressure and volume the steam is now led to another cylinder, where its expansion is completed. Its work is thus divided up into two stages, a high-pressure, and a low-pressure, cylinder. Each cylinder has its own connecting rod and valve gear, but they both drive on to the same crankshaft, which now has two cranks. This is a far more satisfactory arrangement than a single cylinder, when greater power is required.

An engine of this type is known as a " compound engine." For all large steam engines, this process of dividing up the work is carried still further. The steam expands first in the high-pressure cylinder, then goes to an " intermediate-pressure " cylinder, and finally to the low-pressure cylinder. This is the " triple expansion " engine, the expansion taking place in three cylinders. Again, the single " low-pressure cylinder " may be made into two, giving four in all, one H.P., one I.P., and two L.P. This is the " quadruple expansion " engine.

As stated before, the valve gear of a steam engine may have

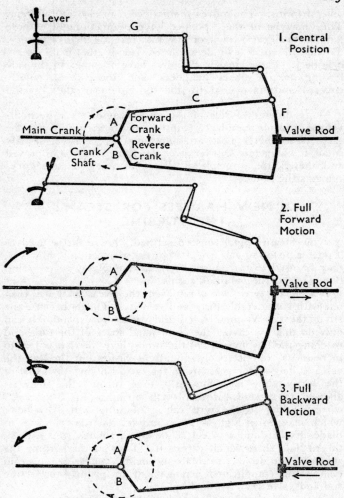

Lever

G

1. Central Position

C

F

Main Crank

Forward Crank

Reverse Crank

A

B

Crank Shaft

Valve Rod

2. Full Forward Motion

A

B

F

Valve Rod

3. Full Backward Motion

A

B

F

Valve Rod

44. THE STEPHENSON LINK MOTION FOR CONTROLLING THE VALVE

The crankshaft (which comes out of the paper) rotates the crank arms A and B as shown by the dotted circles. It is instructive to draw 2 and 3 for several positions of A and B.

several forms. The valves themselves may also be different. They may be of the " poppet " type, something like those familiar to all car owners, or they may take the form of pistons, moving in small cylinders placed beside the main steam cylinders. These smaller cylinders have openings in the side leading to the main cylinders, and these are regularly covered and uncovered by the movement of the " piston valve."

Many different forms of the steam engine have been invented, and no manufacturer produces an engine exactly the same as another. The variations may be extensive, or only small, in character. But however much they may be improved and altered, the principle of all reciprocating steam engines remains the same.

A NEW HARNESS FOR STEAM : THE TURBINE

IN the steam engine, just described, the steam is used to push a piston to and fro. Its powers of expanding, however, may be used to turn a wheel, in the same way as the wind blows round the windmill's sails.

If a bicycle tyre valve is removed, the released air will rush out with considerable force and velocity. This is because the air in the tyre is compressed and wishes to expand. It can only do this by leaving the constricted space of the tyre, and reaching the low pressure of the atmosphere where it is free to increase its volume. Consequently it rushes out through the valve as long as the pressure in the tyre is higher than that of the surrounding air. Similarly, in a turbine the steam is allowed to expand through small openings, or " nozzles," corresponding to the tyre valve. Issuing with a velocity which may be as high as 1,000 m.p.h., it strikes a series of blades fixed round a wheel. The wheel rotates, and with it, the turbine shaft which carries it. Thus in the turbine the steam is used directly to rotate the shaft, whereas in the steam engine the complicated arrangement of piston, connecting rod and valve gear is necessary.

In the simplest form of turbine two or three nozzles are placed round the circumference of the turbine wheel carrying the blades. Steam expands through the nozzles, and in so doing the energy which in the steam engine would move the piston, is now used up in giving the steam its high velocity.

It enters the blades, forces them round by its momentum, and so rotates the wheel. This turbine (called the " de Laval turbine," after its inventor) is used only when very small power is required.

The usual method is to place a disc, or " diaphragm," in front of the wheel. Fixed in this disc are a number of " nozzle plates," opposite the blades of the wheel and somewhat similar to them in shape. These nozzle plates are bent round circumferentially in such a way that the steam expands as in the de Laval nozzles, emerges at great speed, and is directed on to the wheel blades.

INCREASING THE YIELD OF POWER : THE " MULTI-STAGE " TURBINE

THE combination of one diaphragm and one revolving wheel is called a " stage," the two turbines described being each " single stage " machines. In them all the energy of the steam is used in one set of nozzles to give it a tremendous velocity, and, in order to use this speed efficiently, the de Laval turbine rotates at 30,000 revolutions per minute. Speeds of this nature can only be used in very small machines, however ; in anything larger, they would be impossible. Moreover, even if this were not so, this single expansion, because of the extremely high steam velocity, is very wasteful. For this reason, all medium and large size turbines are " multi-stage " machines, in which the steam expands to a small extent in each stage, instead of the whole expansion taking place at once.

The steam issues from the first stage nozzles, but is only allowed to expand to a slightly lower pressure, and has a correspondingly smaller velocity. It passes through the blades of the first wheel and enters the second stage nozzles, where it expands slightly again, and so on through all the stages. Finally it emerges from the last wheel having given up its energy and is led away to the condenser.

As its pressure drops in each successive stage, its volume is increasing at the same time. Because of this, the blades and nozzles must be made longer and longer in each stage to allow the larger volume of steam to pass.

The velocity with which the steam strikes the blades of each wheel is by this means kept within reasonable limits, and far more efficient use is made of the available energy. Moreover, as the size of a turbine increases, the maximum speed at which the shaft can safely revolve is lowered. To allow for this, the number of expansions is so adjusted that the ratio of the blade speed and the steam velocity is correctly proportioned. This would be impossible in a very large single-stage machine, and a large part of the energy of the steam would be wasted. In any case, because of difficulties of manufacture, no single-stage turbine could be made to produce a fraction of the power developed by the huge machines of to-day.

THE MIGHTY GROUPED TURBINES OF TO-DAY

As machines become larger and larger, the quantity and pressure of steam passing through the turbine are also increased in proportion. More and more stages are introduced, and eventually the turbine becomes too big and altogether unwieldy. Then the single turbine is divided into two, as was the steam engine when the single cylinder became too large ; and continuing the analogy, each half of the turbine is called a " cylinder." Each cylinder is complete in itself, and has its own shaft, diaphragms and so on. They are in fact two separate turbines with their shafts coupled together except that the steam from the high-pressure cylinder exhaust is led into the low-pressure cylinder, instead of each having its own supply. The very largest sets have three cylinders and, corresponding to the quadruple-expansion engine, the low-pressure cylinder is usually divided into two, the steam entering at the middle and passing out at both ends. A cylinder divided like this is called a " two-flow " cylinder, as the steam is split up and flows in two directions.

Through these developments, the size of turbines has been increased, until they can produce power to an extent that no steam engine could approach. Because of this, their relatively smaller size, and several other factors, the turbine has practically ousted the steam engine for all purposes but the smaller power installations. In one way only will the old reciprocating engine reign for ever supreme over the turbine. That is the fascination of its movement, that fascination which, on every small passenger boat that exists, eternally draws crowds down below to " watch the engine."

SETTING THE ENGINE TO CONTROL ITS OWN SPEED

The " load " or power required from an engine is varying for different reasons all the time. The reciprocating engines and steam turbines are usually designed to run at a constant speed, and precautions must be taken to prevent them suddenly speeding up to a dangerous speed if the load is reduced, or vice versa. This could be done by the engineer in charge, who would have to close the valve and reduce the amount of steam supplied, as soon as he saw the engine begin to speed up. This, however, is not a practical method, as he could not prevent the speed varying to quite an appreciable extent. It must be done automatically by the engine itself, so that steam is reduced or increased as required, the movement on altera-

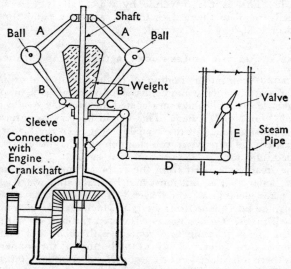

45. The " Governor," a mechanism by which the engine controls its own speed.

tion in load speeds up or slows down the engine. This is achieved by a mechanism driven from the engine shaft.

Fig. 45 is a diagram showing the action of a simple form of " Governor," as this device is called. A weight, revolving at the end of a string, exerts a pull on the hand. The same " centrifugal " force makes the balls of the governor tend to fly upwards as the shaft on which they are mounted is rotated by the engine. They are attached to this shaft by the arms AA and BB, and it is so arranged that the balls have a certain definite position for each speed of the engine.

Suppose now the engine is running on " full load " at its

correct speed, with the valve in the steam pipe wide open as in the diagram. The load is suddenly decreased, the engine starts to speed up, and the balls begin to fly outwards (due to the increased centrifugal force). As they do so, the arms BB raise the sleeve mounted on the shaft, and this action, through the mechanism CDE, closes the valve a little. The engine is now receiving the correct amount of steam for the particular load, and its increase in speed has been checked as soon as it started. This is the principle by which all engines automatically regulate themselves to suit whatever conditions of speed or load may be required.

REVERSING THE BOILER'S JOB : A USEFUL LAST STAGE

THROUGH continually boiling off fresh quantities of ordinary tap water, which contains dissolved mineral salts, an ordinary kettle gradually becomes coated all over the inside with a hard " fur " or " scale." This would be very harmful in a boiler, causing much of the available heat from the furnace to be wasted. To prevent this happening, the water is first purified, and then used over and over again.

The steam exhausted from the turbine cannot be returned to the boiler as it is, but must first be made into water again. This takes place in a " condenser." The steam is taken from the turbine into a large iron shell, in which are a large number of small tubes. Cold water is circulated through these tubes, and the steam, coming into contact with their cold surface, condenses into water and falls to the bottom of the condenser. From there it is sucked out by a pump and eventually returned to the boiler.

The condenser has also another function. If the pressure of the steam at the turbine exhaust can by some means be lowered, this will have the same beneficial effect as raising the initial steam pressure—and this is done automatically in the condenser. Water has a much smaller volume than the quantity of steam it would form, and when the latter condenses into small drops of water, it leaves behind it—space. Consequently a " vacuum " is formed in the condenser, and the pressure into which the steam exhausts is in the neighbourhood of $\frac{1}{2}$ lb. per square inch, instead of the atmospheric pressure of 15 lb. per square inch. This is a very important point, and condensers must be carefully designed for this reason.

TIDYING UP THE FRAGMENTS OF POWER

An outline has been given of the fundamental components of a steam power station. In practice, several minor additions are made to these, with the object of converting the absolute maximum of energy contained in the fuel into actual power delivered by the engine or turbine, from which, in an efficient modern station, only about a quarter of this available energy is actually converted into useful work. Improvements in the design of turbines, boilers and condensers have been, and are continually being, made. It is impossible to trace here all the developments in design that have taken place in the past, and the possible improvements of the future. All that can be done is to give some indication of the principal modifications to the simple " cycle of operations " of a steam power plant as first described in this section.

Water entering the boiler must first be heated up to its boiling point before it becomes steam, and this uses up some of the heat of the furnace. Consequently every effort is made to raise the water from the condenser to as high a temperature as possible before it reaches the boiler. It may pass from the condenser through one, two or three " feed-water heaters." Steam is taken from the turbine at various points before it reaches the exhaust and led to these feed heaters, where it raises the temperature of the water considerably.

A large amount of heat escapes up the boiler-house chimney with the flue gases, which are still very hot. This loss must be reduced, and, consequently, the flue gases and the feed water are taken to another heater called the " economiser," where the gases give up a large amount of their heat to the feed water, which in its turn is raised to a still higher temperature before finally entering the boiler.

The cold air which enters the furnace (whether as " forced," " induced " or " natural " draught) also uses up some of the heat, without serving any useful purpose. To reduce this, the air is sometimes led through an " air preheater," where again the flue gases give up some more of their heat to the ingoing air.

All these are measures taken to avoid wasting the least bit of available power, in order to reduce the coal bill. This, however, is only part of the cost of reducing power. To reduce the capital charges, the machinery must be arranged in as compact a manner as possible, otherwise a larger building will be necessary, and this will increase the necessary capital and the interest to be paid. Also the cost of maintaining the plant in good condition must be low, and many other factors must be considered. It is long since the day of James Watt, when it was a question of whether power could be produced at all—to-day the engineer is chiefly concerned to see that there is no waste of power that can possibly be utilised, and he is constantly devising means for improving the performance of power plants to a still greater extent.

THE ENGINE ITS OWN FURNACE: INTERNAL COMBUSTION

IN a steam-power plant, a furnace, boiler, economiser, etc., are all necessary before the latent energy of the fuel can be utilised in the form of high-pressure steam, whether by a reciprocating engine or turbine. Liquid and gaseous fuels, however, are not subject to the same limitations. They can be introduced into the engine itself, and the energy they give off in the form of heat can be made to do work there directly, without any such intermediate stage, as the generation of steam for a steam engine. Any engine in which the combustion of the fuel takes place in the engine itself is called an " Internal-Combustion Engine."

In the furnace of the steam boiler, the gases given off by the burning coal are free to expand in the large space of the furnace and escape up the chimney. If, however, the fuel were burnt in a small confined space, the gases given off would have no room to increase their volume. Consequently, as they are heated to a very high temperature by the process of combustion and cannot expand, their pressure rises. This is what occurs in the cylinder of an internal-combustion engine, and these high-pressure gases are used directly, in the same way as steam is used in the steam engine. The means by which the energy of the gas is made to rotate the shaft are the same in principle as the steam engine, that is, by the use of cylinder, piston, connecting rod and crankshaft. But the conditions of operation, and the gases used are so different that in practice there are wide differences in the design of the two types of engine.

In the great majority of internal-combustion engines, only one side of the piston and one end of the cylinder are employed. The other end of the cylinder is open to the atmosphere and, as there is no necessity for a piston rod in these circumstances, the connecting rod is joined to the piston direct. The piston is not now a flat disc, but is really a small cylinder itself, sliding inside the cylinder proper. The end against which the gas expands is of course solid, but the other end is open. The connecting rod is attached in the middle of the piston, and passes through the open end to the crank-shaft. The valves which are of a type different from slide valves, are situated in the cylinder head, as shown in Fig. 46. They are shaped somewhat like a mushroom, and open and close circular openings in the cylinder, through which the gases pass.

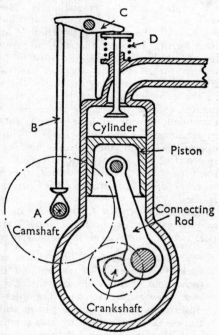

The manner in which these valves are operated is illustrated in Fig. 46. An aux-iliary shaft A, driven by the crankshaft, has protuberances called "cams," which at every revolution of this "camshaft," push the rod B upwards. This movement rocks the arm C pivoted at its centre, which in its turn pushes against the end of the valve stem and opens it as shown. Normally the valve is held closed by the spring D. The valves themselves may be placed in any position in the cylinder, provided of course that they are in direct communication with the "combustion space."

46. An internal-combustion engine in section, showing the valve mechanism.

The gases in the cylinder reach such a high temperature that it is necessary to cool the cylinder. In motor cycles and aeroplane engines, where the cylinders are exposed to the air, they may be " air-cooled " by the cold air rushing past them. Most engines, however, are cooled by circulating water through a jacket placed round the cylinder.

HOW THE INTERNAL-COMBUSTION ENGINE WORKS

VARIOUS fuels may be used in the internal-combustion engine, but the operation is substantially the same in each case. The fuel is usually introduced in a gaseous form, mixed with the correct proportion of air for combustion, and then burnt. In order that the mixture of gas and air may be ignited easily and rapidly, it must first be heated to a certain temperature. Anyone who has used a bicycle pump knows it quickly becomes warm, and in the same way the mixture in the cylinder is heated by compressing it, but to a much greater extent. After the gases have been burnt and have expanded, they must be removed, and the cylinder emptied in readiness for the next charge. The complete sequence of operations, from the introduction of the mixture to the removal of the spent gases, is called a " cycle." The piston itself performs all these duties, the method depending on whether the " four-stroke cycle " or the " two-stroke cycle " is used.

THE FOUR-STROKE CYCLE.—As its name implies, in this system each cycle occupies four " strokes " of the piston (i.e. two revolutions of the crankshaft).

1. *Suction Stroke.*—The piston moves downwards and sucks in a mixture of gas and air through the inlet valve (now held open by the camshaft).

2. *Compression Stroke.*—The inlet valve is closed and the upward movement of the piston compresses the charge to the necessary temperature and pressure.

3. *Working Stroke.*—As the piston reaches the top of its compression stroke, the mixture is ignited and burns so rapidly that the pressure rises instantaneously. The piston is pushed down by the force of the " explosion," so doing the work on the crankshaft.

4. *Exhaust Stroke.*—The piston moves upwards by its own momentum and forces the exhaust gases out through the open exhaust valve.

It will be seen that in a four-stroke engine, each cylinder produces only one impulse driving the crankshaft, in two revolutions of the engine. The rest of the cycle is occupied in receiving the fuel, preparing it for combustion, and removing the spent gases after they have given up their energy to the crankshaft. This has its disadvantages since, unless the engine has several cylinders, the crankshaft will have a rather uneven jerky motion, necessitating the use of a heavy flywheel. A great advantage, however, is that the cylinder is almost completely emptied of the useless exhaust gases, enabling a full charge of fresh mixture to be drawn in. The valve gear also is quite simple.

The inlet and exhaust valves are each driven by cams mounted on the same crankshaft. It will be noted that each valve is only open during one stroke of the cycle, and for this reason, the camshaft must only make one revolution per cycle, and is therefore driven at half the speed of the crankshaft.

From the foregoing explanation of the operation of the internal-combustion engine, it will be understood why motor cars can only be started by turning the engine round first. The cylinders must first be charged with mixture, and this compressed, before ignition takes place and the engine begins to drive itself.

THE TWO-STROKE CYCLE.—Here the crankshaft receives an impulse during each revolution of the engine. The operations are performed as follows :

1. *Firing Stroke.*—The piston is sent down the cylinder at the same time compressing fresh mixture which has been drawn into the " crank case " (which totally encloses the crankshaft) through an inlet valve in the side of the case, now closed for this compression. As it nears the bottom of its stroke, the piston uncovers an opening in the cylinder wall through which the exhaust gases from the previous combustion escape. Immediately afterward another opening on the opposite side of the cylinder, which is connected by a pipe with the crankcase, is uncovered by the piston. This allows the fresh mixture, already compressed by the piston downstroke, to escape into the cylinder, from which most of the exhaust gases have gone. On the top of the piston is a deflector which prevents the incoming mixture from going straight out into the exhaust pipe. The incoming charge is directed to the top of the cylinder, and to a certain extent helps to drive out the remainder of the exhaust gases. Thus at the end of the

downward stroke, the cylinder is already filled with a fresh charge of fuel and air.

2. *Compression Stroke.*—The mixture is now compressed in the cylinder by the piston moving upwards, and is ready for firing at the top of the stroke. At the same time, the inlet valve is opened, and through this the piston sucks a fresh charge of mixture into the crank case. This again is compressed during the following firing stroke.

The whole sequel is performed during two strokes of the piston and each cylinder fires once per revolution, instead of every alternate one as in the four-stroke cycle. This is a distinct improvement and means that this engine will develop twice the power of one similar in size and speed, but working on the four-stroke cycle. It has however one great disadvantage — the difficulty of removing the exhaust gases from the cylinder before the fresh charge is introduced. They are not driven out by the direct action of the piston as in the four-stroke engine,

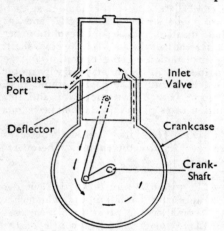

Exhaust Port

Inlet Valve

Deflector

Crankcase

Crank-Shaft

47. Cylinder and crankcase of a two-stroke engine, showing the piston moving downwards.

they are only " allowed to escape " at the end of the stroke. As a result, there still remains a considerable quantity in the cylinder. The fresh charge, compressed to a certain extent in the crank case, drives some of this remainder out, but not all. Moreover, some of the new mixture itself is liable to escape through the exhaust opening. Because of this, the power developed does not reach quite double that of the four-stroke engine. Another disadvantage is the more difficult cooling of the cylinder-head, which is subjected to the heat of the explosion once in every revolution instead of once every two revolutions. The metal forming the cylinder does not have as much time to cool, and consequently a two-stroke engine is always liable to run hotter than the four-stroke type, calling for additional care in manufacture and selection of material used for the cylinder.

In the oil engine, air only is drawn in and compressed, the fuel itself only being introduced at the point when ignition takes place. Two-stroke engines using oil for fuel are fitted with a separate pump, which blows clean air into the cylinder at the end of the firing stroke. This drives the exhaust gases out much more effectively, and the air left in the cylinder is then compressed. Some of the new charge escapes itself, of course, but as air only is blown in, this is immaterial. In engines where a mixture of fuel and air is introduced, however, the exhaust gases cannot be blown out of the cylinder so effectively for fear of a considerable amount of fresh mixture escaping. Because of the superior " scavenging " obtainable in the oil engine, the two-stroke cycle is chiefly adopted for engines of this type, although two-stroke petrol engines are used extensively for motor cycles.

SETTING FIRE TO THE FUEL

After the fuel and air have been compressed to the correct temperature and pressure, a means must be found for " exploding " the mixture. Explosion is really only burning taking place in such a short time as to be almost instantaneous. Although ignition (that is, firing of the fuel) may occupy less than 1/200th of a second, during this period the gases must be completely ignited, and the mixture of air and fuel must be so adjusted that no fuel is allowed to escape wholly or partly unburnt. Ignition is usually effected by starting the flame at one point in the cylinder, whereupon this flame travels through the combustion space, and the rest of the mixture is burnt. In all except oil engines this first flame is started by external means.

At one time, the gases were " set fire to " literally. At the end of the compression stroke, the piston uncovered a very small hole through the cylinder wall. A small flame was situated outside the cylinder and at the right moment set fire to the gases through this hole, which was then covered again by the piston moving downwards on the working stroke. This was a rather crude form. Next came the " Hot Tube " method of ignition, used extensively on gas engines. A hollow tube is mounted on the cylinder, communicating with the inside, but usually kept closed by a valve until the appropriate moment. This tube is kept red hot by an external burner. At the end of the compression stroke the valve opens, the gases are forced into the tube, and on contact with the red-hot metal, burst into flame. This flame travels back into the cylinder and sets fire to the main volume of gases.

Nowadays, however, nearly all engines are ignited by electrical means (the "sparking plug" familiar to all car owners). The sparking plug comprises two metal points across which an electric spark travels after the compression of the mixture. The gases in the vicinity of the spark are ignited, and the flame thereupon spreads through the cylinder. The intermittent sparking may be produced by a magneto or by an electric battery and coil which is in circuit only at the moment of ignition.

Fuels used by internal-combustion engines may be of various kinds, the chief requirements being cheapness, ease of handling, simplicity of operation and ignition, and the absence of any residue left after burning, which would foul the inside of the cylinder. For this reason alone, coal is impossible as a fuel, by reason of the ash left after combustion. Fuels are chiefly compounds of carbon, and a little unburnt carbon which may be left in the cylinder after each combustion gradually accumulates until the inside of the cylinder and piston are coated, and the engine needs " decarbonising " (though the partial burning of the lubricating oil on the sides of the cylinder also helps to cause this). The fuels universally used are gas, petrol and oil, each calling for a distinct type of engine.

ENGINES WHICH USE GAS AS FUEL

GAS engines, as their name implies, use gas for fuel which is drawn in together with air on the suction stroke, the mixture being compressed and fired in the normal manner. Most gas engines are horizontal and the arrangement of a small engine of this type is shown diagrammatically in Fig. 48.

The long cylindrical-shaped piston moves in the cylinder and is connected to the crankshaft by the connecting rod. Only the left-hand side of the piston is used, the right-hand side of the cylinder and piston being always open to the atmosphere. The cylinder is surrounded by a water jacket, through which cooling water is circulated. Air and gas are admitted through valves of the mushroom type (not shown) and the used gases are exhausted through a similar valve, placed as illustrated. A camshaft beside the engine, rotating at half the crankshaft speed, operates these valves at the appropriate moments. Ignition may be of the " hot-tube " method for small engines, but to-day electric ignition is employed almost exclusively.

The gas engine is little used in America, and only to a moderate extent in this country. It is in Germany that the greatest development has taken place in the extensive use of gas engines for large industrial power production. In 1923,

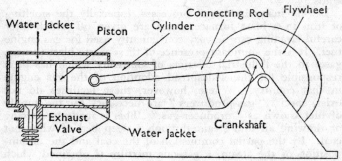

48. *The arrangement of a small horizontal gas engine*

the installation of these engines totalled 2,000,000 H.P. Gas engines have been manufactured capable of developing 10,000 H.P. and more. These large machines may be of a variety of types, operating on the two-stroke, or, more usually, the four-stroke cycle. They are generally horizontal, and may be " single-acting " or they may be equipped with piston rods, valve gear at both ends of the cylinder, etc., as " double-acting " engines in a similar way to the reciprocating steam engine.

The development of the gas engine for large power production in some form or another is of some significance. The present world resources of coal and oil (which includes petrol) are by no means unlimited, and it is possible that eventually some anxiety will be caused by the dwindling of these reserves and the question of power production in the future. At present, priority of place is given to the progress of the steam turbine and the oil engine. It may well be that this attitude may change eventually and the problem of developing the gas engine for large power production, utilising as it can the waste gases from other industrial processes, may perhaps occupy more attention than it does at present.

Gas engines may operate on either ordinary town lighting gas or on some special " power gas." The former is used only for small installations where the quantity consumed is not too large for economical operation on this supply, and not large enough to warrant the additional expense of installing a special " gas-producer." All medium and large-sized engines, however, use other gases which may be of various kinds.

During many industrial processes, especially the smelting of iron in a blast furnace, gases are given off which after careful cleaning can be very conveniently used for gas engine fuel. It is the abundant presence of these waste blast furnace gases in the industrial districts of Germany which has been responsible for the widespread adoption of the gas engine in that country. Where, however, these facilities do not exist, special " gas-producers " are necessary for the supply of fuel known as " producer-gas." This is made by forcing or drawing air and steam through a deep bed of white-hot coal. By the partial combustion of the coal and the decomposition of the steam, a gaseous mixture is obtained which after thorough cleaning is led into the engine. The air and steam may be either forced through or simply sucked through by the piston of the engine on its suction stroke.

MODERN CARRIER OF MAN : THE PETROL ENGINE

THE petrol engine is almost exclusively used in the form in which it is known by everybody—in the motor car, motor cycle and aeroplane engine and for transport purposes in general. It is light in construction, easy and simple of control and operation, and petrol itself is light and easily handled and distributed to meet this special demand.

The principle of operation of the motor car engine is exactly the same as that of the gas engine and most people will be familiar with its construction. With the exception of some motor cycles, most petrol engines work on the four-stroke cycle, and are, of course, " single-acting." A mixture of air and petrol vapour is drawn into the cylinder through one inlet valve and fired by the electric spark of a sparking-plug, after which the exhaust valve opens and the gases escape through the exhaust pipe. The camshaft controlling the valves is driven by gearing from the crankshaft and may be situated in the crank case operating through push rods as in Fig. 46. In the popular " overhead camshaft " engine of to-day, it is situated on top of the cylinder head, close to the valves.

As it is used almost exclusively for transport of one form or another, the petrol engine is only built in comparatively small sizes. It must be as light and compact as possible and must be capable of running with the minimum of trouble. Usually constructed with 4 or 6 cylinders (though as many as 12 are sometimes employed) the engine is built as one unit, all cylinders driving a common crankshaft enclosed in one crank case on which the cylinders are mounted. Nearly all petrol engines are water-cooled, the chief exceptions being aeroplane and motor cycle engines. After circulating round the cylinders, the water is taken to a radiator, exposed to the air where it is cooled, before being returned to the cylinder jackets once more. The engines work at very high speeds, and for this reason all materials used for the construction of the moving parts must be as light and strong as possible, special metals and alloys being extensively used for pistons, connecting rods, etc.

Apart from those features of design and construction necessitated by its peculiar nature and use, the petrol engine differs fundamentally from the gas engine in only one respect. This is the use of a special apparatus called the " carburettor " for converting the liquid petrol into gaseous or vapour form, and mixing it with the air before it enters the cylinder. The action of a carburettor may be seen from Fig. 49 which illustrates diagrammatically a simple form.

Air is sucked in through A and rushes past a jet B in the middle of its path. This jet is kept filled with petrol from a small tank, and as the air travels past its end, some petrol is sucked out and mingles with the air in the form of vapour. The proportion of air to petrol is controlled by the adjustable opening C, through which air is also sucked, in a greater or less quantity according as the final mixture is required weak or strong. The speed and power of the engine itself is controlled by means of the throttle valve, varying the total quantity of mixture admitted to the engine. The tank is supplied from the main petrol tank through the small hole, D, which can be closed by dropping the needle valve E. The float is for the

purpose of keeping the petrol in the tank (and therefore the
jet also) at the required level. If this is too low, the float
sinks, the levers drop and lift the needle valve, so that the
pressure of petrol in the main tank forces more petrol through
the hole, D. When enough has entered, the float rises, lifts
the levers and closes the needle valve, shutting off the supply
of petrol.

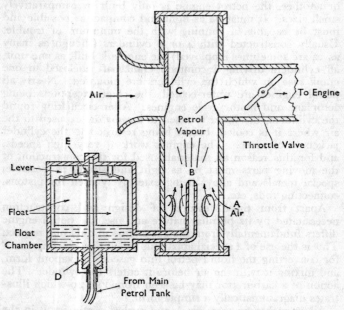

49. *The carburettor of a petrol engine, which converts
liquid petrol into vapour and mixes it with air before it
enters the cylinder via the throttle valve.*

The conditions of load and speed are continually varying
in a motor car engine and it cannot be designed for a constant
speed as are all industrial power units. Because of this variation, it is necessary to control the *quality* as well as the *quantity*
of the mixture admitted to the engine, and this is achieved
by the adjustable opening C. In practice, many carburettors
function with several jets, which can be brought into action
or not as required.

USING THE HEAVIER OILS AS FUEL

THE gas used in gas engines is, of course, readily mixed with air to form a combustible mixture, and petrol, being a volatile and easily vaporised liquid, needs only the carburettor to achieve the same end. The problem of the engine using oil fuel, however, is rather different, since oil is a far heavier liquid than petrol and cannot be vaporised and mixed with air in the same way.

Engines such as the gas and petrol engines in which a *mixture* of fuel and air is drawn in and compressed as a whole, are known as *mixture* engines. Some oil engines are also made to operate as mixture engines, but in this case special

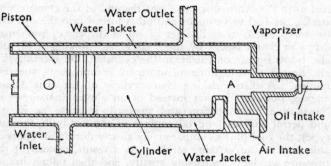

50. *The " hot-bulb " engine, made to use the heavier oils*

means are required to vaporise the fuel and form the mixture. The manner in which this is achieved is interesting and Fig. 50 shows diagrammatically the cylinder of an engine of this type—known as the " hot-bulb " engine.

At the end of the cylinder is an extension A, only part of which is enclosed by the cooling water jacket. As a result, the end outside the jacket becomes very hot and forms a vaporiser. Air is sucked in by the piston, and at the same time fuel oil is injected through an opening into the vaporiser. The oil becomes vaporised by the temperature of the latter, and mixes with the air to form an explosive mixture. The mixture is compressed during the return stroke of the piston, to a degree such that at the end of compression the pressure (and temperature) are sufficient to cause the mixture to be exploded automatically by the hot walls of the vaporiser.

The working stroke follows, and on the return of the piston the exhaust gases are expelled. After an engine of this type has been standing idle for some time, the vaporiser becomes quite cold and the engine will not start until this has been heated by means of an external lamp.

THE "NON MIXTURE" OR DIESEL ENGINE

THE "hot-bulb" engine is not used for large power and the more usual form of oil engine is a development of the original engine invented by Dr. Rudolph Diesel. In the cycle of operations of a four-stroke Diesel engine, air only is admitted through the inlet valve on the suction stroke and compressed by the piston, instead of a mixture of air and fuel as in "mixture engines." At the end of the compression stroke, the fuel valve opens and oil is forced into the cylinder by compressed air. The jet of oil is dispersed into small drops or "atomised" by the "air blast" forcing it in, and also by its impact on the air in the cylinder. On meeting this air, heated to a high temperature by compression, the fuel ignites. A distinguishing characteristic of the true Diesel engine, however, is that instead of an almost instantaneous "explosive" combustion and pressure increase as in gas and petrol engines (and oil engines of the hot-bulb, mixture type), the fuel burns comparatively slowly during an appreciable part of the working stroke. As a result, instead of the pressure suddenly increasing greatly, and then falling immediately as the piston moves outwards, there is no initial increase but the pressure is maintained for the first part of the working stroke. After the combustion is completed, the action of the expanding gases carries out the remainder of the stroke.

The oil engine has been developed greatly in many directions. As a massive reciprocating engine, it cannot compete with the steam turbine for the production of very large power in land installations, but in the field of marine power production, it is extensively used, even in very large sizes, for providing the motive power for ships. Large Diesel engines are subject to several variations. Great advances have been made in dispensing with the air-blast injection by means of compressed air. Fuel may be pumped directly into the cylinder by means of an accurately made fuel pump, a small unit, mechanically driven from the engine itself, thus avoiding the necessity for a special air compressor for this purpose.

Also the peculiar nature of non-mixture engines makes

them particularly adaptable for operation on the two-stroke cycle. Efficient removal of the exhaust gases can be achieved by the incoming charge of pure air, without the fear of losing fuel through the exhaust openings. It is in the Diesel engine that the two-stroke cycle has seen its greatest popularity, although, perhaps, the four-stroke cycle is still more extensively used. Diesel engines are in use for marine propulsion of all descriptions, using either " air " or " solid " injection, single- or double-acting, and operating on the four-stroke or two-stroke cycle.

HEAVY OIL FOR THE MOTOR CAR

THE petrol engine has certain definite disadvantages, both for motor car and aeroplane, and a large amount of research has been and is being done in the endeavour to produce an oil engine which has all the advantages of the petrol engine for this type of work, without its inherent disadvantages.

Oil is superior to petrol in that there is no risk of accidental fire and also in that an oil engine requires less weight of fuel than a similar petrol engine—both factors of paramount importance for aircraft in particular. Moreover there is no complicated, and possibly delicate, electrical ignition apparatus to cause trouble and increase the chance of engine failure.

Although the prices of petrol and oil (for transport purposes) have been adjusted at the same level by taxation, the oil engine consumes less fuel for the same power, and is therefore cheaper to run.

The oil engine, as developed for transport work, does not work as a true Diesel engine, and for this reason it is referred to merely as a " compression-ignition " engine. The peculiar demands made on road vehicles, the constantly varying speed and load, call for an engine of very special design if the necessary high engine speed and flexibility is to be obtained. It is also essential that no black, evil-smelling smoke be allowed to contaminate the air, and great care is necessary to ensure complete and perfect combustion. Much higher pressures are encountered in an oil engine, and in order to withstand them, the cylinder, etc., must be stronger, with the result that the petrol engine has advantages for engines of small-car size. With future development, however, these disadvantages will probably be overcome.

The " combustion-ignition " engine for transport purposes

is in operation almost a compromise between the Diesel and
" mixture " engines. Air only is sucked in and compressed,
but when the fuel is introduced, combustion takes place so
rapidly as to give the rapid pressure rise of the petrol and gas
engines. In order to effect this, the air and fuel in the cylinder
may be given vigorous relative motion to each other, to atomise
the fuel jets and ensure every particle of oil reaching the necessary oxygen for rapid combustion. Different firms adopt different designs, however. Some rely on the atomising effect
of a nozzle with very fine holes to distribute the oil throughout
the air, while others give the air a rapid swirling motion past
the fuel valve which ensures each part of the fuel jet meeting
fresh oxygen as it leaves the valve.

The oil-engined transport vehicle is now well established,
and there are thousands in use throughout the country.
It may also be mentioned here that there are in existence
vehicles propelled by gas engines, the gas being taken from
cylinders carried on the chassis. These, however, are a long
way behind the oil engine in development and popular
acceptance.

THE POWERFUL LIGHTWEIGHT OF THE AIR

RAPID as the advance of the motor car in this century has
been, it has been equalled by the development of its
younger brother, the aeroplane. Although not subjected to
the same extent as the motor car engine to continually varying
conditions, the aero-engine has its own peculiar demands,
which are even more exacting. It must be absolutely reliable
and, above all, the weight of the engine and fuel carried must
be the absolute minimum. The development of higher speeds
and larger flying range depends largely on reducing the weight
to be carried in proportion to the power available, and the
aero-engine must be as light and compact as possible, and its
fuel consumption must be a minimum for the power required.
For this reason, the metallurgist has been called in to provide
the lightest and strongest alloys obtainable for the construction
of these engines.

In the early days of aviation, the small rotary " Gnome "
engine was very popular, and was capable of really wonderful
performances. In this engine the normal procedure of the
reciprocating engine was reversed. The single crankshaft
was fixed, while the cylinders and pistons themselves rotated
round this, being arranged in a star-shaped pattern on which

the propeller itself was mounted. The cylinders were air-cooled by means of metal fins on the casing to radiate the heat to the air. Difficulties of lubrication, limitation in power and other factors, however, have led to the development of the normal engine with stationary cylinder block and rotating crankshaft for aeroplane work. Engines of to-day are very much larger and more powerful and are almost all of this type except in the smaller engines. Considerations of weight and space have given rise to many types. They may be either air- or water-cooled.

The absence of fire-risk and ignition complications, make the oil engine particularly desirable for aeroplane use in these respects. Much experiment is being conducted with this object in view, and it is probably only a matter of time before the oil-engined aeroplane is universally accepted. Unfortunately at present this means an unavoidable increase in weight of engine, due to the inherently heavier nature of the oil engine with its higher pressure.

THE GAS TURBINE—CAN IT BE DESIGNED ?

JUST as the steam turbine followed and has largely displaced the reciprocating engine for all but the smallest steam power plants, so the engineer always visualises the possibility of the gas- or oil-driven turbine. Probably no engineering subject connected with power production has had so much discussion as this problem. For many years experiments have been made and a few trial machines made, but it cannot be said that to-day the gas-turbine has become a practical proposition. It is only feasible as a large power unit, and the fundamental difficulties attending its design have not yet been overcome. In all internal combustion engines, the compression of the charge, whether mixture or air alone, is a vital factor on which the efficiency of the engine fundamentally depends.

It is the problem of arranging in an efficient manner for this compression, to an extent sufficient for economical working, which is the chief obstacle to the successful invention of the gas turbine. The reciprocating engine achieves this by piston compression, but the slow piston speed required and great bulk, render the use of separate reciprocating air compressors undesirable. Rotary air compressors, driven by turbines using steam generated by the exhaust gases have been tried, but it is extremely difficult to obtain by this means adequate compression, without which the efficiency of the whole set cannot approach practical demands.

Another great difficulty is also an acute form of one fundamentally associated with internal combustion engines, as opposed to steam engines. It is that of finding a metal to stand up to the high temperature of the gases. In the only practical form of gas turbine yet produced, air and gas are compressed, ignited, and the hot gases are expanded through nozzles on to a turbine wheel as in the de Laval turbine, previously described. The cylinder, and in large sizes, the pistons and other parts, of gas and oil engines are water- or oil-cooled to enable the metal to withstand the high temperatures, but water-cooling of turbine blades would lead to impossible complications.

It would be foolish to deny the possibility of the gas-turbine ever being successfully produced. Far stranger things have been condemned as impossible, and have subsequently developed beyond their inventor's most optimistic dreams. It may even be that the future will see the large gas-turbine as the successor to the steam-turbine in all large power plants —if so, it is too far ahead to be even visualised as yet. All that can be said at the moment is that up to the present there has been no real indication that the gas turbine will ever be able to compete with other power units on an efficient, economical and practical basis.

POWER FROM RUNNING WATER: THE WATER ENGINES

AFTER combustible fuels, the next most important natural source of power is the energy possessed by water. The saying that " water finds its own level " is the basis of water-power production. The water is made to work before it is allowed to reach the level it seeks.

Water is evaporated from seas and lakes to form clouds which drop rain on high ground. Gravity makes the rainfall run down hill sides, through valleys to the sea, and in so doing gives vast quantities of water energy in the form of motion from one level to a lower. Owing to the inherent limitations of the position of a water-power station, its use was for long restricted to isolated riverside mills. The development of electricity, however, has made possible the transmission and utilisation of huge quantities of power, generated in hydro-electric power stations far away from the scene of its application.

Water is virtually an incompressible liquid, and therefore anything in the nature of the expansion of gases in a heat engine is impossible. Mechanical work is obtained from the "kinetic" energy possessed by a mass of moving water; or from the "pressure" water is able to exert by reason of its weight and its urge to reach a lower level. If a long vertical pipe closed at the bottom were filled with water, the weight of the column of liquid above it would exert a force or pressure on the bottom of the pipe. The water at the bottom would also be under pressure. If the pipe were imagined to be a cylinder with a sliding piston at the bottom, this pressure would drive the piston downwards and could be made to

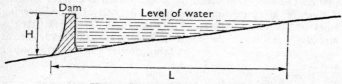

51. *How a dam produces a head of water*

drive a crankshaft through half a revolution. Alternatively, if a hole were pierced in the pipe near the bottom, a jet of water would rush forth which could be made to rotate a wheel of blades in the same way as the high-velocity jet of steam from a steam turbine nozzle.

The energy of motion of a river is not so important from the engineer's point of view, as the drop in level throughout its course. Let us consider a valley through which a river is pursuing its normal course. The only way of extracting work from this river is by the use of a paddle wheel more or less the same as the old mill wheel, thereby utilising only a fraction of the total flow ; an inefficient method, and incapable of producing large quantities of power.

If now a dam be erected across the valley as in Fig. 51, the water will mass itself up behind it as shown. To reach its own level, this mass must fall through the height " H." This is called the " head " of water, and corresponds to our vertical pipe, only on a vast scale. By this means the whole of the fall in level throughout the length of river marked " L " is concentrated at one point to provide a single large

" head." Moreover, if necessary, all the water flowing down can be diverted through the hydraulic power-plant. In this way the energy of the river over a considerable length of its path can be as it were " collected " and used at one point.

Alternatively, water may be conveyed through pipes to a power station situated several miles down the river. By this means a greater head still may be obtained where the river falls steeply. The head of water available at a dam is of necessity limited by the height of the dam which can be economically built. Water can be led through pipes to a power station 3,000 feet below. The choice of method depends on the nature of the ground and quantity of water.

A hydro-electric power station consists only of the engine room—there is no equivalent to the boiler house of the steam plant. On the other hand, it is very often necessary to dam a river or lay pipe lines which entail great civil engineering work and a large expense. In some cases a natural dam is already provided in the form of a waterfall, in which case it is only necessary to direct the falling water through the power station.

HARNESSING A HEAD OF WATER : THE TURBINES

IN practice, water is rarely made to drive a piston engine, only for very small installations, where a high head is available, and only a slow rate of rotation is required. For all practical purposes, hydraulic " prime movers " are always water turbines, giving purely rotational movement. They are of two kinds, the " impulse " turbine, in which the jet of water from our vertical pipe is utilised, and the " pressure " or " reaction " turbine, in which the energy utilised is partly " kinetic " energy, and partly pressure energy.

The choice of which type is most suitable depends on the nature of the water supply available. There may be a high head or a low head of water, with a large quantity available or a small. A high head is most conveniently converted into a comparatively narrow jet, while a low head will not provide a jet of very high velocity. For this reason, impulse turbines are usually installed where there is a large head of water available, and reaction turbines are employed in " low-head " installations.

The suitability of hydro-electric productions of power depends, of course, on the possibility of obtaining sufficient quantities of water at the necessary head to produce the amount of power necessary to make it an economical proposition. For this reason, it is not very adaptable to the conditions prevailing in England. In Galloway, however, a large hydro-electric installation has been constructed in which water from several Scottish lochs is led through pipe lines to five power stations. It is abroad, however, that the water turbine has seen its greatest development, and single units developing up to 70,000 H.P. have been installed by the Niagara Falls Power Co.

"MILL-WHEELS" WHICH YIELD 26,000 H.P.

THE old form of mill-wheel was fixed a little above the level of the stream, but the lowest of its straight paddle blades, projecting radially from its rim, were in the water which carried them round as it flowed by. In the only form of impulse turbine used to-day, the "Pelton Wheel," the head of water obtained from the dam is utilised in causing a jet of water to issue at a high velocity from a nozzle. This is directed on to the "buckets" (corresponding to the paddle blades) of the turbine wheel as shown in Fig. 52. The shape of these buckets in cross - section, and as seen looking from the nozzle, is also shown in Fig. 52.

As each bucket comes round, it meets the jet issuing from the nozzle, which strikes the central partition of the bucket and divides into two streams which flow round each half, and leave at the sides. In this way nearly all the velocity energy of the water is removed in doing work by rotating the wheel. The

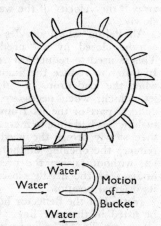

52. *The Pelton Wheel, with (below) a section through a "bucket" showing how the water stream is divided into two.*

wheel is completely enclosed in a casing, into which the nozzle protrudes. One or two nozzles may be employed, the second one being arranged at an angle of about 60 degrees to the first.

Two Pelton wheels, each with its inlet pipe and nozzle,

are sometimes arranged on the same shaft, at the end of which the electric generator is coupled. Pelton wheels are not made for such large capacities as reaction turbines. They have been constructed, however, to produce 26,000 H.P. and more, operating with a head of water of over 3,000 feet.

The manner in which these Pelton wheels are governed is interesting. Like all power units, they are subject to variations in load which make it necessary to reduce or increase the supply of water. If the load is suddenly reduced, however, it is not possible suddenly to cut down the water. Tremendous pressure in the pipe line would be created by the sudden stoppage of the huge column of moving water, and the pipes would be burst. Thus, while the water supplied to the turbine must be suddenly reduced to prevent its " running-away," the velocity of the water in the pipes must be reduced slowly.

All Pelton wheel nozzles have a circular opening, which can be closed by a " needle-regulator " sliding internally. This is used to reduce the supply coming through the pipes. In order to reduce the amount of water hitting the buckets when the load drops, a " deflector hood " is fixed over the jet, which, when necessary, rapidly moves forward. This deflects part of the jet from the buckets at once, before the turbine has had time to increase its speed. Another mechanism then slowly brings the needle regulator up, which gradually reduces the opening of the nozzle, and therefore the size of jet, without raising the pressure in the pipes to dangerous limits. As the needle closes the deflector slowly returns to its original position.

Instead of the deflector hood, a pressure release valve may be fitted in the pipe line. In this case the needle regulator closes rapidly. The pressure in the pipes opens the release valve, which allows water to escape and then slowly closes again as the pressure falls.

THE REACTION TURBINE

ALTHOUGH water is incompressible, and cannot expand like a gas when its pressure is reduced, it can nevertheless exist at a high pressure as instanced by the water at the bottom of the vertical pipe. If the water at this pressure is released, by opening a nozzle to the atmosphere, the pressure energy will be converted into velocity energy. In the Pelton wheel all the energy is converted into velocity energy before it reaches the wheel, but in the reaction turbine only part of the energy is used in giving the water velocity, with the result that the water enters the blades, still at a higher pressure than that due to the atmosphere. This remaining pressure energy is then converted into kinetic energy in its passage through the blades. This change produces a " reaction " on the turbine blades further tending to drive them round.

The distinction may be a little difficult to understand, but the " reaction " principle is clearly shown by the apparatus which is sometimes used for watering lawns. A stand carries a vertical pipe at the top of which is pivoted a hollow tube shaped like one half of a swastika, as shown in Fig. 53. Water

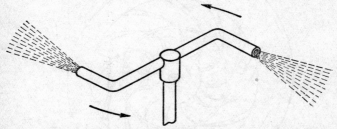

53. *The reaction turbine in principle—the apparatus used in watering lawns, in which the " reaction " pressure of the water on the pipes causes them to rotate backwards.*

is supplied at a small pressure from the mains, travels up the vertical pipe and out at the end of each arm. In pushing itself forward out of the pipe, at the same time it pushes this backwards. The horizontal bent pipe therefore rotates, and the water is sprayed round in a circle. This actually is a reaction turbine in principle.

A Pelton wheel cannot be designed with more than two jets, and the volume of water used is therefore comparatively small. In a reaction turbine the water is admitted all round the circumference and large volumes of water at a low head can therefore be utilised. The largest water turbines are of reaction type, and are slightly more efficient than impulse turbines.

A reaction turbine is usually mounted on a vertical axle. Water is admitted through guide vanes round the circumference, passes through the blades, where it gives up its

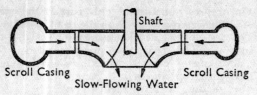

a. Elevation showing direction of Water-Flow

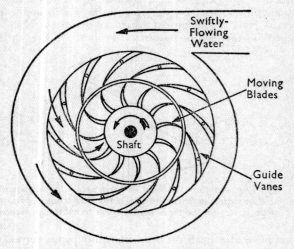

b. Plan showing motion of Water and Wheel

c. How the Guide Vanes work

54. THE ESSENTIALS OF THE " REACTION " TURBINE

energy, and its direction is changed so that it leaves tangentially as shown in Fig. 54.

The turbine is surrounded by a " scroll casing " of the form shown. The cross-sectional area decreases on the way round,

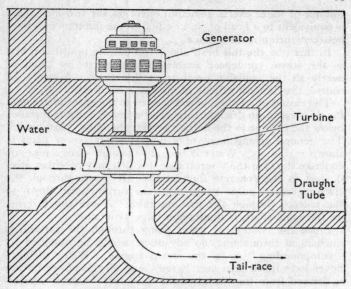

55. The arrangement of a water power plant

as water leaves the main body through the guide vanes. Governing is effected by adjustment of these guide vanes, which are pivoted in the middle as shown in Fig. 54(*c*). As they are moved round, the width of the opening x between them decreases, thus reducing the amount of water admitted to the turbine. Pressure release valves or " surge tanks " are installed in the system to prevent a dangerous rise of pressure when reducing the load.

USING A WATER " HEAD " BELOW THE TURBINE

IF the full head is to be utilised, the turbine must be situated as near as possible at the level of the " tailrace," that is, the water leaving the power station. This, however, would entail difficulties of construction, so that usually the turbine is placed some distance above the tailrace. In order not to lose this part of the head, the turbine discharges into a " draught tube " which ends some distance below the level of the tail-race water. Thus the draught tube is kept full of water not in contact with the atmosphere, so that the weight of this column of water exerts a suction effect on the turbine. This is equivalent to a head of water equal to the difference in level between turbine and tailrace.

In this way the full head above the tailrace is utilised, just as the steam condenser enables advantage to be taken of nearly all the available pressure of the steam. Actually, of course, the draught tube is in no way a condenser.

The casing of a Pelton wheel is open to the atmosphere, and for this reason no draught tube can be fitted, and the distance below the turbine to the tailrace level is therefore " lost head." The general arrangement of a typical water power plant is shown in Fig. 55. Water is brought through a large pipe, or concrete duct, to the " scroll case," which may be either steel or cast in the concrete foundations. It passes through the circumferential guide vanes, into the turbine, and down to the tailrace through the draught tube. Above the turbine, on the same shaft, is mounted a huge generator.

Since the volume of water going through the turbine is unchanged throughout, no advantage would be obtained by " compounding " as in the steam engine. Water turbines never have more than one "stage," and all the power output is derived from the blades of the one great " runner wheel."

TURNING THE OPERATION UPSIDE DOWN: THE PUMPS

ALTHOUGH not a means of power production, the pump is, next to the water turbine, the most important type of hydraulic machinery. Indeed pumps are far more extensively used than turbines, although, of course, they are not on the same scale as regards size and power.

Most hydraulic machines are with modifications capable of being reversed, and when driven by an external agency provide a means of raising water from a lower to a higher level. For pumping work the reciprocating motion, practically ignored for power production, to some extent comes into its own, being suitable for steady work against high pressures, and where the quantity of water is not large. The reciprocating pump is conveniently driven by a small steam engine, to which it is connected by a common piston rod. The two fundamental types of pump are shown in Figs. 56 and 57. In the " Bucket Pump " illustrated in Fig. 56, a piston slides up and down in a pipe connected below to the water supply. Below the piston, a " suction " valve is fitted in the pipe. There is also a valve on the piston. These valves are circular discs made of some flexible material such as rubber, and fixed at their centres, opening upwards when subjected to a pressure below.

On the upstroke of the piston, the " vacuum " beneath it causes the suction valve in the pipe to open, and water rushes into the " cylinder." During this stroke the same vacuum keeps the piston valve shut. On the down stroke, the pressure of water trapped beneath the piston closes the suction valve. At the same time the piston valve opens, and the water passes through to the other side. As the piston rises again the pressure of the water on its upper side closes the piston valve. Consequently while sucking a fresh lot of water into the bottom chamber, the piston forces the first quantity out into the

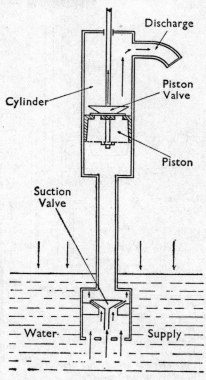

56. How the village pump works

delivery pipe. The flexible valves of course are operated solely by the pressure of the water, and no valve gear is required.

For higher pressures, the plunger pump of Fig. 57 is more suitable. In this there is no " piston " or piston valve, and the action all takes place in one chamber. The withdrawal of the plunger on the up-stroke creates a partial vacuum, and water enters through the suction valve. On the down-stroke the plunger forces the water out of the delivery valve, above which is a chamber filled with air which " cushions " the jerky delivery of water. The action of the valves is the same as in the bucket pump.

Both these pumps are " single acting," and give a very uneven delivery for this reason. By various combinations of bucket, piston and plunger, " double acting " pumps are obtained. The majority of reciprocating pumps are double acting, and for all but small sizes and low pressures, operate as plunger pumps.

THE CENTRIFUGAL PUMP

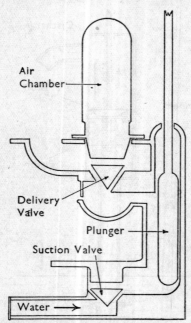

Air Chamber

Delivery Valve

Plunger

Suction Valve

Water →

57. The plunger pump, used for higher pressures. The air chamber acts as a " cushion " and thus helps to steady the delivery of the water.

IF a weight is whirled round on the end of a string, it will be felt to exert a pull on the hand. This is due to the " centrifugal force," by which the weight tends to fly off at a tangent. All bodies when revolving in a circle or curved path have this tendency, to an extent depending on the velocity, weight and radius of path. Perhaps some may have tried the experiment of twirling a bucket of water round in a vertical circle, without spilling the water. Any success which may have attended their efforts was due to this same centrifugal force, which counteracted the weight of the water and prevented it falling out.

It is on this principle that the centrifugal pump is based. It has a strong resemblance to a reversed reaction turbine. In the centrifugal pump, the inlet or suction pipe is led to the centre of the wheel or " impellor " as it is called. Before starting, the pump casing must first be filled with water from an external source. As the impellor is rotated by some external source of power, the water in the vanes is flung out round the circumference by centrifugal force. In order to fill the vacuum that would be formed, more water must enter to take the place of that which has been discharged. In this way a steady flow of water enters the middle of the pump, is whirled out and discharged into a scroll casing terminating in a delivery pipe.

Still following the analogy of the reversed turbine, the energy of the water, now mostly kinetic, must be converted into pressure energy. This to a certain extent takes place in the scroll casing. Often, however, specially shaped guide vanes are fitted round the circumference as in the turbine. The area of the passage between these gradually increases outwards, so that the water is slowed up and its kinetic energy is changed into pressure energy. The pump as now constructed is indeed in all essentials a reversed turbine, and for this reason is known as the " turbine pump."

WORKING IN STAGES TO MEET HIGH PRESSURES

THE pressure or head against which a centrifugal pump is capable of working depends largely on its velocity, and for this reason the suitability of a single impellor is limited by practical considerations of size and construction. The difficulty was however overcome by the introduction of the multistage pump, which bears a strong resemblance to the steam turbine. Several impellors are all mounted on the same shaft. The main suction pipe leads to the centre of the first impellor and from there is thrown out into a circumferential chamber. From this it is led back through guide passages in the pump casing, to the centre of the next impellor, and again thrown out into the next chamber.

By this means the water enters the inlet of each successive stage at the delivery pressure of the preceding one, and the pressure is built up in steps throughout the machine. Within limits therefore the pressure can be raised to any desired extent, by constructing a pump with enough stages. Multistage pumps are capable of pumping against high heads, and have to a great extent replaced the reciprocating pump for this duty. One example of their use is the boiler feed pump, which is usually constructed in this way and must pump water into the boiler against a pressure of several hundred pounds per square inch.

Owing to its freedom from valves, even delivery and suitability for dealing with large quantities of water, the centrifugal pump is almost universally used. One great advantage is its ability to deal with water containing grit, etc., in suspension, which although undesirable in any machine, is not likely to cause so much damage to a centrifugal pump as to a pump fitted with valves. It is also readily driven by an electric motor mounted on the end of its shaft.

FITTING THE POWER TO THE JOB IN HAND : THE PURPOSE OF MACHINES

MACHINES are devices for canalising power. " Power supply " means the availability of a " force " to do physical work, that is, to move a body against a resistance. How then is the machine made to do the work ? The problem is independent of the source of power, whether it be obtained from a steam engine or the human biceps. Usually the energy supplied is not in a convenient form for doing the work, and means must be found for overcoming this obstacle.

First a few words of explanation are necessary of the engineer's conception of " work," which for him has a very definite significance. A man who has been trying for a long time to push a barrow or lift a heavy weight probably feels at the end that he has done some hard work, even if he has not succeeded in moving it at all. The engineer does not recognise unsuccessful work, only that in which the object is achieved to a greater or less degree. If the labourer moves his barrow or lifts his weight but a fraction of an inch, to the engineer he has " performed work." But without movement against the resistance, he has not.

In accordance with this conception, the amount of work done is measured by multiplying the force exerted on an object by the distance through which its point of application is moved. Again, as previously explained, energy cannot be destroyed. It follows therefore that the amount of work or energy put into a machine at one point is given up by it at some other point (disregarding for the moment losses due to friction, etc.).

In Figs. 58 and 59, two of the simplest methods of applying power are illustrated—the lever and wedge. In Fig. 58 if the man pushes his end of the lever down, the other end pressing against the stone will rise, but through a smaller distance. If he moves his end the distance a in Fig. 58 by exerting a force P, the other end will exert a force W on the stone, moving it through the distance b. From what has just been said, it follows that $P \times a = W \times b$ and $W = P \times \dfrac{a}{b}$.

Similarly in Fig. 59, where a hammer and wedge are used to open a window, if the hammer strikes the wedge with a force P and pushes it in a distance a, the wedge will exert a force W on the window, and again $W = P \times \dfrac{a}{b}$.

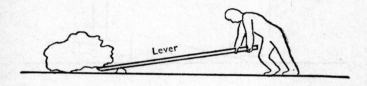

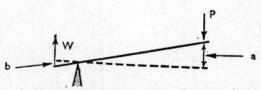

58. How the lever can be used to lift a heavy weight

This illustrates how a force which is not large enough to perform a certain task direct, can by these simple means be made to exert a greater force which will. The work done or energy used is the same, but a small force moving through a large distance is converted into a large force acting over a short distance. This principle is constantly being unwittingly applied in everyday life. It applies not only to forces moving in straight lines, but also those having circular motion.

Not only do the lever and wedge make a large force available, but they must also be regarded as means for the application of power available in an inconvenient form. The man can put his whole weight on the lever, which is one of the easiest ways in which he can exert his strength. He cannot do this directly on the stone, the lifting of which is a very different matter. The hammer again cannot be used directly for opening the window, it can only provide a blow, and this cannot be applied underneath the window frame. It can be utilised, however, by means of the wedge.

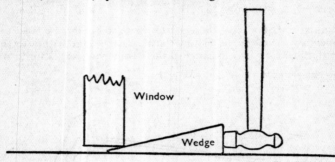

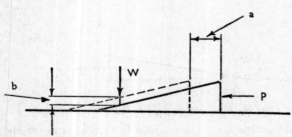

59. *How wedge and hammer help to open a window*

Thus the lever and wedge are both elementary methods of applying power in the general form of a " crude force " to specialised purposes. They also illustrate another function of machines, by which they receive a small force at one point, and exert a large force (but for a smaller distance) at another.

UBIQUITOUS MOVER OF HEAVY WEIGHTS: THE SCREW

SCREWS, nuts and bolts enter into every side of existence, engineering or otherwise, and their action is well known. The spiral " thread " of the screw enables it to be twisted into wood or a steel nut in the same way as a corkscrew enters a cork. Screws are used universally for fixing two machine parts together as in Fig. 60, the nut being tightened with a spanner and so gripping the plates.

In action the nut is merely another form of wedge. Instead of being straight, the faces of the wedge—the " thread "— are bent round into a circular spiral form. They slide on the corresponding thread of the screw and wedge up against the parts being clamped.

Like the wedge, screws are able to exert a larger force than is applied to them. If a spanner 6 inches long rotates a

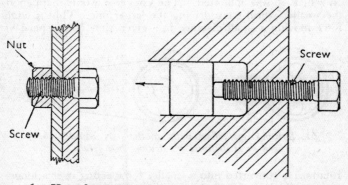

60. *How the screw may be used (left) to fix two plates together. (Right) The screw being used as a machine for moving a heavy object slowly.*

$\frac{1}{2}$-inch diameter screw through one turn, the movement of the latter in the direction of its axis will only be the distance between one thread and the next—about $\frac{1}{20}$ of an inch. The man's hand will move about 36 inches each revolution, and so if the screw is arranged to push an object between grooves in the direction shown in Fig. 60, a force about 720 times as great as that exerted by the hand will be available for pushing the object against resistance.

The ordinary motor car jack works on this principle, and by rotating a screw, the mechanic is able gradually to lift the whole weight of the car. In large machinery, power-driven screws are used in the same manner to move very heavy weights in guided paths.

DISTRIBUTION AT CONVENIENCE : THE PULLEYS AND BELTS

IF two wheels with leather covered rims were pressed together as in Fig. 61, and one were rotated, the friction between the rims would cause the other also to rotate. If also there were no slipping between their surfaces, the small wheel, half the diameter of the large one, would revolve at twice the speed of the other. Suppose the larger one was the " driving wheel," rotated by a certain force, the smaller wheel would revolve at twice its speed, but only half the " torque," or turning force, would be available from the shaft on which it was mounted. The converse would happen if the smaller wheel were driving the larger one. Thus a large force moving a small distance in a given time (slow speed of

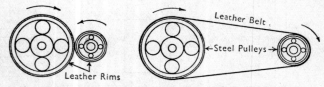

*61. Driving one wheel with another, by contact (left)
and at a distance by driving belt (right).*

rotation) is converted into a smaller force acting over a longer distance (high speed) in the same way as by the lever.

By this arrangement the shafts on which the wheels are mounted must necessarily be close together, which limits the application of this arrangement.

If, however, a leather belt is passed round steel " pulleys " as in Fig. 61, the driving pulley will move the belt, and the belt will drive the other pulley, due to the friction between the surfaces. By this means the driven shaft can be mounted at a distance from the driving shaft, in a variety of convenient positions. Moreover, its speed can be adjusted in accordance with requirements and the " turning force " necessary to do the work. There are various different arrangements for transmitting power between shafts in this manner. In Fig. 62 is a series of pulleys by which four different speeds of the driven shaft can be obtained from a constant-speed driving shaft, according to which pair of pulleys the belt connects. This is much used on machine tools.

THE TOOTHED GEAR WHEEL, MASTER OF SPEED RATIOS

IN the two friction wheels just described, the drive is trans-mitted purely by the friction between their surfaces. To this end, this surface must be of special material (which frequently needs replacing) and much power is lost by slip-ping. Although a belt also slips to a certain extent, the whole of the friction surface is contained in the belt, which can easily be tightened when necessary. Moreover the friction area extends half round the pulley, instead of the narrow strip of contact between the friction wheels. Consequently although the belt and pulley are widely used, friction wheels are never employed for any but the most in-significant applications.

If the friction surface be replaced by teeth round the rim of the wheels, the objections vanish. This provides a strong positive drive without slip, giving an exact ratio of speed, impossible where the driving action depends on friction. Belts and pulleys are restricted in the power they can transmit, and have other

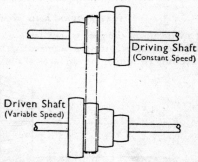

Driving Shaft
(Constant Speed)

Driven Shaft
(Variable Speed)

62. How the speed of the driven shaft can be varied by using a series of pulley-wheels.

disadvantages. Their chief use is for driving machine tools from countershafts, where comparatively small power is required. Gear wheels can be made up to any size, and are used universally where power is to be transmitted at a different speed. By this use, small high speed electric motors rotate slow heavy machinery with a minimum waste of power and at exact speeds. Gear wheels are employed both for connecting the high speed steam turbine shaft of a ship to the propellor shaft, and in the gear box of the smallest " baby " car.

Greater force is needed to drive a car up a hill than on the level. The power developed by the engine, however, depends on its speed, so that as a car slows down on mounting a hill, the power of the engine also diminishes and eventually the car would stop. The driver accordingly "changes down," whereby the engine can rotate at a higher speed in relation to the speed of the car, thus producing sufficient power to move it up the hill. This is equivalent to a man who increases the length of his lever when he comes to an extra heavy stone.

Where the shafts are a considerable distance apart, and large powers are to be transmitted, exact speed ratios required, or other objections exist to the use of a belt and pulleys, chains connecting gear wheels are used instead. The most familiar example of this is the bicycle, where the motion of the feet is transmitted to the back wheel, which revolves at about three times the speed of the pedals.

SCREW GEAR AND WORM WHEEL

By means of the gear wheel drive, shafts may be made to drive one another at right angles, by the simple modification of bevelling the engaging surfaces of the gear wheels. But in these,

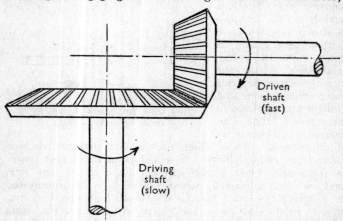

Driven
shaft
(fast)

Driving
shaft
(slow)

63. Gear wheels with bevelled edges, by means of which shafts may be made to drive one another at right angles.

and in the other gear wheels so far described, motion can only be transmitted between shafts whose axes are in the same plane, whether parallel or at right angles. This is not always the case, and frequently one shaft is required to drive another not in the same plane. For this purpose "skew gearing"

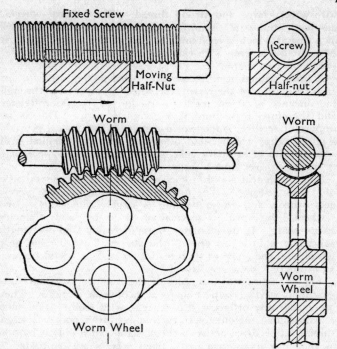

64. How the principle of the screw and nut (above) can be adapted in the worm-wheel drive (below), to move a toothed wheel (cross-sections are shown on the right).

is employed, which has points of resemblance both to the ordinary gear wheel and to the common screw.

A particular case of " skew gearing " is the " worm " and " worm wheel " drive. Imagine a rotating screw to be fixed in position, and the nut to have linear motion. Further, consider only one half of the nut. If the screw does not move, the half nut will move to the right, as shown in Fig. 64. If the surface of a wheel were provided with teeth on its circumference cut in such a form as to correspond to the thread of the nut, the wheel might also be moved by the rotating screw.

This is the principle of the " worm " drive as shown in Fig. 64. The " worm " is nothing but a screw fixed in position, with a very large and strong thread. The " worm wheel " has teeth round its circumference, which are really sections of a thread which corresponds to that of the worm, fitting it as a nut fits a screw. In this way motion is transmitted between the two shafts.

A great reduction of speed takes place in this drive, as for each revolution of the worm, the wheel revolves only through the distance of a few teeth—a fraction of its circumference and therefore a fraction of a complete turn. This is an important feature of the worm drive; its use makes possible a speed ratio, which could otherwise only be obtained with several pairs of ordinary gear wheels, and a small force may be made to overcome a larger resistance.

The worm gear is only a special example of the general type of " skew gearing." The difference between ordinary screw gear wheels and worm gearing is largely dimensional; one " wheel," the worm, is so small as to be the same diameter as its shaft. If its diameter were increased and its length shortened a little, to give it the shape of an average gear wheel, and the angle of its thread increased, it would become an ordinary " skew gear wheel."

Fig 65 shows two examples of the manner in which skew gearing is used to connect shafts at inconvenient angles. They are really only ordinary gear wheels, with teeth cut in such a manner that the outside of each wheel forms part of a screw thread. The drive between them is the same sliding motion as that of a screw in a nut. Skew wheels are expensive to make, and because of their sliding motion, a certain amount of friction and wear takes place. They are only employed in special cases, although the worm reduction gear is extensively used.

ENERGY WHICH ESCAPES THE ENGINEER

As already stated, the performance of any work requires motion in some form or other. The nature of this motion depends entirely on the nature of the machine and the work it has to do, be it a motor car or a sewing machine. It is by such means as those described and others, such as the crank or connecting rod, that power is taken from the main supply, whether countershaft or electric motor, and applied in the form and motion required.

Whenever any part of a machine is in movement, it must be in contact with other parts which constrain its motion, whether they are fixed or themselves moving. Throughout the machine there are many points of contact of this nature, where metal rubs against metal ; and this frictional resistance to movement between the surfaces is overcome, with the resultant wastage of power in the form of heat. Between piston and cylinder, turbine shaft and bearings, connecting

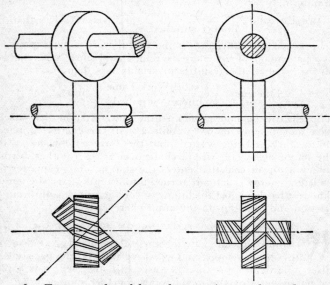

65. Two examples of how skew gearing can be used to connect shafts at inconvenient angles, showing (below) the arrangement of the threads.

rod and crank pin, the teeth of geared wheels and at the thread of a screw—always there is friction, whatever the nature of the motion. Without friction, man would be powerless to walk or do anything—nevertheless to the engineer it is in most cases an eternal obstacle to the creation of the " perfect machine."

Throughout the whole process of utilisation of energy, some power is constantly escaping in various ways. Heat disappears up the chimney stack with the flue gases from the furnace, some is radiated to the air from steam pipes and engines, some is lost to condenser or cylinder jacket cooling water, and some is dissipated as friction. All this is lost energy. For this reason, whatever the nature of a machine, the useful work obtained from it is always less than the energy originally supplied to it. Some of the latter always escapes in some form. The term " efficiency " is used to denote the success achieved in reducing these losses to a minimum.

It is the ratio $\dfrac{\text{Useful Work done}}{\text{Energy supplied}}$, and is always less than 1.

In practice, the efficiency is the useful work done expressed as a percentage of the energy supplied, and since some energy always escapes, the result is invariably less than 100%.

$$\text{Efficiency} = \frac{\text{Useful Work Done}}{\text{Energy Supplied}} \times 100\%.$$

The electric generator of a steam power-station may itself have an efficiency of 98%—only 2% of the energy supplied by the turbine being wasted—but the " overall efficiency " of the station as a whole will rarely be over 25%. In other words, for each ton of coal that enters the station, only a quarter of its latent energy is actually turned into useful electrical energy. The rest has been lost to chimneys, cooling water, and through friction and radiation to the atmosphere.

30 TONS OF STEEL FLOATING ON A FILM OF OIL

WHEN two metals rub together, there is a great deal of friction developed and excessive wear on the parts takes place. Particularly is this the case with steel, which is liable to get so hot that the metal welds together momentarily, or " seizes." If it is still dragged round, the surface of the metal is all scarred and scratched, and is useless as a " bearing surface." To avoid this, the sliding surfaces must be lubricated with oil. This has a soothing effect in every way. It reduces friction greatly, prevents the metal getting hot and " seizing," reduces wear, and increases the life and efficiency of the machine to a very great extent. Actually the oil penetrates between the surfaces, and prevents their coming into harsh contact with each other.

It was originally thought that the lubricant simply greased the surfaces, and by making them smoother, reduced the friction. This has been shown not to be the case, and with efficient lubrication, no actual contact takes place between the surfaces at all. This, however, is the ideal condition of lubrication, when the power wasted in friction is a minimum ; and it is the constant endeavour of the lubrication engineer to attain it, but the measure of his success depends on the nature of the sliding contact. In some motions, such as that of a piston in a cylinder, the metal surfaces and edges of the piston continually tend to break up this thin layer of oil, and make contact with the cylinder walls. In others, this destructive tendency is not present, and the movement actually helps to retain the lubricant between the surfaces.

One of the most striking examples of efficient lubrication is the steam turbine. The shaft may weigh anything up to 30 tons, but, because of the very high speed and uniform motion, it drags the oil round with it and a film of oil is maintained which prevents all contact between the metal surfaces. Thirty tons of steel rotating at 1,500 revolutions per minute, and entirely supported by a thin film of oil less than a thousandth of an inch in thickness !

That this effect is produced by shafts rotating at high speeds is strikingly shown in some light spindles used in the watch-making industry, where air is used as the lubricant. When started up, the noise and roughness of running shows that metal-to-metal contact is taking place ; but when the speed has risen to a certain extent, the noise ceases and the spindle runs smoothly and quietly, showing that the speed and " suction " effect are maintaining a thin layer of air between the surfaces, preventing all contact. Again, when stopped, the spindle slows down for a while and then suddenly begins to run noisily and roughly again, showing that the speed has dropped too low, and the film of air has been broken through.

Considerable attention is paid to the question of lubrication to-day. In former years, the feeling was that anything would do. Now it is realised that only by supplying the correct kind of lubricant in the best way can the friction waste be kept down, and the life and condition of the machine be maintained satisfactorily.

SLOW-MOVING FORCES TRANSMITTED BY WATER

OWING to its incompressibility, if an enclosed column of water be subjected to a pressure at one end, this pressure will be transferred to the other end of the column. Consequently if a pump be supplying water at a pressure into a pipe line, this can be tapped off and used to drive hydraulic machinery at points down the pipe. It would not be a practical proposition to pump water into one end in order to drive a huge water turbine at the other end, of course, but there are many classes of machinery which are conveniently driven in this way.

This method of power transmission is indeed employed extensively for certain types of work. Frequently it has advantages over other methods, and particularly where a machine requires a large, slow-moving force, or a large force at infrequent intervals. It is thus well adapted for the operation of large press tools, lifts, hoists, cranes, dock gates, large sluice valves and other purposes. Usually gearing in the hydraulic machine is unnecessary, the force being transmitted direct from the piston. Perfect regulation and great precision are easy, losses are small, and leakages easily detected, and of course there is no fire risk, as must always be the case to a certain extent with electricity. In a limited field, it is extremely useful, although of course it is unsuitable for high speed machinery or power transmission over long distances.

The pressure water is supplied in iron or steel pipe-lines, into which it is pumped in the main power station. It usually comes off the same supply as the town's mains, and special " hydraulic intensifiers " raise its pressure from that of the ordinary domestic supply to that required for hydraulic machinery. Alternatively, factories and even individual machines may have their own plant for raising water to the pressure required.

A steady and even flow is required in the pipes, and the velocity of the water must be low, otherwise excessive losses in transmission will result.[1] Equally important however is a steady pressure. Fluctuations in the water taken by machinery or in that supplied to the pipe-line would cause great fluctuations in pressure were no means taken to prevent this.

To this end " hydraulic accumulators " store any surplus energy being supplied by the pumps, and give this out when for short periods the demand is greater than the supply. These work rather on the principle of the gasometer. A heavy weight is supported on water at the pressure in the pipe line, and rises and falls according to the quantity of water being drawn off or supplied. By this means the pressure is always kept at a constant value, and the energy of the system is kept in equilibrium. If more is being supplied than is required, the weight is raised and energy is then stored in the accumu-

[1] See p. 120.

lator. If the demand exceeds the supply, the weight falls and drives the necessary extra amount out of the accumulator still at the same pressure.

CREATING WAVES TO CARRY THE ENERGY

IN the ordinary hydraulic transmission of power just described, the necessity for steady flow and pressure was emphasised. In all normal use of water power this is the case, but for some purposes just the opposite conditions prevail, and rapid fluctuations of pressure are actually encouraged and used to drive machinery.

If pressure is suddenly applied to a piston in a hydraulic cylinder full of water, " compression " in the sense of that of the internal-combustion engine cannot take place. The piston does not move, and the force is merely transferred practically instantaneously to the other end of the cylinder. If, however, a sudden pressure is applied by a plunger to the end of a long column of water enclosed in a pipe, a very short but appreciable time elapses before the pressure reaches the other end. Actually it travels with the velocity of sound and the pressure is transmitted by waves travelling through the pipe. Just as a piece of paper rises and falls on the ripples of a lake, so the pressure at any one point in this pipe line is alternatively high and low. It is as though the column of water were vibrating to the impulses received at one end, the vibrations being transferred to the other end.

If a plunger A be fitted in one end of the pipe line, controlled impulses can be given to the column of water. The reciprocating motion of the plunger causes " ripples of pressure " down the pipe. If the length of pipe be correct, these impulses will be exactly repeated (except for transmission losses) at the other end. In other words " waves of energy " are transmitted down the pipe line by the plunger. If now a piston B of the same stroke and speed be fitted at the other end, this will be able to utilise these waves of energy. It will receive impulses exactly in accordance with those transmitted from the plunger, and it will be given a motion which is a repetition of that of the latter. In this way, energy can be transmitted through a pipe line without any constant flow of water as it remains enclosed in the pipe permanently. This is known as the " Wave Transmission of Energy."

One of the more important applications of this method was in the machine-gun equipment of certain aeroplanes during the war. In these machines, the gun fired between the moving blades of the propeller, and of course very exact timing of the shots was necessary to avoid hitting the propeller as it passed in front of the muzzle. An oil pipe connected a certain mechanism on the engine to another on the machine gun. As the crankshaft of the engine—and therefore the propeller —passed certain points, impulses or waves of energy were transmitted down this column of oil. These were received at the other end, and there actuated the timing mechanism of the machine gun. By this means exact timing and control was possible, ensuring that the bullets always had a free path between the whirling propeller blades.

HOW POWER IS PASSED ON TO THE WAITING MACHINES

THE power produced in the various power-production plants which have been discussed is like some huge pent-up force, bursting to find an outlet somewhere. It is a tremendous energy, ready to perform all the tasks which man may ask of it. But these are all of different kinds and descriptions, varying in magnitude and in the nature of the work required. The " prime movers "—steam engines, gas engines, steam or hydraulic turbines—all transform natural energy into the form of a revolving shaft. But the revolving shaft in the power house of a factory is no use as such to the man operating a machine on the top floor of a building a hundred yards away. The next step therefore is to find means to apply this great force to all the various uses. Nature has been tamed and controlled to a certain degree in the power station, but this was only the first stage.

A power station is analogous to a water works where huge quantities of water are stored, and must be distributed throughout the locality in water mains and pipes, until finally each householder takes off his small quantities from his tap. So the power generated must be split up and distributed to every point where it will be required, available in a form suited to the work done. Several ways of doing this are possible, and the choice depends entirely on the scale of operations and the particular circumstances.

Mention has already been made of hydraulic power transmission, in which the analogy with the water-works and distribution is very strong. Here the fluid medium is supplied, charged with "pressure energy" all ready for operating hydraulic machines. Water is not the only fluid which can be used in this manner, however. High-pressure steam itself could be distributed through pipes for operating many small steam engines at the various points. This is not good practice, however, as too much heat and energy is lost in the pipes.

Air, however, is not subject to the same disadvantages, and does not need to be at a high temperature. Many auxiliary machines, hand-operated tools, etc., in a factory are driven by compressed air. The "revolving shaft" drives the crankshaft of an air compressor, in which a piston sucks air into a cylinder and compresses it. This of course is the action of a heat engine reversed—the "gas" enters at a low pressure and is discharged at a high one, instead of *vice versa*. The air is distributed throughout the factory in pipes and is used to drive various pneumatic tools, drills, spanners, lifts and hoists.

Again the various machine tools of a factory must be driven, and these require far more power than it is possible to transmit with compressed air. Belts and pulleys may connect the prime mover to long "countershafts" supported overhead and extending through the workshop. The machine tools are arranged on the floor under each of these rotating countershafts and are driven from it by belts and pulleys.

THE ELECTRIC TRANSMISSION OF POWER

THE methods of power distribution outlined above, however, are only possible on a small scale. Compressed air machinery is limited in size, and hydraulic machinery in applications. Distance and the practical difficulty of connecting the various countershafts to the power unit, together with the complicated system of shafting, belts and pulleys, are disadvantages in the use of this means. Moreover its use is only possible in one particular building, in which the power plant must also be installed.

The vast majority of the power produced is turned into the form of electrical energy. This is the only way by which the huge outputs of the modern power station can be utilised. The "revolving shaft" is coupled to an electrical generator, and from this the energy is readily transmitted through wires and cables. Since these are the only connections required with the points of application, their flexibility and negligible size enable electrical power to be obtained at any point and in any quantity.

To-day electricity is used for the transmission of practically all power required for use at many different points. Countershafts may be retained in factories, but each of these is now driven by an electric motor obtaining its power from the main generator. Many machine tools, however, are fitted with their own motors.

Distance is no obstacle to the transmission of electrical energy. Each factory may have its own power station, connected by cables to the different points of application throughout the workshops. Electricity can, however, be generated in far larger quantities and at smaller cost in big power stations and distributed in the same way as electric light for domestic use, all over the surrounding country. In either case, it is the cleanest, most efficient, and adaptable method of conveying the precious output of the " power producer " to the " power consumer."

WILL WIRELESS ONE DAY DRIVE THE RAILWAY TRAIN ?

THE distribution of energy has reached a high stage of development with the introduction of the electric cable. It is doubtful though whether it has yet reached the end of its advance. Even the cable, flexible and convenient though it is, imposes limitations on the use of power, particularly for transport. The ideal, of course, would be a method by which energy might be dispatched to its points of application without the necessity of intervening connections of any sort.

Every wireless set requires a minute quantity of power for its operation, power which is controlled by waves in the ether. Already we have experimental aeroplanes and boats without pilots or crew, controlled entirely from a distance by means of wireless. Power can be controlled by wireless—can it be transmitted ? Possibly the future will see this development. If so, the whole of the power production and distribution side of engineering may be revolutionised. No more steam locomotives or petrol engines, but silent, smoothly operating trains and omnibuses all equipped for the reception of power transmitted by wireless from a few vast central power stations. Radio-transmission of energy is at the moment but a dream, but the day may come when it is a commonplace of existence.

" POWER ON THE MOVE "

IN effect the employment of power in stationary machines is merely a question of directing it to give certain components of a machine the necessary force and nature of movement to perform the necessary operations. The question of transport, however, is a specialised branch of the application of power.

The problem of utilising power to produce movement on land presents few difficulties, once the driving force has been provided in a suitable form. Only solid surfaces enter into consideration, and movement is effected by the friction between revolving wheels and a road or rails. In a motor-car, the engine crankshaft drives the back axle through a clutch and gear box ; in a locomotive the driving wheels are mounted directly on the crankshaft. Constant developments are always taking place in the production of the necessary power, but its actual application to the achievement of motion presents no difficulty.

Off the land, however, the question is different. There is no solid surface, but the " vehicle " is now surrounded entirely by a fluid, whether water or air. Consequently friction in the nature of that existing between road and tyres does not exist. Walking comes inevitably to man, but he must learn to swim in the sea. So other means must be found for propelling ships and aircraft. The two necessities are a driving force to produce motion, and means to control the motion.

A fluid will not support a heavy weight, but it will offer some resistance and reduce the speed of its fall. The hands of the swimmer " slip " through the water to a certain extent, but the mass of water resists sufficiently to enable him to " push " himself on a bit farther. In the same way the revolving paddles of the old river steamers propelled them forward. To-day, however, the " propeller " is almost universally employed for " fluid " propulsion.

As so often happens in engineering, the propeller is merely the converse of something else—the windmill—just as an air compressor is an engine working backwards. On the left-hand side of Fig. 66, the wind blowing on the blade of the windmill as shown forces it downwards in the direction of the arrow, and rotates the wheel. Now if the wheel itself were driven round in the opposite direction, the rotating blade would force the air back as in the right-hand diagram. Since, however, the air resists the whirling blades, it exerts a force P on the windmill itself—and if the speed were sufficiently high the latter would push itself over because of this force.

The blades of a propeller really correspond to small sections of a large screw thread, revolving in the " nut " provided by the fluid. If neither the nut nor bolt were held in any way, and the bolt were rotated by some means, both would move in opposite directions. In the same way, a revolving propeller drives air or water backwards, and on so doing, pushes itself

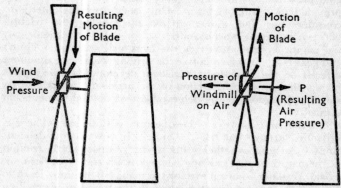

66. *How the propeller (right) reverses the action of the windmill (left).*

(and the ship or aeroplane) forwards. The distance through which a propeller would travel forward in one revolution, if rotating in a solid nut, is known as the " pitch " of the propeller.

The " driving force " through a fluid is thus provided— it is now necessary to control the movement obtained. The way in which this may be done is exemplified by the " rudder." Fig. 67 gives three views showing the action of the rudder of a ship. In (a) the ship is in a straight course, the rudder is in a central position, and the minimum resistance to motion is offered. If the rudder is put over as in (b) the water will offer increased resistance to its motion, and the reaction will tend to push the rudder round in the direction of the arrow. As it is fixed to the ship, the whole vessel turns and finally has a motion as in (c).

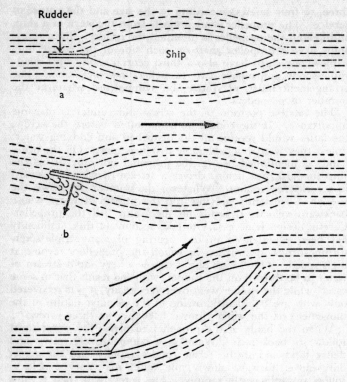

67. *The action of the rudder in turning a ship* (*which is moving in the direction of the arrow*).

It is thus possible both to drive and steer an object through a fluid medium. The propeller and rudder are to the ship or aeroplane, what the driving wheels of the back axle and the steering wheels of the front axle are to the motor car. No brakes can be provided on a ship, however, which can only be stopped quickly by reversing the propeller.

PROBLEMS OF PROPELLER AND RUDDER DESIGN

ALL ships except small river steamers and the like are driven by propellers—sometimes called "screw propellers," or more usually, simply "screws." There are ships with one, two, three, or four screws, according to the size and the nature of service. The propeller shaft projects from the stern of a ship, and behind the propeller is mounted the rudder. Twin-screw ships have a propeller shaft on each side of the centre line, triple-screw ships have also a third central screw, and quad-ruple-screw ships have two propellers on each side. The arrangement must, of course, be symmetrical whatever the number of propellers.

The relative position of the screw and rudder is of some importance. If the rudder were mounted before the screw, the latter would receive all the disturbed and eddying water, unless they were a considerable distance apart. On the other hand, as mentioned before, the propeller not only drives the ship forward, but it also drives a stream of water backward in a corkscrew motion. Whatever the number of screws, the rudder is constantly moving into this stream of water whose backward velocity depends on the " slip " of the propeller. Careful design is necessary to take account of this. Difficulty has been experienced in the steering of many triple-screw turbine-driven destroyers, in which the propellers revolve at high speed. The " high slip " causes a very rapid stream of water to be thrown on the rudder, with the result that in some cases, while the rudder went over very easily, it was recovered only with great difficulty, owing to the peculiar nature of the movement of the water thrown back by the three screws.

When the blade of the propeller revolves, the water must follow its back face. Water is a comparatively heavy and dense fluid and if the screw rotates rapidly and the vessel only moves forward slowly, the water may not be able to follow up sufficiently rapidly. The screw will then revolve in " cavities " of air and water vapour—a phenomenon known as " cavitation."

To avoid this, marine propellers must be carefully designed in relation to size of blade, speed of revolution, power trans-mitted and the speed of the ship itself. They were originally made of cast iron, but are now nearly always of a special bronze, which is both lighter and stronger. They may either be cast as a whole, or the blades may be made separately, and bolted on to a central hub or " boss " on the propeller shaft. Fig. 68 shows two varieties of propellers used: the one on the left is a form used for slow-speed merchant ships, that on the right is a naval propeller for high speeds. The propellers for H.M.S. *Repulse* each weighed $13\frac{1}{2}$ tons.

Because of the weight of water, and the problem of cavitation, ship propellers are limited in the speeds at which they may be run. While ships were driven by large slow-speed reciprocating steam engines, this created no difficulty and engines could be coupled direct to shaft. A steam turbine, however, works best at high speeds. A compromise may be struck between the best speeds for propeller and turbine, and direct turbo-drive may be used.

The discrepancy between these two most suitable speeds is so great, however, that large ships are now usually designed to allow both engines and propellers to work under the best

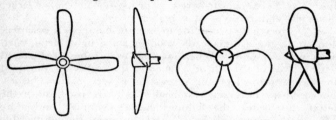

*68. Two types of propeller seen from front and side—
on the left for slow speeds, on the right for high speeds.*

conditions. This is done by using high-speed turbines, which either drive a slower-speed propeller shaft through reduction gearing, or else an electric generator. The electric current produced drives slow-speed motors coupled direct to the propeller shaft. The same variations are possible with Diesel engine drive.

TRAVELLING THROUGH THE AIR

In the air, the same considerations apply as regards the means of propulsion as in the water. Nothing in the nature of a " friction " drive is possible, and aircraft must push itself forward by driving air backward, just as the ship does in the sea. For control also, of course, the same conditions apply.

Here, however, the resemblance ceases. Air as a medium is some 800 times lighter than water, and is consequently a very elusive substance from which to derive anything in the way of support. Even if a man were suspended in the air by some means, he would have difficulty in propelling himself, to any perceptible degree, in the manner in which he is able to swim in water. The air, being so much lighter and more mobile, would provide negligible resistance to the strokes of his moving arms and legs. In the same way the " air-screw " must revolve in a correspondingly less substantial " nut " than the marine propeller, which is a screw revolving in a liquid " nut."

Actually, in order to drive a body forward, a propeller must drive a weight of fluid backward. Owing to its lightness, a far greater volume of air than water must be so driven backward in order to propel an object of the same weight. For this reason, an air screw is proportionately of a larger diameter, and revolves at a higher speed.

As in everything pertaining to aircraft, lightness is essential, and air screws are made of wood or some light metal, such as aluminium alloys. When made of wood, they are covered with a layer of varnish or lacquer for protection. Compared to marine propellers, air screws have very narrow blades. For ordinary purposes two blades only are used, since the fewer the blades, the lighter, cheaper, simpler, and more efficient the screw will be. Where, however, the permissible diameter is limited, or for some reason (such as the proximity of an unsymmetrical body, or another air screw) the air flow through a two-bladed screw would be unsymmetrical, three or four blades may be used. Wooden air screws are usually made with two or four blades, but metal ones with seldom more than three.

A car with no gear box cannot make the best use of its engine power. An aeroplane has no gear box between engine and air screw and consequently if the latter is of constant " pitch," the engine will not always give its best performance, for different conditions of speed, climbing altitude and density of the air. To remedy this, " variable-pitch " propellers are coming into use, by means of which the pilot may alter the pitch or angle of the blades while in flight, in the same way as a motorist changes gear. In one form of " variable-pitch " propeller this is done automatically as the load on the screw lightens.

WHY AN AEROPLANE STAYS IN THE AIR: THE " AEROFOIL "

A SHIP is lighter bulk for bulk than the water it displaces, and floats upon the surface. It has only " two-dimensional " motions; its weight is supported by the water, and all that is necessary is a rudder to steer it in a horizontal plane. An airship is also lighter than air, and " floats " in a similar manner to a ship, in that no effort is necessary to keep it suspended in the air.

The airship, however, is a special case, and for the aeroplane the most vital thing is to make it leave the ground, and to keep it in the air at all. Its movement is " three dimensional," and it must be controlled and directed in all three directions. For this reason a few words are necessary as to how the lift of an " aeroplane " is obtained. Although, of course, it is the aeroplane which moves through the air, it is more convenient to consider the aeroplane as stationary, and the air as flowing past it.

69. " Eddies " of air formed by a flat plate (with consequent force on the plate) inclined at a small angle to the direction of the air flowing past it.

The force exerted on an object by air flowing past it depends on the size and shape of the object and the velocity of the air. If the object be a flat plate held at a small angle to the direction of air flow, the reaction, a force exerted by the air, will be nearly at right angles to its surface as shown by the arrow R in Fig. 69. This is because the air is as it were " piled " up on the underside, and rushes past the upper side, leaving a space of low pressure filled with " eddies " of air. The total force on the lower side is therefore greater than that on the upper side, and the plate tends to move in the direction of the arrow R. (Contrary to what might be supposed, the lifting force is due rather to the reduction of pressure above, than the increase of pressure below the plate.) It has been found that the most suitable shape for obtaining a force at nearly right angles to the windflow in this way is not a flat one, but a curved and tapered section as in Fig. 70. This is called an *aerofoil*.

The wings of an aeroplane are *aerofoils*, so shaped that when moving horizontally through the air, the force exerted by the air is as nearly vertical as possible. It can never be absolutely vertical, however, and its direction is always tilted back owing to the " angle of incidence " of the aerofoil to the direction of flow necessary to produce any force at all, and also to friction between the air and surface of the aerofoil.

Actually the force R is equivalent to two forces L and D at right angles as in Fig. 70, one vertical and one horizontal. It will be seen that while the " lift " L tends to raise the aerofoil, the other component, " D," tends to move it in the direction of the air flow, or in other words, retards the

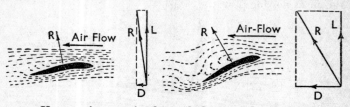

70. *How an increase in the angle between the air flow and the aerofoil increases the " lift " L but also the " drag " D.*

motion of an aeroplane in flight. A perfect aerofoil would give the maximum vertical " lift " and no " drag " as D is called.

From the two cases illustrated in Fig. 70 it will be seen that as the angle of incidence increases, the suction on the upper side becomes more violent, and the total force R increases. Actually it reaches a maximum at an angle of about 15° to the direction of flow, and after that begins to decrease again. At the same time, however, the " drag " increases at a rapidly growing rate. Thus although it is necessary to get the maximum lift from an aerofoil, it cannot be done without increasing the drag, and the best compromise must be sought, giving the maximum ratio of lift to drag. The angle of incidence at this optimum point may be in the region of $4\frac{1}{2}$°.

BALANCING ON THE WIND

AN aeroplane has been aptly said to " create its own hurricane, and ride on it." It must be possible to ride it, however, in any direction required. Steady controlled motion is only possible if the aeroplane is as it were delicately " balanced on the wind," or perhaps more accurately, balanced on the forces exerted by the air on its various surfaces. To this end all aircraft must be equipped with " control surfaces " by which these forces may be controlled and its movement in three dimensions may be directed. These surfaces are nothing more than subsidiary aerofoils corresponding to the action of a ship's rudder.

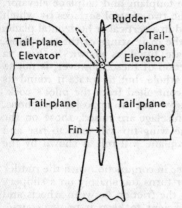
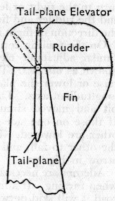

71. The tail of an aeroplane from above (left) and from the side (right), showing how the rudder and tail-plane elevator control the direction of flight in horizontal and vertical planes respectively.

A smaller aerofoil is mounted at the tail of the aeroplane, which is normally set so that it has no incidence or lift, and the aeroplane is supported by the main wings. This is called the tailplane. If due to any disturbance of the air, the incidence of the main wings is increased, the resulting greater lift tends to increase it still further, and by so doing depresses the tail. The tailplane, however, will now have some incidence itself. This will create lift on the tailplane, which, being at such a long " leverage " from the centre of gravity of the aeroplane, will tend to elevate the tail and restore the plane to its level position. This small subsidiary aerofoil therefore has a stabilising effect during normal flight. A vertical fin mounted on the tail will have a similar effect in the vertical plane.

If the " trailing " (or rear) edge of these aerofoils be tilted, the equivalent of " variable camber " aerofoils will be obtained. By lowering this " tailplane elevator " as shown by the dotted position in Fig. 71, the air will have a lifting effect on the tailplane due to the angle of incidence thus obtained. The tail will rise, the nose will dip and the aeroplane will move in a downward direction. If the elevator is raised, the aeroplane will begin to climb. In the same way, if the vertical rudder behind the fin be moved, as in Fig. 71, the aeroplane will turn to the right or left. The tailplane and tailplane elevator, and the rudder and fin, are the two control surfaces by which the direction of flight is altered in a vertical or horizontal plane.

On the trailing corners of the main wings of the aeroplane, similar adjustable elevators are fitted as shown in Fig. 72 known as *ailerons*. The function of these, however, is not to raise or lower the plane as a whole, but to rotate it round its longitudinal axis. They are controlled from the pilot's cockpit and moved simultaneously—but in opposite directions. If those on one side of the fuselage are raised, those on the other are lowered. Thus one wing-tip will tend to rise and the other to fall, and the aeroplane will roll as shown by the arrow in Fig. 72.

Ailerons are necessary for use in conjunction with the rudder when turning. If a motor-car turns too sharply on a slippery road it will skid outwards, as the friction between wheels and the wet road is now not sufficient to keep it on its course. An aeroplane has the same tendency to " skid " sideways when turning. There are no wheels to keep it on its course, however, so in this also it must be balanced by the wind. By " banking " or turning on its axis by means of the ailerons in the manner just described, the surface of the wings is presented to the air at the side. The force exerted by the latter is now directed at an angle to the vertical, tending to prevent side movement of the aeroplane while still supporting its weight. In this manner the pilot uses the surrounding air to assist his turning, in the same way as a racing motorist uses the " banking " of a race track.

On the combination of elevators, rudders and ailerons the pilot relies entirely for his control over the movements of the aeroplane. By suitable adjustment of any or all of these control surfaces, the aeroplane can be guided in any direction required. Control wires connect the various elevators, etc., to controls in the cockpit. By simple movements of the " rudder bar " at his feet or control column by which the elevator and aileron controls are operated, the pilot may loop, roll, turn, bank, climb, dive or do anything he wishes.

In the case of airships, of course, there are no wings, and no advantage would be derived from banking. Moreover the surface area is so large as largely to resist the skidding tendency. Airships are therefore fitted with rudders and elevators only —situated symmetrically at the tail.

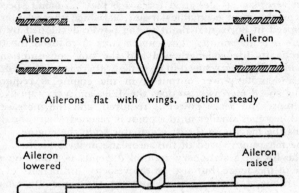

Ailerons flat with wings, motion steady

Aileron lowered   Aileron raised

Ailerons moved for rolling motion

72. How the ailerons, moved simultaneously but in opposite directions, cause an aeroplane to roll in the direction shown by the arrow.

HOW AIRCRAFT ARE DESIGNED

VARIOUS considerations govern the design of an aeroplane, and the particular nature of the service for which it is intended is responsible for the distinctive features of its construction. It may be a huge commercial air liner, carrying many passengers with their luggage and weighing many tons, or it may be a Schneider Trophy racing seaplane with a speed of over 400 miles per hour. Between these two extremes lie all the combinations of weight, lift, airscrew thrust, speed, etc., which are found in the various types of machines.

The chief forces acting on an aeroplane in flight are its weight, the lift, airscrew thrust and drag. In effect it is the lift which counteracts the weight, and the thrust of the air-screw which overcomes the drag which is inseparable from lift, and also the general resistance of the air to movement. The weight is an inherent feature of the machine, but the airscrew thrust, lift and drag are all variable factors, depending on the height, speed, design of airscrew and angle of incidence of the aerofoils.

An aeroplane is designed for a specific " cruising speed." This is the most economical point, at which the relation of the speed in horizontal flight to the power developed by the engine is a maximum. The engine runs at reduced throttle, whereby its life is lengthened and the fuel consumption is kept low. For every speed in level flight there is a certain drag, and a definite power output from the engine is required. As the speed increases, so does the drag, and very rapidly, so that more and more power is required, and the increase in speed becomes smaller until a point is reached where the drag equals the maximum thrust obtainable from the engine. This is the maximum speed of the aeroplane in level flight.

The lift on a stationary aerofoil depends not only on the angle of incidence, but also on the velocity and density of the air. Thus if the density is constant the same lift can be obtained with a high velocity and small angle of incidence, or a low velocity and large angle. As has been mentioned before, however, the lift only increases up to an angle of about 15 degrees, after which it rapidly decreases. This is the angle of maximum lift and corresponds to a minimum air speed. As the speed of an aeroplane decreases, in order to obtain the necessary lift to support its weight, the angle must be increased until this maximum is reached. If the speed falls still further, the lift decreases, and increasing the angle now further decreases it, with the result that the aero-plane will fall. This is said to be " stalling." The angle of maximum lift, and the minimum speed, are known as the " stalling angle " and " stalling speed " respectively.

The distance the aeroplane runs along the ground after land-ing is of considerable importance, affecting as it does the size of aerodrome or of an emergency landing ground in the case of a forced landing. For this reason its " landing speed " must be low, and of course, for the same reason, the minimum " take-off " speed. If, however, the landing speed is too low, the machine will be unmanageable when landing on a gusty day. The stalling speed and landing speed depend largely on the wing-design, and a compromise must be found most suitable for all the requirements of the aeroplane. Low landing speed may be obtained at the expense of flying speed and *vice versa*.

EVERY AEROPLANE HAS ITS " CEILING "

As previously stated, when the engine is developing its maximum power, the aeroplane reaches its maximum speed in level flight. At all other points in the practical speed range of the aeroplane, the engine is not working at its maximum. There is thus a reserve of power available for climbing, in which not only has the drag to be overcome, but the weight of the aeroplane must be raised to a higher level. Climbing is achieved by raising the nose of the aeroplane to a certain angle. Every aeroplane has its best " angle of climb," depending on its weight, power and the form of its wings, etc. Good " take-off " characteristics and a good " angle of climb " go together to a great extent and are a very important consideration in the design of all commercial, and the majority of military aeroplanes. If the angle of climb be increased beyond this critical angle, the aeroplane will not gain height and eventually will lose flying speed and stall.

The density of the air has an important effect on the lift of an aeroplane. Though in normal flight it is of secondary importance, at high altitudes its influence is pronounced. As the air becomes " thinner," the lift for any angle of incidence decreases. When climbing, the pilot must therefore increase the angle of incidence, which in its turn increases the drag, and lowers the maximum speed obtainable.

As the altitude increases, the angle of incidence necessary to maintain the lift becomes larger, and therefore the minimum speed to prevent stalling increases. The maximum speed obtainable is being reduced, the speed necessary to prevent stalling is becoming higher, and eventually they will equal each other. At this point the aeroplane can only just keep on level flight. If the angle of incidence be increased, or the engine power be reduced, the machine will stall. This maximum attainable height varies with each aeroplane, and is known as its " ceiling."

THE IDEAL AIR-SCREW

Mention has been made of the effect of the form of aerofoil on the performance of the aeroplane. Equally important is the design of the airscrew, which very greatly affects its characteristics.   Maximum speed, arriving speed, rate of climb, take-off, etc., are all affected greatly by the form of this.   A certain combination of pitch and diameter may give the maximum flying speed, but will give an unsatisfactory angle of climb.   Each characteristic may require a different form from the others.   For high speeds a very high pitch screw is required; on the other hand, large diameter and low pitch are necessary for a good take-off and angle of climb. In actual fact an airscrew in which not only the pitch but the diameter can be varied at will is really required.

All the different factors affecting airscrew design, shape of aerofoil, wing area, necessary engine power, etc., must be weighed up and judged in accordance with the type of service for which the aeroplane is to be used.   Benefits obtained in one direction must be balanced against disadvantages in another.   The final forms must be chosen with a view to the principal requirements, whether it be good all-round performance, high speed, high angle of climb for fighters, or any other special feature.   In addition, adequate control surfaces must be provided, and finally the air-resistance must be decreased as much as possible by " stream lining."   By this means the air is made to flow in smooth, easy curves, and all sharp corners and flat surfaces are eliminated where possible.

A HURRICANE IN A TUBE

ADVANCE in aviation is only made possible by continual research and experimental work.   Each new machine brought out must be thoroughly tested by actual flight.   Its lift and drag characteristics, take-off and general behaviour in the air must be thoroughly investigated before any conclusions can be formed as to its merits.   The effect of improvements and alterations to existing aeroplanes must also be observed in the same way.

There are certain serious disadvantages to flight tests of this nature, however.   Airscrew thrust cannot be accurately measured, and delay in tests due to variable atmospheric conditions, inability to repeat trials under identically the same conditions, and the necessarily short time of observation all make it difficult to obtain accurate and exhaustive results. Moreover for the safety of the test-pilots it is essential that as much as is possible be found out about the machine before it is allowed to leave the ground.   On the other hand, no tests are possible unless carried out in air, on which the performance of the aeroplane depends entirely.

It has been said that an aeroplane in flight is equivalent to a stationary aeroplane in a flow of air. This is made use of in the " wind tunnel," in which a great deal of experimental research is carried out. There are several of these in existence. In principle the wind tunnel is simply a long tube through which air is blown at a high velocity. Model aircraft, aerofoils, airscrews, etc., are suspended in this current of air in such a way that the lift, drag and other data may be measured. The models are exact reproductions of the real machines, and the corresponding results that may be anticipated for the latter are deduced. Air is drawn through the tunnel by a large fan at its mouth, which gives it a velocity of more than 100 miles per hour through the " tube."

By this means the conditions prevailing in actual flight may be closely resembled, and valuable information about the adjustment of the centre of gravity with reference to the air forces, the loading of wing and control surfaces, the resistance of the body and fittings, airscrew thrust, and other particulars can all be found in this way.

THE MATERIALS FROM WHICH MACHINES ARE MADE

WONDERFUL machinery for an infinite number of purposes may be invented and designed, but without the necessary materials the brains of the designer are useless, his calculations and drawings all in vain. Advance in the science of engineering depends largely on the metallurgist and his ability to produce the necessary material for each new development.

The basic metal for mechanical engineering is of course iron or steel in some form; but as time goes on, " iron and steel " become the general names for an ever-increasing variety of metals, which, although mainly consisting of the same material, have in fact widely differing properties. The iron and steel industry, old-established as it is, has by no means reached the end of its development. Research to-day is as active as ever it was, and new applications are constantly being found for which new and better materials must be produced.

Non-ferrous metals too play an important part. From the

point of view of strength, steel is superior to all other metals, but this is not everything. For many purposes it is not suitable, and instead brass, bronze and other special metals are employed. Aluminium and its alloys are being increasingly used for rapidly moving parts, where strength and lightness are essential.

Gold and silver may hold the proud title of the " precious metals "—but how small is their real worth, and how value-less they appear in comparison with iron! Iron is the corner-stone of this twentieth century Age of Steel—the whole of our material civilisation is based on it, in its infinite variety of forms. Engineering could not exist without it—modern life depends fundamentally upon it. Truly the world to-day may be said to live in a house built on iron. So long has this precious metal been the faithful friend of man that its existence is taken for granted, its various uses extended automatically as the machine age advances.

In the British Museum is a wedge of wrought iron buried in the great pyramid of Cheops probably as early as 3500 B.C. From the primitive little furnaces of those days, holes in the side of a bank of clay, with charcoal from forest trees as fuel, to the huge blast-furnaces and steel works of to-day, is a far cry. It is not possible here to trace the history of the develop-ment of iron and steel in any detail, but no book on engineering would be complete without some mention of the metal to which it owes its existence.

HOW THE WORLD'S MOST USEFUL METAL IS OBTAINED

IRON in its metallic state is not found in nature—it must be obtained from its " ore." This is essentially a natural " iron-rust," being a compound of the metal and oxygen. Iron smelting consists of splitting up this combination of iron and oxygen. The process takes place in the blast-furnace, by " reduction " with carbon in the form of coke which, under the action of great heat, combines with the oxygen of the ore, leaving the metallic iron. Coke and iron ore are fed into the top of the furnace, and the fiery mass raised to a temperature of about 1,500 degrees Centigrade by means of a blast of hot air and gas blown through from underneath. Molten iron runs to the bottom of the furnace and is drawn off as required, while the gases resulting from the combination of carbon and oxygen escape from the top of the furnace.

In addition to the iron ore and fuel, limestone is added to

the charge. This is because the ore contains much dirt and impurities most of which are removed by the action of limestone as a molten " slag " floating on the metal, and periodically drawn off. The slag itself is sold and used in a crushed form in concrete mixtures for road building and other applications. About 2,000 tons of iron may be obtained from 7,500 tons of raw material, after about 24 hours' burning. The molten metal may be taken direct to the steel furnaces and made into steel, or it may be poured into moulds and cooled, when it is known as " pig iron."

The gases issuing from the furnace top are taken to one of several " blast stoves " and also to gas engines. The latter drive air compressors for supplying the blast, which passes through another blast stove in which are fire bricks raised to white heat by previous contact with hot furnace gases. Thus by alternatively using each blast stove, first to take the heat from the gases, and then to give it up to the cold blast air, a constant supply of hot blast is available. This is led to a large pipe passing right round the bottom of the furnace, from which it is blown into the burning mass inside, through branch pipes penetrating through the furnace walls.

THE FIRST FINISHED PRODUCTS : WROUGHT AND CAST IRON

THE smelting of iron ore in a blast-furnace, however, does not give us the material we need to make the tremendous variety of machines, tools, and all those forms in which iron and steel enter our daily lives. Pig iron itself as such has no significance as a material for the engineer. It is only the first stage, and acts as a starting point for the various processes which will eventually produce the different irons and steels which are required. Some of the pig iron produced in the furnace is further treated and converted into the forms in which iron, as distinct from steel, is used, such as wrought iron and cast iron.

Wrought iron was the pioneer of the iron and steel family, and it was chiefly in this form that it was produced in such a primitive manner in early times. It is still used in many ways for decorative work such as beautiful wrought-iron gates, and for various pipes, bolts, etc., but to a great extent has been replaced by steel.

Cast iron still plays an important part in industry to-day. It is made by what amounts to a repetition of the blast-furnace process—but in a smaller furnace known as a " cupola."

Pig irons of various composition are charged into the cupola, together with cast-iron scrap, and the correct quantity of coke and limestone as before. The molten metal runs to the bottom and is poured out in a glowing, white-hot stream into big ladles. From these ladles it is poured into the moulds where it cools into the desired shapes. Many parts of machinery casings, baseplates and wheels besides domestic articles such as gas stoves, electric fires, etc., are made of cast iron. It is a cheap and convenient metal, and very suitable for use where no unusual forces are to be encountered.

It is, however, hard and brittle, and for important, highly stressed parts of machinery, cast iron cannot be trusted, and steel must be used. Nevertheless, for many and varied purposes it is an admirable medium, and its use dies slowly before the relentless march of steel.

VERSATILE STEEL, THE ENGINEER'S STRONG RIGHT ARM

BUT the majority of pig iron is made into steel, and it is into this form that the red, earthy iron ore is finally transformed. "Steel," that fascinating word beside which "iron" seems somehow dull and ordinary. Steel, in its infinite variety of forms, so soft and pliable that it can be bent double or tied in knots without cracking, or so hard and strong that it cuts ordinary steel as if it were cheese. Its uses are so wide, the demands made on it increase so rapidly, that new types of steel must constantly be developed to keep pace with the needs of civilisation. Perhaps some rustless metal is required, or a still harder and stronger cutting tool for the factory—whatever the problem may be, eventually it is solved and more is added to the ever-increasing knowledge of the research worker and steel manufacturer.

It seems strange, somehow, contrasting their uses and the wide difference in their applications, to reflect that in its chemical composition, steel is nearer to pure iron than is cast iron. Both contain iron and a certain amount of carbon, and it is upon the small variations in this carbon content, together with carefully regulated heating and cooling in manufacture, that the final nature of the metal depends. Wrought iron usually contains 0·1 to 0·2% of carbon, cast iron about 3·5%, and steel 0·3 to 0·4%, though it may be as low as 0·03%, or as high as 2%. These are the so-called "carbon-steels," or alloys of iron and carbon.

"Alloy steels" on the other hand, depend not only on their

carbon content for their properties, but on the usually small amounts of other metals added as well. As a general rule steels with a low carbon content are soft, while those with a high percentage of carbon are hard and less ductile (or less easily bent). The " tenacity " or strength of a steel increases until the carbon content is just over one per cent, and then decreases. It will be appreciated that with such small variations in composition, the manufacture of iron and steel is a highly developed and specialised science.

THE BIRTH OF THE MODERN STEEL TRADE

IT was in 1856 that an Englishman, Henry Bessemer, invented his process for the manufacture of iron and steel which revolutionised the ideas of those days, and led to the greatest commercial development the world has seen. Though largely superseded by the " Open Hearth Process " to-day, it was Henry Bessemer who first made it possible to make steel rapidly and cheaply, and it is he who will always be the outstanding figure in the history of steel.

As mentioned above, pig iron contains an excessive quantity of carbon, which makes it hard and brittle, and lacking in that all-round strength which is necessary for its wide use. It also contains other impurities, occurring naturally in the earth, and remaining in the metal after separation from the ore. All these must be removed, and just as the furnace was used to obtain iron from iron ore, so it is used to convert iron into steel. This it does by burning out these impurities and most of the carbon.

Until this time all metallurgical processes had required the use of a furnace, with the consequent high cost of fuel. Moreover, steel as it was being made could only be obtained in small quantities at a time, and the enormous demand of to-day could not possibly have been met.

Bessemer's genius led to the utilisation of the heat generated by the burning of the impurities themselves, to produce the same result, without the necessity for an external furnace. Coal (or carbon) if burnt in air generates a large amount of heat, and heat is generated in exactly the same way by the burning of the impurities in iron. Thus a mass of molten iron at 2,300° F. say, may, by blowing air through it, in a few minutes become steel at 3,000° F. simply by the combustion of the impurities.

The apparatus devised by Bessemer for the manufacture of

steel in this way, is famous as the "Bessemer converter," shown in Fig. 73. Molten iron of suitable composition is poured into the mouth of the converter which can rotate about its centre and a blast of air is blown through about 200 holes in the bottom. Smoke and a shower of sparks issue from the mouth, and soon develop into a fierce roaring flame. From the colour of this flame the operator can judge the state of the metal inside, and after 15 to 20 minutes the blast is shut down. Special irons are now added to give the final steel the carbon content and characteristics required, after which it is run off into a ladle and cast into moulds or "ingots."

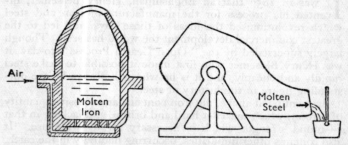

73. How the Bessemer converter is used in making steel

THE OPEN-HEARTH METHOD INVENTED BY SIEMENS

IN 1861, Siemens introduced his "open hearth furnace," and this led to a new method of steel manufacture which to-day has largely superseded the Bessemer converter. By a special arrangement of the path of the furnace gases, Siemens was able to produce the necessary heat to keep the iron molten, which before had been impossible. In the open hearth process to-day, the molten iron is turned into the furnace and mixed with scrap steel, carbon and other substances, according to the nature of steel required. There it is subjected to a temperature of about 1,700° Centigrade by blasts of combustible gas and compressed air. These gases are subsequently taken to regenerators, where they heat the ingoing blast gases in the same way as is done in the blast stoves of the blast furnace.

The open-hearth process requires a much longer time than the Bessemer, and usually takes from 8 to 12 hours. When the steel is ready it is drawn off into the ladle, and cast into moulds as before. The great advantage of this method is that throughout the operation there is complete control over the metal, and it is possible to make frequent tests and secure a steel of the exact composition required. Moreover certain types of iron can be used which are not suitable for the Bessemer process. Sometimes the procedure is not continuous, that is the molten iron is not taken direct to the steel furnace. In this case, pig iron is distributed over the bed of the open hearth, together with some steel scrap and other ingredients required. (It takes about 4 or 5 hours to melt a 30 ton charge.) So important are these advantages to be gained by the use of the open-hearth process, that in all high-class construction work, such as bridge building, steel made by this process is invariably specified.

CASTING AND MOULDING THE WHITE-HOT METAL

WHETHER it be iron from the cupola, or steel from the Bessemer converter or open-hearth furnace, the molten metal has now been poured into a huge iron ladle ready for use. The next step is to convert this mass of white-hot liquid into a solid metal body roughly resembling the final shape required, so that the work of the machinist may be as little as possible. Its treatment now depends on the nature of the metal, its final shape, and the use for which it is intended. Steel may be allowed to solidify and subsequently be rolled, forged, etc., when required, but cast iron can be used in only one way. The molten metal must be taken straight to the foundry to be " cast," and in practice the cupolas are situated in the foundry itself.

Molten metal from the cupola is poured into previously prepared moulds, where it cools and takes up the required shape. The principle of this use of the metal is exactly the same as the way in which jellies, moulds, and similar delicacies are made for the table. In this case a glass mould is used, with sundry designs and patterns on its inner surface. The hot liquid jelly is poured in and allowed to cool, and when removed from the mould it is quite solid and has taken permanently the shape of the inside of the mould. In exactly the same way is cast iron given its shapes, providing castings for different uses, except that the form of the moulds is usually very much more complicated than that of any jelly seen on the table.

The material which forms the moulds of the iron-founder must be capable of withstanding the heat of the molten iron, and it must bind together so that it will not be broken down by the pressure of the liquid metal. It must also be porous to a certain extent to enable certain gases to escape as the metal solidifies. The material used is chiefly sand, carefully selected and prepared by mixing with other substances to give the final moulding compound. For small castings an iron box is filled with this sand, a wood " pattern ", the shape of the required article, is placed in the sand, which is then packed closely all round it. When the pattern is removed, the sand now bears its exact impression, in the same way as a piece of wax does when a key is pressed into it, so that its shape may be matched. The mould, however, is split into two, a top half and a bottom half.

When these are assembled together, nothing is seen of the " shape " left in the sand by the pattern, as it is right in the centre of the mould. Molten metal is now poured into this internal cavity through a hole in the mould, and is allowed to set. After some hours the sand is broken away and the solid metal casting is revealed identical in shape with the wooden pattern. For very large castings, no single box could be made large enough to contain the whole mould. Then a pit is dug in the sand which constitutes the foundry floor, and the bottom half of the mould is built up in this. The top half is held in a massive iron framework, and placed on top.

Castings made in this manner take a considerable time to cool, as the sand retains the heat. For this reason the iron is fairly soft, and can be easily machined. For some purposes, however, a very hard surface is required for some parts of the casting, such as the outer rim of an iron wheel, gear wheels, and similar parts where heavy wear will be experienced. In this case, the sections of the mould in contact with these surfaces are made of iron. The molten metal enters the mould and, coming in contact with the cold iron of the mould, becomes solid almost at once, cooling very rapidly. These " chilled " portions are extremely hard, and castings of this nature are known as " chilled castings."

THE CASTING OF STEEL—FOR GREAT HEAT AND HIGH PRESSURES

CASTING is a very convenient method of transforming at one step the liquid metal into a solid closely approaching the final product. By this means complicated shapes can be made which could not be easily obtained by any other method, whether by machining or forging. For such items as the huge exhaust casings of a large turbine, or the cylinder head of an internal combustion engine (made integrally with its surrounding water jacket), the foundry is invaluable. Indeed it is difficult to imagine how the same forms could be obtained by any other means, unless the many parts were made separately and subsequently assembled together.

Cast iron itself as a material, however, has its limitations. With the advent of higher pressures and temperatures in turbines, Diesel engines, steam-pipe valves, etc., cast iron has proved unequal to the task. Its brittle nature, and generally inferior quality as a metal make it unsuitable. For these purposes, where the form required can still only be obtained by casting, but where a metal superior to cast iron is necessary, cast steel is used. For instance, in a two-cylinder turbine, the low pressure cylinder casing is made of cast iron, but the high pressure cylinder is a very carefully designed steel casting made from the finest quality steel.

The process followed with steel is very similar, and the castings are of course obtained by pouring molten metal into moulds. The problem is rather more involved, however, because of the high temperature at which the molten metal must be used. Moreover difficulty is met with on account of the high " shrinkage " of the cooling steel and also the quantity of gases dissolved in the molten metal. On cooling, these gases are liberated from the metal, and as they cannot escape through the solid external crust (for the outside of the casting cools first) they form hollow cavities or " blow-holes " in the solid metal. These of course are not visible, and if not revealed in the process of machining, may seriously weaken the casting. Steel castings are made of special metal and with great care, only the best sand and moulding materials being used.

THE MIGHTY STEAM SMITHS OF THE MODERN FORGE

IRON and steel in elementary forms have long been known to man, and the blacksmith, that " mighty man " hammering red-hot horse shoes at the anvil of his smoky forge, is an historical figure. He and his kind have sadly dwindled in numbers, but their methods still exist to-day—and in a form which the noble smith of antiquity could never have visualised.

Steel which is not to be cast is poured into other moulds of plain rectangular shape called " ingot-moulds." Here the

" ingots " solidify, and are kept at a uniform temperature in the " soaking pits " ready for the next process. This is to ensure that the metal is in the same state throughout, without any partially solidified centre or uneven composition in any part. If now a plain round shaft is required, the white-hot ingot is taken to the steam hammer and hammered and hammered. Gradually its corners disappear, the short thick form of the ingot lengthens, and finally becomes a long round shaft of the required description, which needs only to be finished off by the machinist.

The forging of such mass-produced parts as motor car crankshafts by this method however would be a lengthy process. Forgings of this nature are therefore made by a process known as " drop forging," which combines the advantages of forging and casting. While still retaining the superior qualities of better " grain," greater uniformity and freedom from defects, etc., which distinguish forged from cast metal, it is at the same time possible to perform the rapid and exact repetition work of the foundry.

Indeed, drop forging is a compromise between the two methods. The hammer and the anvil are now given an " impression " of the finished article, as are the two halves of the moulding box in the foundry. Now, however, they are called " dies," and are made of hard steel. Between these dies, the white-hot steel is rapidly forged into the exact shape required. The dies themselves are expensive, however, and this method is really only suitable where large numbers of identical parts are required.

The steam hammers used for the forging of large machine parts are indeed formidable monsters. Able to deal a blow which even Vulcan in his smithy could not have imagined, they are yet such exact and finely controlled machines that they can smash a watch glass without harming to the least extent the mechanism of the watch itself.

A great deal of forging, however, is done by hydraulic presses which are operated by water power. These do not deal hammer blows, but the operation is more a squeezing of the metal into shape so that the whole metal flows, instead of the mere surface battering of the steam hammer. This is very advantageous, as it is particularly necessary that the innermost part of the metal (always the site of faults and bad quality) should be worked in this manner, and so obtain the beneficial effects that the process of forging actually confers.

PUTTING STEEL "THROUGH THE MANGLE"

STEEL may be cast or forged to take up any shape desired within reason, but sometimes neither of these methods are suitable. If for instance steel rails for railway lines, girders for bridges, or anything of this nature is required, where the shape of the section is constant throughout its length, the foundry or the forge are both impractical and uneconomical for this purpose. Instead the white-hot steel is " rolled " into the required shape, almost as the housewife rolls her lump of dough into piecrusts and tarts.

The lump of dough in this case is the steel ingot—still hot though solid from the soaking pits. It is taken to rolling

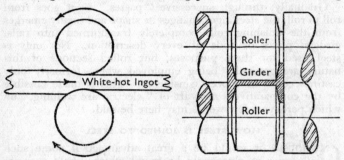

74. Rolling white-hot steel into shape. The rollers on the right are forming an " I "-beam.

mills, huge steel " mangles " driven by enormously powerful electric motors. The " rollers " of the " mangle " are steel, and are placed at an adjustable distance apart. The white-hot ingot is brought up and in a moment it is through the first " pass " through the rollers. To and fro it goes until finally it emerges from this first stage. It is now very much smaller in section than the original ingot and proportionately longer and is known as a " bloom " or " billet " according to its size. Fig. 74 shows the action of steel rolls on an ingot. It is cut up into suitable lengths and next taken to the " roughing mills."

Here the rolls have ridges and serrations round their circumferences, of various shapes, so that when it emerges the steel has already acquired something of its final form. It is next taken to " finishing " rolls, where it is finally given the exact shape required.   On the right-hand side of Fig. 74 are shown a pair of rolls such as might be used for the manufacture of those girders which are constantly seen being erected as the skeleton of some large new building.   The shape of the girder itself as it comes through the rolls is shown shaded.

This rolling of steel is indeed little more than putting it through some huge mangle. The metal must be white-hot (except for the smallest sections) and the rolls very strong and powerful, but the action is identical. It is used for the manufacture of everything that can be produced in this way, and which has no alterations in its section throughout its length.

Gradually, through successive " passes," as it goes from roll to roll, the steel ingot changes its shape and finally emerges from the finishing rolls completely transformed into rails, girders, plates or rods of every description. Not only is steel used for these purposes, but rolled sections of this nature are gradually being employed where formerly only castings could have been considered. This is made possible by the comparatively new art of " electric arc welding," on which perhaps a few words may here be said.

HOW STEEL IS JOINED TO STEEL

Obviously it would be a great advantage if some such substance as glue could be found which would successfully hold steel structures together. The forces involved, however, and the necessity for making a secure and lasting joint, rule out the possibility of any such substance as glue being used. Nevertheless, very much the same thing is done in electric welding by using metal itself as the jointing medium. By this means different parts may be fixed together without the use of any bolts, nuts or rivets at all.

The plates are held in the position required, and electrically connected to an " earth." If now a metal rod or electrode be brought near the plates, and a suitable voltage applied, an electric arc will be struck between the electrode and the " earthed " metal. A form of electrolysis takes place, and metal leaves the electrode and is deposited on the joint as required, forming with the two plates a sound and permanent joint.

The " welded " or " fabricated " structure has not reached the limit of development ; experiments are still being made to test its suitability for a wide range of purposes. As yet it is not used for the rapidly moving parts of machinery, but neither are castings, and it is the casting which so far the welded structure has largely replaced. Stationary frames for electric motors and generators, engine base-plates, condensers, all items of this nature, formerly huge massive castings weighing many tons, are now usually made by welding together a few rolled steel sections, bars and plates. Great saving in weight, cost of material, time and labour is possible by this means. Particularly does this apply to the largest sizes of casting, where weeks are saved which before would have been necessary for pattern making and moulding.

The advantages of welding are many, and its uses are steadily increasing. Already it has been used in the construction of ships and bridges. A saving of no less than 550 tons in weight was effected in the construction of the German " pocket battleship " *Deutschland* through the adoption of the welding process.

SMOOTHING OFF THE ROUGH EDGES

STEEL rails and girders for stationary structures in which they are only weight supporters do not need any further process, except the drilling of a few holes for joining purposes. The carefully designed parts of moving machinery, however, are by no means ready for use when they leave the forge or foundry. Many of these items must be of exact dimensions, and they are not allowed to vary from these more than one or two thousandth parts of an inch. No foundry or forge could produce an article anything approaching this degree of accuracy, so that the castings and forgings are only roughly shaped, and the task of giving them the final exact dimensions as laid down by the draughtsman is left to the " Machine Shops."

The roughly shaped parts as they enter the machine shops are slightly oversize. Moreover, the surfaces are rough and uneven from the hammer or mould. On certain sections this coarse surface does not matter, but wherever metal joins metal a smooth " machined " surface is essential.

The work of this part of the factory consists therefore of cutting and shaping the rough materials until finally the accurate and smoothly finished part is ready for assembly with the whole. Actually forgings and castings are chiefly used for the major components of the machine. Many of the smaller parts enter the machine shop as plain round steel bars, rods and strips. These must be shaped and machined until finally the finished part emerges, as the statue from the block of stone. The hammer and chisel however are replaced by the mechanically driven machine tools.

The machines themselves will be described in greater detail later on, but a few remarks may be made here in connection with the material of which the cutting tools themselves are made.

STEEL CUT STEEL

WHATEVER the nature of the metal to be cut, whether it be hard or soft, the tool itself must be very much harder. During the cutting process great heat is given out from the friction produced between tool and metal. Heat has a very marked effect on steel, and the heat treatment of the steel itself is an important part of the steel industry. If the cutting tool is of inferior material, or gets too hot, it will soften and becomes useless for its work.

To avoid this, tool steel must be specially made, and its history is the story of continual development of tools that are harder and will cut at greater speeds than ever before. The greater the speed, the less the cost of manufacture, but greater also is the heat evolved and the strain on the tool. Consequently the tool-maker must constantly produce a tool that is not only still harder, but which can be used at still greater speeds without suffering damage.

In the early days of machines, tools were made from ordinary carbon steel of high carbon content. When this steel is heated to a cherry-red and suddenly cooled by " quenching " in water or oil, it becomes extremely hard and brittle. Owing to this latter quality, tools made in this way are liable to break. They are therefore " tempered " by careful reheating to a lower temperature and quenching once more. By this means they lose some of their hardness, but much of the brittleness is removed, and the steel is considerably tougher.

Tools were made in this way until 1857, when Robert Mushet introduced the first " self-hardening " or tungsten steel containing a small amount of tungsten. This represented a great advance on the ordinary carbon steels, being capable of cutting harder materials at considerably higher speeds. Since that time, experiments have been made with the introduction of other metals such as vanadium, and gradually the performance of these " high-speed " steels has been improved. When the friction heat of cutting raises the temperature of a carbon-steel tool to about 500° F., it begins to soften and rapidly deteriorates. With high-speed steel tools, however, this temperature can be increased to about 1,200° F., or higher, without the tool softening or deteriorating.

Recently high-speed cutting alloys have been produced whose hardness approaches that of a diamond, and which freely cut materials which formerly could only have been machined by diamond tools ! Ordinary tools are sharpened by grinding, but these can only be slightly altered in shape even by grinding. A cutting tool of this nature at work is an awe-inspiring sight. The tool tears along the metal at a tremendous speed, and the steel is machined off so hot that it is blue. One wonders how any metal or machine can stand such treatment, and expects something to give way at any moment.

THE HARDEST METAL SURFACE KNOWN TO MAN

IT is not only tool steels which need to be very hard however. Many parts of machines are subject to a severe sliding motion which tends to produce excessive friction or wear. A typical instance of this is the cylinder of the internal combustion engine, a fact which most motorists know to their cost. The friction, great speeds, and the high temperature which makes good cylinder lubrication difficult, all too soon lead to that " knocking " and high oil consumption which indicate that the cylinders need re-boring. In the endeavour to provide bearing surfaces to stand up to work such as this, the use of nitrogen has been introduced. By heating cast iron at a high temperature in the presence of " nascent " (newly formed) nitrogen, the casting is given an extremely hard outer skin. The nitrogen enters into the surface of the metal where it forms an outer layer of a hardness which gradually decreases inwards. Thus this hard skin does not extend to the main body of the metal which retains all the toughness and strength of the ordinary casting.

A bearing surface produced by this " nitriding " process, as it is called, is so hard that it cannot be touched by a file, but will itself cut glass and even scratch quartz. It is also very resistant to the corrosive action of steam and air. It retains its quality up to a temperature of 500° C., and will recover on cooling any hardness lost at higher temperatures.

THE METALS WHICH CONTAIN NO IRON[1]

As we have seen, the progress of the motor car and still more the aeroplane made it essential that engines should be made as light as possible. For this reason materials were sought which would be capable of withstanding the same forces but would be much lighter in weight. As a result largely of the demands of these two branches of engineering, the aluminium alloy has come into its own. This metal, unknown a hundred years ago, now ranks with copper, lead and zinc (the most important non-ferrous metals). Aluminium is not often used alone, however, as it is weak and awkward to cast. It is necessary to add small percentages of one or more other metals, to give it other qualities equally as important as lightness. An alloy to be of use must be not only light but strong, easily cast or wrought, and easily machined.

Aluminium itself weighs approximately one third as much as brass or iron. With the object of giving it sufficient strength so that its lightness might be utilised, a large number of alloys have been produced in the past under proprietary names. Many of these, however, were superfluous and only introduced for reasons of business competition, and to-day the useful aluminium alloys are to a great extent standardised. The metals chiefly used with aluminium are copper, zinc, silicon, magnesium, manganese, tin or nickel.

The use of aluminium alloys is extremely wide, and it is not possible to detail all their various compositions. In motor-car and aeroplane engines, for instance, it is usual to have a particular alloy for a special purpose. Different compositions are accordingly used for pistons, crank cases, gear boxes, cylinder heads and carburettor bodies. By this means the weight per horse power of aeroplane engines has been very greatly reduced.

The strength and hardness of aluminium alloys may be greatly improved by heat treatment, and to this they are usually subjected. They are heated to a temperature of about 500° C., and " quenched " in water, after which they are kept at room temperature for some days. By this means the mechanical strength of certain alloys may be improved to a point comparable with brass or iron.

The use of aluminium is not of course restricted to engineer-

[1] See also p. 78.

ing, its adoption both in alloy form and as pure aluminium is very wide. Pots, pans, cookers, wheels, pistons, aeroplanes all use it in one form or another. But perhaps the best monument to this metal and its place in our daily lives is the aluminium statue standing in Piccadilly Circus, Eros, the God of Love.

THE ELECTRICIAN'S METAL: COPPER AND ITS ALLOYS

AFTER iron and steel, copper is the most widely used metal in industry to-day. It has many applications in its pure state, and copper pipes and tubes are used to a considerable extent to convey steam and liquids. Its chief use is in the electrical industry, where its resistance to corrosion from the air, and high conductivity make it an admirable material for wires, electric cables, bus bars, armature windings, etc. A very large amount of copper, however, is used in the form of its two most common alloys, brass and bronze.

Brass is one of the most valuable of the alloys. It consists of the metals copper and zinc, the proportion of copper varying from about 55% to 99%. It bears somewhat the same relation to copper as steel does to iron, though for different reasons. It is harder than copper, takes a high polish, and does not change much on exposure to the air. Owing to its cost it is not suitable for heavy castings or construction work, and since it cannot be tempered like steel it is not adapted for cutting tools. But besides its wide use for domestic wares, it is used to manufacture many auxiliary items which are always found in engineering equipment. Its range of composition offers a material suitable for a wide variety of applications.

Bronze is an alloy whose chief constituents are copper and tin. Usually its properties are adjusted to suit requirements by the addition of a small amount of some other metal. Phosphor, manganese, aluminium and lead bronzes are among the strongest, and most expensive, alloys in use. They are harder and less " pliable " metals than brass and are suitable for a variety of uses where a strong, tough and non-corroding metal is needed. Ship propellers, springs, electrical parts, gear wheels and bearings are some of their principal applications.

CONNECTING THE MOVING PARTS: THE BEARING METALS

IN all machines, some of the moving parts must be attached to the framework or bed-plate, otherwise there would be no restraint on their movement whatever. At the same time they

must be free to move and fulfil their part in the operation of
the machine. A shaft must be held in place, though still free
to revolve. Consideration will show that, although a connecting-rod is joined to the crankshaft, here too, motion takes
place, and the connecting-rod may be imagined to be swinging
about the crank pin. In all such cases, " bearings " are necessary, which, while holding the part in position, leave it free
to move in its appointed manner.

In each case the rotating part is held in a close-fitting " hole "
of some special bearing metal. The motion need not be rotating,
however, it may be reciprocating, for instance the " cross
head," where the other end of the connecting rod joins the
piston rod. Here parallel plane surfaces must be provided
to guide the to and fro movement of the cross head. In all
these instances, metal is moving on metal. Shafts, crank pins,
etc., are usually steel for reasons of strength. The surfaces
on which they move must be made of special " bearing metal,"
so that they may move freely, with the minimum of wear and
power wasted in overcoming the friction between the two
surfaces.

Bearings may be made of several materials. Cast iron is
used for rough or extremely high temperature work, while
wood and even rubber are sometimes employed for special
purposes. The great majority of bearing surfaces, however,
consist of special bearing metal against which the particular
item of machinery moves. This special metal must be able to
carry the weight of the shaft or whatever it is supporting, and
stand up to steady or suddenly applied load without giving way
or cracking. It must have a low coefficient of friction and rate
of wear, but at the same time must wear more rapidly than
the shaft, since this is usually more costly to replace.

The most commonly used material is " white-metal," so
called from its extremely light-coloured appearance. Several
varieties are used, but they are essentially alloys of lead, tin,
antimony and copper. White metal bearings are used in all
classes of machinery, from 7 H.P. petrol engine bearings, to
100,000 H.P. turbine bearings. They are easily machined to
a true surface and accurately adjusted, while owing to their
slightly plastic nature, they will automatically mould themselves to the surface of the shaft.

The strength of white metal is not sufficient for the bearing
as a whole to be made of it however, and it is used in the
form of a lining supported by an outer shell of cast iron,

brass or bronze. The second metal provides the necessary strength to support the load, and the white metal lining makes an excellent bearing surface. One feature of these bearings is that should they get overheated owing to insufficient lubrication or overloading, the white metal will partially melt without damaging the shaft.

Under certain conditions, or where the service is severe comparatively soft linings such as white metal are not always suitable. In this case bronze bearings are usually fitted. When well fitted, these will run cooler and with less friction than any other bearings. They are strong, and so need not be used as the lining of a cast iron shell, and will stand up to severe loading. On the other hand these bearings wear most of all, and owing to their hard nature and lack of plasticity, they do so only at the expense of almost certain deterioration of shaft, leading to overheating.

PROTECTION WHICH LENGTHENS THE LIFE OF THE METALS

THE foregoing very brief resumé of the manufacture of iron and steel, special alloy steels and non-ferrous metals such as brass, bronze and aluminium alloys, may perhaps serve to convey some idea of the vast extent and importance of the science of " Metallurgy." Unfortunately, however, the engineer is not only concerned with the production of appropriate materials, he must also constantly endeavour to prevent their destruction.

Everyone is aware of the tendency of iron and steel to " rust," and it is a phenomenon which affects industry and the home alike. Perhaps the problem of the engineer differs only in degree from that of the man whose eternal quest is the razor blade which does not need drying after use. Certainly the problem on the larger scale is serious. In 1922 Sir Robert Hadfield estimated that the annual cost due to corrosion throughout the world was over £700,000,000.

Rust is the form in which iron and steel deteriorate when exposed to the atmosphere, but it is only one instance of the " corrosion " in general, to which most metals are subject. Many machine parts are not subjected to any great stresses, or to any abnormal atmosphere, but even in this case rust is objectionable and causes a very unsightly appearance. When, however, machinery of a vital nature is exposed to excessive heat or other severe conditions, the corrosion is very much more severe and becomes a serious matter. Various factory fumes, impurities in river water, sea water, moisture in turbine steam, gases at very high temperatures are only some of the factors which assist the process of corrosion. Modern use of higher and higher temperatures has made the matter even more pressing, and great developments in special steel to resist corrosion have been made.

The steps taken to prevent this insidious attack vary, depending on the nature of the metal, the part it has to play, and the corroding medium to which it is exposed. These factors range from a steel bridge exposed only to the wind and rain, to the metal parts of a furnace subjected to the gases and full temperature of a raging fire. The difference is chiefly one of degree, and it is equally important that the bridge should be protected from the corrosion, which would ultimately eat into the metal and render it no longer safe.

A NEW SURFACE TO COMBAT CORROSION

THE simplest protection against corrosion is to cover the metal with a coat of paint. This is done to all steel girders and similar parts for use in structural work, and in a host of miscellaneous cases where metal is exposed to no very severe conditions, and plays no very active part. The Forth Bridge is an excellent example of this, a gang of men being employed there permanently for this duty alone. It takes them three years to paint the entire bridge from end to end, and when they have finished they go back and start all over again.

The paint used must be of a special kind for this work. It must be fluid enough to ensure that the covering is of even thickness; it must dry rapidly and evenly, and must not harden on the surface and leave a soft layer underneath. The skin formed must be of such a nature that it can take other coats of paint without softening, and must also be hard enough to be washed clean by rainfall. Finally it must wear well and must entirely exclude air, moisture or gases from the metal—that is, prevent its corrosion.

The protective coating need not necessarily be of paint. Many metals are immune from corrosion in ordinary conditions, and the practice of covering iron and steel with a thin layer of some "non-rusting" metal is of very long standing. "Galvanised iron" roofs (with a zinc covering), chromium-plated car fittings, "electro-plated silver," are all well-known examples of this method ; while " tin-plate " (iron plate covered with tin) was being made in Bohemia as early as the sixteenth century, and to-day the production of plates for the manufacture of tin-plate is an important part of the steel industry. Articles " plated " in this way combine the virtues of cheapness, strength and freedom from rusting of the two components.

Several metals, including zinc, tin, cadmium, copper, nickel, chromium, lead, aluminium, gold and silver are used to form the protective covering, according to the nature of the metal and the work for which it is required. Various methods of application are also possible. The " base " metal may be dipped into a bath of the molten " protective " metal, a method which forms the basis of the production of " galvanised iron " and tin plate. " Electro-plating " is, of course, very widely used. In this method the article to be plated is immersed in a solution of a salt of the coating metal. Another piece of metal is also inserted, this and the article forming two " Electrodes," and the metallic solution the " electrolyte." On the application of an external electric supply to the electrodes, a current passes through the electrolyte, and a metallic covering is deposited on the article by electrolysis.

The thickness of the film depends on the length of time for which the current passes, and is therefore easily and accurately adjusted. Lastly, molten metal may be sprayed on to the article from an electric or gas-fired " pistol." The coating metal is fed into the pistol in the form of a wire, melted and sprayed on. This method has the advantage that it can be applied to finished constructions, irrespective of their size or shape.

STAINLESS STEEL : MOST MODERN FORM OF ALL

IN comparatively recent years, however, new discoveries have been made which have revolutionised the question of corrosion-prevention. In 1913 Brearley discovered that steel containing a high percentage of chromium possessed very high resistance to corrosion. This steel, when heated to a high temperature and quenched, hardened readily and led to the production of stainless steel cutlery during the war. This was its first and probably most famous application, but war conditions soon awakened engineers to the value of this new material, and its use increased very rapidly.

Owing to the fact that during its heat treatment this steel

becomes hard, it was not suitable for all purposes. It was later found, however, that a greater proportion of chromium and substantial addition of nickel produced a steel which became softened and not hardened by this treatment. To-day a whole range of stainless and rust-resisting steels can be obtained, suitable for almost any purpose.[1] Although the results of this addition of chromium and nickel were remarkable, the reason why they were so successful in resisting corrosion was not understood for some time. Further advances in the understanding of corrosion in general have made it reasonably certain that it is due to the formation of a passive oxygen-containing layer on the surface of the steel in contact with the air.

There is no need to call attention to the widespread application of stainless steels to-day. In every direction their use is being adopted. As knowledge and experience in their production increases, special steels are being produced to meet abnormal conditions, combining all the necessary mechanical qualities with this priceless boon of resistance to corrosion. So varied are the characteristics obtainable from rustless steels of one type or another, that to-day, trains, aeroplanes, and even battleships could be constructed of such material in their entirety. Moreover, the development of " alloyed " stainless steels, with the addition of small quantities of rarer metals for special purposes is probably as yet only in its infancy.

THE STEEL THAT CONTAINS NO IRON

PERHAPS before we leave the subject of preventing corrosion in iron and steel, mention may be made of one development which represents a great advance in the problem of steels for use at great heat. With the advent of ever-increasing temperatures and pressures in many branches of engineering, the difficulty of finding materials to stand up to these conditions becomes more and more pressing. The high temperatures common to-day in steam pipes, internal combustion engines, furnaces, boiler-tubes, etc., all demand the production of steels that will be as little affected as possible.

At these temperatures most metals have a tendency to oxidise, and as with ordinary " rusting," this is great in the case of iron and steel. Oxygen in the air combines with iron to form iron oxide or " scale." The scale formed drops off,

[1] See p. 70.

and the oxygen " eats " its way farther and farther into the metal. Where machine parts at this temperature have also to withstand great pressures, as is often the case, this continual oxidation may seriously weaken and endanger the machinery. In any case the depreciation and replacement costs will be very heavy, so that it must be avoided at all costs.

To meet this situation special " heat-resisting steels " have been developed, which actually may contain no iron at all. In these, the addition of nickel and chromium is carried to the limit, and the " steel " consists solely of these metals. These alloys are far more resistant to oxidation than any steel containing iron (the addition of 10% of iron to the alloy materially reducing its useful period of service at the highest temperatures). At the same time the strength and other mechanical qualities of the metal are quite adequate. An alloy of 80% nickel and 20% chromium will give excellent life and service, even when working at a temperature of 1,100° C. and higher.

Pipes for the hottest gases, furnace parts, internal combustion engine valves, electric heating elements in radiators and coolers, all these and many other components are nowadays made of these special nickel-chromium alloys.[1]

A TARNISH TO STOP TARNISHING

When aluminium or its alloys are stored in a comparatively dry place, the metal is not even tarnished, much less corroded, over long periods. Under other conditions, however, for instance when exposed to the action of sea water or sea air, it tends in time to become corroded, and its surface pitted. In the former case, contact with the air produces a surface skin of aluminium oxide or hydroxide. This film, unlike iron rust, adheres to the metal and though so thin as to be invisible, effectively prevents any further tarnish or corrosion. It has, however, its limitations. If frequently wetted and dried it is apt to crack and detach itself locally, while impurities or cracks in the metal are liable to cause defects in the film. When exposed to sea water or sea air corrosion begins at these weak points, is progressive and ultimately leads to pitting.

For these reasons special steps are generally necessary to prevent the corrosion of aluminium and its alloys on board ship, in seaplanes, etc. Various methods are available, including

[1] See p. 71.

painting, enamelling, varnishing, and of course electro-plating. By a simple but ingenious device, however, known as " anodic oxidation," the tendency of aluminium to oxidise is itself encouraged and utilised to prevent any further corrosion. This process is in a way similar to that of electro-plating, and the article to be " anodised " is made the anode in a bath of electrolyte. This is not a metallic solution, however, but is such that on the passage of a current a layer of aluminium oxide is formed on the metal, instead of a coating of some other metal as in electro-plating.

The " tarnish " thus produced electrically is much thicker and stronger than the natural film (it has been estimated to be 100 times the thickness of the natural film formed by exposure). Moreover, one of the most important features is that as the oxide is formed on prominent parts, the current continually seeks admittance through the unprotected aluminium, which offers less resistance to its passage than the oxide. In this way small holes, cavities and cracks which would not be completely covered by electro-plating are sought out and entirely coated by the artificially produced oxide.

The results of " anodising " aluminium in this way are remarkable. The film resists sea water corrosion to a considerable extent, even at the wind and water line it is quite strong, and the metal can be freely bent and handled without damaging it. It is not suitable for all alloys, but several give satisfactory resistance to corrosion after this treatment—and excellent results are obtainable with magnesium and of course pure aluminium.

A MACHINE TO MAKE MACHINES: THE LATHE

No less wonderful than the finished products of engineering are the means by which they are made. The machine-tool industry itself is a very important part of the general engineering activity. With ever-increasing competition, new methods of manufacture must be found for producing articles even more quickly and cheaply. Time taken in manufacturing must be reduced, and this has led to the development of the high-speed tool steels previously referred to. But as cutting-tools progress, so the machines in which they are used must be made faster, stronger and more efficient to utilise their advantages.

The number of machine tools used in the various sides of engineering is very large. It is therefore impossible to give more than a brief description of the operation of a few fundamental machines. The machine shop receives material in much the same way as the tailor receives his cloth, and out of this the finished parts must be produced according to the drawings, just as the tailor cuts his cloth to his measurements. Broadly speaking, therefore, " machining " is the process of removing metal from the rough material, until the required shape is obtained, accurate in dimensions and smoothly finished. This is usually done by means of a hard, sharp tool which gradually cuts away the superfluous metal, leaving a true " machined surface."

The majority of machines belong to this class. In others the process is different, no cutting tools in the strict sense of the word being used. The metal is as it were forced into shape by blows. These are known as Press Tools and are referred to later.

The most widely used and fundamental machine of the workshop is the lathe. It is used for all purposes and for all sizes of machine parts from the smallest to the largest. It cuts " surfaces of revolution," and its principle of operation is as follows: The part to be machined is held by some means, and rotates about a fixed axis. The tool moves either, (1) parallel to this axis, cutting a cylindrical surface, (2) perpendicular to the axis, as in cutting the end of a cylinder, (3) in any combination of these two directions, cutting any variety of " surfaces of revolution."

The cutting action is in a way similar to the peeling of an apple. The knife pursues a spiral course round the apple, and thus brings the skin off in one long piece, instead of removing one circle each time the apple is turned round. In the same way, if the tool of a lathe were brought up to the revolving work, and held still, it would cut one groove and no more. Instead it is given a slow movement in one of the directions as above. By this means after one revolution of the work, it has moved on a little, begins a new groove, and so on.

Fig. 75 shows diagrammatically the operation of a simple chuck lathe. A cylindrical bar (known as the " work ") is shown having its surface machined. It is held in the revolving " chuck," which is a disc in which the " jaws " move in radially and grip it. The other end may be steadied by the centre point D pressed against its end, and mounted in the movable tailstock which is clamped to the lathe " bed " or framework. The tool is clamped in the saddle which is mounted on the lathe bed and free to move in a direction either parallel to the axis of revolution, perpendicular to it, or a combination of both. The chuck is rotated by a belt and pulleys from a main rotating " countershaft " extending through the shop and driving many machines.

In the operation illustrated, the cylinder is having its side machined. It revolves at a fixed speed, and the tool is moved slowly but steadily to the left by a mechanism driven by the lathe itself, to ensure smooth and steady motion. Actually of course the tool describes a spiral round the surface

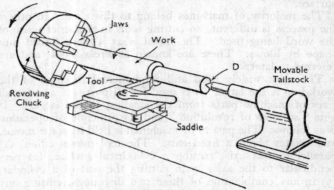

75. The operation of a simple chuck lathe

of the cylinder, but the turns of the spiral are so close as to give practically a smooth cylindrical surface. The " feed," or rate at which the tool moves sideways, depends on the speed of the " chuck." It can also be varied to give a slow or fast rate of feed, according to the size of the " work," the depth of " cut " and the smoothness of the finish required.

For machining the end of the cylinder, the saddle is clamped so that it cannot move sideways, but travels inwards perpendicular to the axis of rotation. A different shaped tool is used for this. If a tapered or cone surface is required, or the sharp edge of the cylinder is to be rounded off, the tool has a combination of both movements so arranged as to produce whatever effect is called for in the drawing of the finished part.

Another operation frequently required from the lathe is

the drilling and boring of holes in the work. If an accurate hole is required through the cylinder, it is first drilled roughly by a drill mounted in the tailstock. It is then made into a smooth hole of accurate dimensions by a long " boring tool " held in the saddle and fed through, machining the inside of the hole in the same way as the outside of the cylinder.

THE PARTS WHICH MAKE UP THE SIMPLE "CHUCK" LATHE

FIG. 76 shows the arrangement of a lathe such as that referred to. The strong cast-iron bed, mounted on four sturdy legs, carries in bearings A and B at its left-hand side a series of pulleys driven by a belt from the main counter-

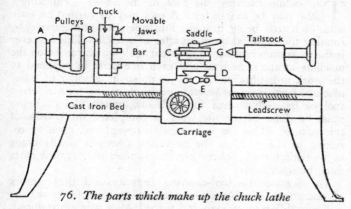

76. The parts which make up the chuck lathe

shaft running through the shop. By altering the pulley on which the belt runs, different speeds of rotation are obtained. To these pulleys is attached the chuck, holding the cylindrical bar to be machined, by means of the movable jaws. The tool C is clamped in the " saddle," which is free to move across the lathe (perpendicular to the axis of rotation) on the " cross slide " D. This itself is fixed to the " carriage," which slides to left or right along the lathe (parallel to the axis of rotation). The saddle and tool are moved in either direction across or along the lathe bed by means of an auxiliary rotating shaft or leadscrew driven by gears (not shown) from the main pulleys. On the carriage are mounted the various controls E, F, etc., for regulating the movements and feed of the saddle. The tailstock, containing the centre point G is shown at the right-hand side separated from the "work."

To take a "cut" along the side of the cylindrical bar, the tool is brought near and adjusted so that it will take off the required thickness. The chuck is set in motion, and the leadscrew engaged with driving gears in the carriage. This slowly moves along to the left, carrying the tool, which steadily cuts its way down the surface of the cylinder. These machines are capable of producing very accurate and highly finished work.

INGENIOUS IMPROVEMENTS IN THE MODERN LATHE

THE saddle carrying the tool in the above "chucking" lathe may be four-sided. A tool may be carried on each side, each tool being brought into operation successively by rotating the saddle through quarter of a circle. This however is the maximum number of different tools which can be on the machine at the same time and each one must be adjusted to the work individually. As the complete machining of many machine parts involves several operations calling for a different tool or tool adjustment for each one, much tool changing must be done before the work is completed on a lathe of this nature. This frequent tool changing, and possibly re-setting of the work in the chuck, is a serious disadvantage in repetition work, where a great number of identical parts must be machined.

To increase the tool-carrying capacity and the number of operations possible without removing tools or work, the radically different capstan and turret lathes were introduced. In these lathes the tailstock is replaced by a revolving hexagonal turret as shown diagrammatically in Fig. 77. Each face of this turret is accurately machined and bored to take a tool attachment, a suitable tool being fitted for each operation required by the work.

The turret itself is mounted on a slide and is moved by a hand wheel along the bed of the machine as the tool is fed to the work. It will be noted that in these machines the tools carried by the turret are fed from the end, and not the side of the work. At the same time one or two cross travelling saddles may be fitted as in the chuck lathe, and these also may carry tools for further operations.

Suppose a part requires five machining operations. The work is held in the chuck, and three tools are attached to the turret, the other two being carried by the saddles at the sides. The first tool performs its work, the turret is revolved, the next tool brought into line, and so on, each tool remaining in adjustment ready to perform the same operation on the next part. By this means, once the tools are " set-up," no further adjustment to them is necessary while that particular part is being machined.

These lathes are particularly adapted for machining parts of mass-produced articles, owing to the enormous saving in time required for setting and adjusting the machine. This is especially the case for parts to be machined and cut off from a long steel bar. The bar is fed through the hollow

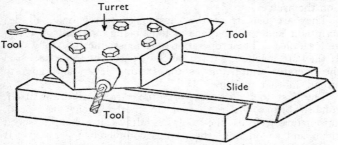

77. *The " turret," designed to prevent frequent tool changing*

centre of the pulleys, the length projecting from the chuck being fixed by a stop mounted on one face of the turret. The part is machined all over by the various tools, cut off by another tool, another length of bar fed in, and so on.

Both chuck and turret lathes are extensively used—the former more for individual or complicated parts, the latter for repetition work, where many identical parts are to be made. Lathes are made in all sizes for all classes of work from machining a ship's propeller shaft to the production of thousands of small bolts from plain steel bars. They may be belt-driven from a countershaft, or may have their own electric driving motors built integrally with the machine.

Since different operations, sizes of work and types of tool all require different cutting speeds, the simple system of pulleys for changing speed is usually replaced to-day with a gear-box as in a motor car. A lever changes the gears when required, and as many as 30 different speeds of rotation may be obtained on one machine.

A MECHANICAL CRAFTSMAN :
THE WONDERFUL AUTOMATIC LATHE

THE time spent in the operation of machining and the wages of the operator, are a very expensive item in the total cost of the product. It is in the endeavour to reduce this machining time to a minimum, that higher-speed cutting tools, and more highly developed machine tools are constantly being introduced. One of the most wonderful achievements in engineering is the automatic lathe—the machine which works itself. These lathes are used for mass-production work and are entirely self-sufficient, carrying out every operation themselves.

They are usually of the capstan or turret type, all descriptions and combinations of tools being mounted on turret and saddles. Their operation is almost uncanny to watch. If they are machining " bar stock " (parts cut from steel bar) the operator simply moves the starting lever, and goes to attend another machine.

The first tool does its work, the turret withdraws itself, rotates, brings the next tool up, perhaps changes speed, automatically feeds the tool, withdraws it, changes speed again and so on until the part is completely machined. It is then cut off, the necessary length of bar is automatically fed through the chuck again up against a stop, the chuck tightened, and again the first tool comes up, and the whole performance is repeated. Several tools may be performing different operations at the same time—the machine sees to all that itself. The secret of the operation of these machines is a " control drum " slowly rotating with the lathe. Adjustable stops are attached to this drum and at each revolution these actuate levers mounted in the turret carriage and lathe bed which start each operation, change speed, etc., at the correct moment.

Each part, of which a large quantity is to be made, has the whole sequence of machining operations previously planned out. The automatic lathe is then very carefully adjusted by the " machine setter " so that it will perform each operation in the correct manner and sequence.

Once the machine is set up for a particular piece of work, all the operator need do is to start the machine. If each part is a separate casting he must remove the finished product each time and fix another casting in the chuck though some-

times this also is done automatically. If from bar stock, all
he need do is to feed another length of bar to the machine
when one has been used up.

These machines are indeed marvels of human ingenuity.
All descriptions of parts can be machined on them, each
part requiring many operations with different tools, different
speeds, different rates of feed for each one. And in this
not only the turret, but the cross slides also must be operated
automatically. It will be understood therefore that the
process of setting-up an automatic machine for a particular
duty is a considerable task, and calls for highly skilled labour.
Nevertheless, this is more than counter-balanced by the
great saving in time and money. One unskilled operator
may be put in charge of several machines at once, the only
skill required being on the part of the machine setter.

For the production of nuts, bolts, motor car parts, and
all such mass-produced items, these machines are almost
literally " worth their weight in gold."

DRILLING, PLANING AND MILLING IN METAL

NEXT to the lathe, the drilling machine is probably the
most universally used machine tool. Everyone at some
time or other has experienced the discomfort of the dentist's
drill, and the workshop drilling machine is of course identical
in principle though perhaps not quite so flexible or adept at
finding its way into the most sensitive corners.

Holes must be drilled in countless places for the bolts,
shafts and other items involved in an assembled machine.
Fig. 78 shows the type of drill used, and a simple type of
vertical drilling machine. The belt drive is taken by the
variable speed pulleys, transmitted through gears to the
vertical sliding shaft or " spindle " at the end of which is
mounted the drill.

The work is clamped to a table attached to the main support of the machine. The hand wheel shown moves this
shaft and drill up and down, by which means the drill is
fed into the work, and withdrawn when the hole has been
drilled through.

Drilling machines are of three types, Vertical, Radial and
Multi-Spindle. Vertical drills, like the simple form described
above, can only drill holes vertically, though the drill can be

moved up and down, and the table adjusted vertically, this is the only freedom permitted, and its use is to a certain extent restricted.

Radial drills have a greater degree of freedom. Many large castings have holes to be drilled at all angles and positions, and moving the casting in order to bring each hole in alignment for the vertical drill would be far too lengthy a business.

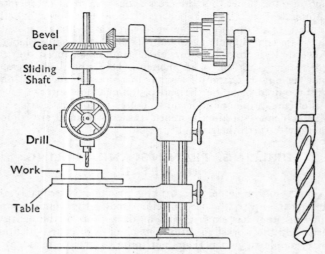

Bevel Gear

Sliding Shaft

Drill

Work

Table

78. One of the most useful machine tools—a simple vertical drilling machine, showing (right) the twist drill on a larger scale.

Radial drills consist of a massive vertical supporting shaft, to which is attached a movable arm. The drill mechanism is mounted on this arm, and can be adjusted to take up the position required for each particular hole. Different degrees of freedom are allowed, according to the type of drilling machine and work to be done.

" Multi-spindle " drills are as their name implies, machines which are each equipped with many spindles and drills. The positions of these are adjustable and by this means many holes can be drilled at once. Like the turret lathe, the multi-spindle drill is particularly adapted for mass production work. The drills can be set for drilling all the holes in a particular casting at once, and then any number of these castings can be drilled without readjustment.

Again, like the lathe, the modern drilling machine has advanced considerably from the simple type illustrated. The variable speed pulleys have given way to an integral electric motor driving through a gear box. Multi-spindle machines are often equipped with a separate motor for each spindle. Automatic feeds are almost universally employed, and the power of the drive is utilised for raising or lowering the table, and moving the heavy radial arms and drilling mechanism about, in order to bring the drill over the hole.

MACHINE TOOLS FOR MAKING PLANE SURFACES

IN many cases a true flat surface is required, for instance where the bed-plate of an engine is to be bolted on to the foundations. For this and other requirements of this nature a " planer " is used.

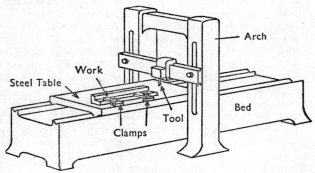

79. *The " planer," for cutting a true flat surface*

One of these is shown in Fig. 79. The work is clamped down on a steel " table " which moves to and fro in the grooves of a solid " bed." As the table moves under the " arch," the work is brought up to a tool which cuts a long strip of metal from its surface. This tool is clamped to a horizontal support which can be moved up and down the two vertical supports as required, and the tool saddle itself can also be moved horizontally on its support. By this means any position can be reached. At each stroke of the table, the tool is automatically fed a little to the right or left, along the horizontal support, ready for the next "cut." By this means, the whole surface is slowly machined to an absolutely flat and accurate plane.

These machines run to very large sizes, as the largest castings usually require their use in some part or other. The largest planers would be quite capable of taking a motor coach on their table, and taking a "cut" off the roof.

At the other end of the scale, many small parts require machining in a similar manner. These are done on a "shaper," in which the tool moves to and fro while the work is clamped to a stationary table. For small work this is a more flexible and convenient arrangement. The machine itself is only light, and small parts can be more rapidly and easily machined in this way than on a heavier and rather more cumbersome planer.

SPECIALIST IN SMALL PARTS : THE MILLING MACHINE

OF equal importance in a machine shop with the lathe, drilling machine and planer is the milling machine. This is extremely adaptable and is a great boon to the manufacturer. In the simple form it consists of a revolving "cutter," with very sharp "teeth." The work is clamped to a table and each tooth of the cutter, as it revolves, takes off a thin cut. Slowly the table carries the work along and the cutter gradually machines the whole of the top surface off.

It may be thought that in this case the operation might have been more simply and easily done on a planer or shaper, but the secret of the milling machine's utility lies in its great adaptability, its aptitude for mass production and its " handiness " and accuracy. The teeth of the cutter may be straight or of any shape to give the required surface.

Several variations of the milling machine itself are possible. The table may be horizontal, with a horizontal reciprocating motion ; it may, however, be vertical or horizontal, moving with rotating or straight line motion in a horizontal or vertical plane. Its movement of course is a slow " feed " motion like that of the tool saddle in a lathe or planer.

Automatic milling machines are much used. Many similar parts are mounted on the same table, and in turn automatically brought under the cutter and machined. All the operator must do is to replace the finished parts by fresh " blanks " as each one comes from the cutter. By this means, setting-up time is dispensed with to a very great extent, as once the machine has been adjusted, nothing further need be done but feed it with raw material.

The milling machine is vastly more suitable for mass production of small parts than the planer, even in those cases when the latter could also perform the operation required. It is quicker, more accurate and flexible, and is very widely used for machining a great number of parts such as are used in a car. In its automatic form it corresponds to the automatic lathe, and brings the same saving in time and labour. Owing to the nature of its operation, however, and the cost of " cutters," it is limited in the size of work with which it can deal.

" JIGS AND FIXTURES " WHICH SAVE THE ENGINEER'S TIME

THE time required to insert a piece of work in a machine, fix it in the correct position, fit the necessary tool, adjust it to take off the right quantity of material is very considerable. This " setting-up " time, as it is called, must be reduced as much as possible. Mention has already been made of the use of high speed tools and the various modifications to the machines themselves, automatic working, etc., which have been introduced. The time required is still further reduced by the use of " jigs and fixtures." These are mechanical arrangements for setting up tools or work.

If holes are to be drilled, a " drilling jig " is clamped to the work. This is a plate in which the holes are already drilled in the correct position. All that has to be done is to bring the drill up to these holes in turn and they " guide " it on to the correct point in the work underneath. Once the jig has been accurately drilled with the " master-holes " as it were, no more marking off on each part is necessary. This is particularly useful with multi-spindle drills. All the drills are set approximately above the holes in the drilling jig, and through these they are accurately guided into place. Jigs obviate the necessity for accurately adjusting the tool each time.

In order to do the same with the work itself, " fixtures " are employed. These are bolted in the correct position on to the machine table and remain there all the time. Each piece of work is placed in the fixture and exactly located in position by stops. No time is therefore necessary to adjust each part in alignment with the tool. By the use of fixtures to locate the work, and jigs to locate the position of the tool on the work, the setting-up time is reduced to an absolute minimum.

MAKERS OF MANY SHAPES : THE PRESS TOOLS

THE machine tools described so far have all been of one class, that in which superfluous metal is, as it were, " carved off " by mechanically driven " sculpturing chisels." The machined surfaces thus obtained are limited to the comparatively few regular shapes obtained by turning in a lathe, drilling, milling and planing. Important and actively employed parts of machines must be made by these methods, in order to provide the necessary strength and thickness of material, accurate dimensions and correct fitting with other parts.

For very many miscellaneous secondary items these methods are unsuitable. To take only two simple analogies from everyday life, it would be far too expensive both in time and material to machine either a tin mug or motor-car mudguard out of the solid, or to cast them in a foundry. Great numbers of unimportant parts which need to be no stronger than these, but must be made cheaply in great numbers, are used in engineering. For this purpose " press tools " are employed, and their applications are rapidly increasing in number.

Tools of this class are employed for the repetition production of large quantities of miscellaneous minor items, chiefly from thin sheets of metal. But first a few words on the nature of the presses used for this work. The simplest form of hand-operated press consists of a heavy framework carrying a strong cylindrical ram which slides up and down in a vertical direction, driven by a screw to which is attached an arm with heavy weights. The piece of metal to be worked is placed between two " dies," and the operation is performed by dealing it a sharp blow with the top die mounted on the end of the ram. The method of working is exemplified in the manner in which addresses are embossed on note-paper. This is done in nothing other than a small hand-operated " press tool." The note-paper is placed between two dies, and pressure on the handle forces these together, the paper thus receiving the impression of the dies, and showing the address in raised letters. The paper-punch for punching holes in the margin of a sheet of paper is an even simpler example of the press tool.

Hand-operated tools are only used for the smallest work. Usually the ram is given its reciprocating movement through a crank and connecting rod from a revolving pulley. Heavy fly-wheels are provided to give the necessary force of blow. The driving wheel revolves all the time and is connected to the crank, connecting rod and ram through a clutch which is engaged, when the blow is required, by pressing a pedal. Hydraulically-operated presses are also used.

JOBS THE PRESS TOOLS CAN DO

THE work performed by press tools on sheet metal is very varied. The principal operations will be briefly described in turn.

CUTTING OR PUNCHING.—This is simply the process carried out by the paper-punch referred to previously. Instead of a plain hole, an infinite number of more or less complicated

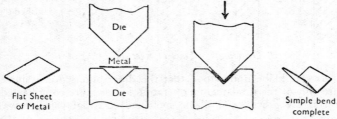

80. *A simple bend formed at one blow*

shapes are obtainable by using different dies, or by operating with two or more dies in turn upon the same piece of work.

BENDING AND FORMING.—In Fig. 80 the simple operation of bending a piece of metal with a pair of dies, at one blow, is illustrated. Very much more complicated bending and forming than this is possible.

DRAWING.—So far the metal has only been punched and bent, operations which could both be performed on paper. If an attempt were made to form from paper a bowl such as shown in Fig. 81, the paper would crinkle and tear. Steel, however, " flows " and stretches from one part to another, and so it can be " drawn " in this manner.

" COINING."—This operation is so called because coins are made in this way. Actually " coining " or " stamping " in this manner is analogous to drop-forging. The " flow " of metal is illustrated in this even more than in " drawing."

Fig. 82 shows dies used for stamping a simple hand-wheel from a blank. The blanks are probably punched out of a sheet, and then heated almost to white heat and stamped into the form shown in one blow. This process may be done cold where copper, lead and other soft metals are employed.

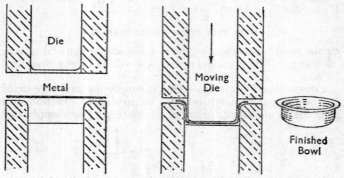

81. " Drawing " a bowl of steel with shaped dies

It should be understood that the descriptions given above are only of the fundamental operations. Far more complicated forms are possible. Pulleys, shell and cartridge cases, trays,

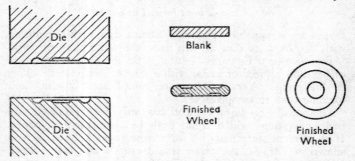

82. Stamping a simple hand-wheel—a process in which the metal must be soft enough (or be heated sufficiently) to " flow."

handles, spoons and forks, fans, wheel hubs, bowls for electric washing machines, motor-car bodies and a host of the miscellaneous irregular and complicated shapes required in engineering are produced in this manner.

Sheet steel is comparatively cheap, and the few operations

necessary to form it into the correct shape in presses take very little time. This is further reduced by automatic feeding of blanks to the dies, and the use of presses with several pairs of dies. Sheet metal is fed in strips into one end of the machine, and from the other the finished products emerge in a totally different form, after having been through several operations. The saving in time and cost of material obtained in this way enables such articles to be produced for a fraction of the cost and time required for machining or casting.

PRESSES FOR PLASTIC MOULDING

GREAT advance has been made in the production of small articles from " synthetic resins." Ash trays, bowls, electric light switches and fittings and many other items of this nature are made of this material. In industry its application is found in small gear wheels, electrical insulating materials, screws and many other articles. Many motor-car manufacturers employ gear wheels made of this material. It is very light, hard wearing and quite strong, and large numbers of a particular part can be produced quickly and cheaply from it. Intricate solid shapes can be produced in a few minutes which otherwise could be obtained only by extensive machining.

The raw material is usually supplied in the form of a " moulding powder." Under the action of heat and pressure this first becomes plastic and then hard, and afterwards cannot be softened by further heat, as a chemical change takes place. Special moulding presses are employed to convert the powder into the smooth, hard finished product. These involve the use of " moulds " or " dies " just like press tools for metal working. " Plasting moulding " is analogous to a casting process in which the bottom half of the mould is filled with material and the upper half subsequently pressed down on top, instead of molten metal being poured into an assembled mould.

A measured quantity of powder is placed in the mould, heated to a temperature of about 350° F., and compressed to a pressure rising from 500 to 2,000 lbs. between the two halves of the mould. Hydraulic presses are chiefly used, in which high pressure water forces down the ram carrying the upper mould. The two halves of the mould are attached to steel plates on the ram and bed respectively, in which provisions are made for the necessary heating, whether steam, electrical or (in a few cases) gas. After being subjected to this compression for a few minutes, the press is lifted, and the completed article is ejected, an exact replica of the shape of the moulds. In mass production, semi-automatic arrangements are made for feeding the raw material and ejecting the finished moulding. Fig. 83 shows the different parts of the moulds for forming the bowl illustrated.

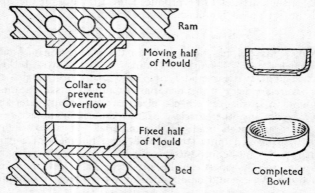

83. Moulds for making a bowl from plastic material

£500 TO MAKE AN ASH TRAY

THE dies necessary for press tools must reach a very high standard. Where thousands of pressings are produced, a minute error in the construction of the die will render the whole production useless. Very fine workmanship is necessary to form the steel dies into the complicated shapes required. Often they cannot be made on machines, but must be laboriously shaped by hand. Extreme accuracy is necessary, and careful heat treatment of the finished die to ensure thorough and uniform hardening of the steel.

Die-making therefore is a lengthy business, calling for highly skilled labour, and is a very expensive item. Large sums must be spent before a single article can be produced, and this first cost must be divided up and added to the price of the final product. Thus if only one ash tray were produced in this way (either from metal or in the plastic moulding press) it might cost as much as £500, less than a penny being the actual cost of the ash tray itself, the rest being necessary to pay for the dies.

If a large number of ash trays is produced, the £500 can be divided up, and is represented by only a fraction of a penny on the price of each one. The economical use of press tools depends to a large extent on a sufficient quantity of the article being required to warrant the expenditure on dies, which may run into many hundreds of pounds.

PUTTING THE MACHINE ON PAPER : DESIGN

ENGINEERING is essentially a practical science which deals with actual forces, real materials and the conditions of everyday use. The magnitude of these forces, the strength of these materials, and the nature of these conditions can never be exactly calculated or foreseen. Moreover, should a machine be designed and built for a certain definite duty, there are few cases in which at some time or other it is not overloaded or used in a manner quite different from that for which it was intended. As a result, the engineer must to some extent rely on certain general rules, and on the invaluable experience which has been steadily amassed since the very dawn of engineering.

Nevertheless, nothing would be further from the truth than to say that engineering is a rule-of-thumb profession. The solution of each new problem that arises, the construction of each new mechanical marvel is made possible only by the use of the keenest brains, the most suitable materials, and a very high standard of skill and manufacturing equipment in the workshop. It may be said that the inventive power of the engineer, the knowledge of the metallurgist, physicist and mathematician, the skill of the workman, the experience of past generations, and (if, as is often the case, a new field is being entered) a little " intelligent guessing," are in engineering all combined and applied to the practical solution of life's problems.

Each machine that is constructed is the answer to some definite demand for a particular type of service. The designer is presented with particulars of the work to be done and the conditions of operation, and is told to design a suitable machine. His designs are useless, however, without suitable materials with which his ideas may be fulfilled, and which will stand up to the strain. The right materials having been obtained, the various parts must be constructed and assembled in the factory until the finished machine is produced ready for use.

Every machine must be completely planned down to the last detail before any production can begin. The factory only deals with the finished plan. It plays no part in the conception of an article; it only follows instructions and converts the designs and drawings of the engineer into the actual machine. Thus, for instance, a new type of motor-car originates solely in the mind of the engineer. He works out and completes every detail of the new car in his mind, and transfers these particulars to drawings on which everything is accurately shown. The workshop receives these drawings, and with the materials provided by the stores, must put them into concrete shape.

Drawings are the language of the factory. They are the " words " by which the designer conveys the ideas of his mind to those in the factory and machine shop. Everything must be put down on paper complete in every detail, in such a way that the workman has there all instructions necessary. It is not for him to play any part in the form of the machine —he merely does what he is told to do by the engineer, through the medium of the drawing. Hundreds of drawings must be made before such a thing as a motor-car can be produced. Many copies of each must be made, and distributed to all who have any hand in the production of that particular part. Not only the workmen in the factory receive them, but if any components are bought from other firms, drawings of these parts must also be sent to them. They are the only language by which particulars and requirements can be stated.

PLANNING THE PROCEDURE : A DRAWING FOR EVERY PART

NOT a single dimension of the finished article can be left undefined. The hundreds of different parts of a car are each of course made separately in the first place. The workman is given his raw material, and a drawing on which are complete details of the part to be made from it. He shapes and machines the parts in accordance with the dimensions and instructions given on the drawing, until he has produced an exact replica.

Machine-shop drawings for the production of each part in this way are known as " piece-part " or " detail " drawings. In the manufacture of a motor-car, the engine, back axle, chassis, etc., are each assembled separately. These " sub-assemblies " as they are called (the complete engine, back axle and other components) are then put together in the final assembly of the finished car. After the various fundamental parts have been machined in the machine shops, they are conveyed to the " fitters," who put them together and make up the sub-assemblies. These men must also be provided with " assembly drawings," showing the position of each item in the finished back axle or other main component.

Many special tools and appliances may be required. Detailed " tool-drawings " are provided for each of these, giving dimensions, material and instructions. As already mentioned, many machine-tools are equipped to perform a sequence of machining operations on one part. Very often it is necessary for the whole procedure to be carefully planned out beforehand —and here again instructions are conveyed to the " machine-setter " by means of drawings. Very careful drawings must also be made of the various dies used in press tools. The drawing office is one of the key departments of an engineering firm, and on its " words " depend all the activities of the workshop.

THE MEN WITH THE PENCIL: CRAFTSMEN OF THE NEW AGE

MASS production and scientifically planned manufacture have almost abolished the old skilled craftsman, with his strong individuality and intense pride in his own skill. The simple article, which he himself fashioned with his own hands from the very beginning, has been replaced by a far more complicated one which has been split up into hundreds of different parts all made on different machines by different operators. In the mass production of to-day each workman has only one function. He makes the same part, hour after hour, day after day. Skill has become intensely specialised for this one class of duty, and at the same time is being more and more replaced by the soulless ingenuity of the machine. The modern workman bears all too little resemblance to the traditional craftsman of the past.

The craftsman's place, however, has not vanished—it has gone to a new class of men. Skill has become of the brain, and far less of the hands. To-day it is the designer and draughts-man who have taken his place. They are the men who devise new methods, develop new ideas, invent new machines. It is in their minds and on their drawing boards that the finished product is visualised, planned, machined, and fitted together. Only after the whole process has been completely thought out by them does the workman begin the actual production. Theirs is the responsibility or credit for the failure or success of the finished machine.

The designer must produce a machine most suited for its particular purpose. He must make allowance for all contingencies, foresee all obstacles. Each part must be correctly designed for its purpose, made of the right material and of adequate proportions to stand up to its duty. All the various forces involved must be calculated, and the maximum stresses to which the part will be subjected must be allowed for. If it is an engine of some description that is being produced, it must be theoretically designed to extract the maximum of work from the energy supplied. It must work efficiently and any possible drawback or irregularities of operation foreseen and avoided.

In charge of the whole department is the chief engineer. He decides the structure of the future product, and superintends the whole design. The details are carried out by his subordinates. Finally, in the drawing office the complete design materialises, and is transferred to the drawing board for actual use. In one connection is this modern parallel of the craftsman particularly evident—in the manufacture of the machine-tools of to-day. They are the nearest approach to the " mechanical man " yet achieved, and in the production of these, the designer may indeed be regarded as the " craftsman of a new age."

This is not to discount the part played by the workman in engineering to-day. True, in the mass-production of huge quantities of identical articles, his skill has largely been both " decentralised " and replaced by the machine. But there must always be good and bad workmen, and other things being equal an article of " good workmanship " will always outdo an inferior one. The designer may detail everything, but in the way in which his instructions are carried out by the workman, small imperfections may make a vast difference to the performance and life of the finished machine. Traditional skill is still significant—and Scotsmen still show a peculiar aptitude for engineering! In other directions the factory may be nothing like so specialised in its functions. Here the workman is far less restricted in his activities, his skill not yet replaced by the machine.

Nevertheless, whereas in the past it was he who had to overcome the difficulties of manufacture, to-day his experience has been transferred to textbooks and added to the training of the engineer. Aided by this accumulated knowledge of the past, the designer is able to overcome these difficulties beforehand, or produce machines which are easily capable of doing what is required.

THE FIRST STEP : WRITING THE MACHINE IN FIGURES

THE design of a machine is rather different from the design of a wallpaper or a new dress—it is not merely a matter of sitting at a drawing board, and by trial and error finally producing a drawing of a machine that looks as though it would do. The machine must first be theoretically designed —the idea must take a definite form. In the case of power-utilising machines, this means a consideration of the work to be done, the force required, the nature of its motion, possible variations, the nature of the power supply, means of converting it and so on. These problems must be theoretically solved, before detailed plans for the actual machine are begun.

If, say, a steam power plant is to be designed, the question is rather more complex. In this case it is not only metal parts which transfer energy and guide it to its uses, but coal, gases and steam all play their part. The engineer must, as it were, " design " the performance of everything which lies in the path of energy from coal to electricity. The process of combustion, heat transference in the boilers, behaviour of the steam in the turbine, none of these are haphazard or left to chance, all must be regulated and controlled. Wide knowledge of the behaviour of steam and the nature of its expansion, the process of combustion, etc., is necessary, as only by means of this can the engineer foretell how much steam or coal will be required to do the work.

By calculations (and helped by experience) he must estimate the various losses of energy which he knows will take place throughout the process. The efficiency of the plant, and the amount of steam, coal, heating surface in the boiler, etc., must all be calculated, as most likely he must meet a guarantee of fuel or steam consumption per unit of power produced. The amount of air required in the furnace for complete combustion must be estimated, and fans designed capable of producing this.

The performance of gases and steam, their expansion and

other behaviour, is a complete study in itself. The engineer, however, must be familiar with all "gas-laws" and properties of heat. From this he is able to find the necessary quantities of steam, size of cylinders, length of turbine blades and other necessary information. And in just the same way in other machinery, internal-combusion engines, water turbines, etc., all items of this sort must first be reduced to actual figures before the machine itself is begun.

DESIGNING THE PARTS TO TAKE THE STRESS: "UNBALANCE"

HAVING "theoretically" designed the machine in this manner, plans and drawings for each of its component parts must then be prepared, so that a machine may be built to give the calculated performance. In the construction of each part several factors enter, but the principal consideration of course is adequate strength for its particular duty. It is useless to prepare designs for an engine using steam at 400 lbs. per sq. inch if the cylinder bursts when steam at this pressure is admitted. At the same time excessive thickness of material must be avoided, as this means increased weight and cost.

Firstly full particulars of the material in use and its strength must be known, and secondly the stress to which it is to be subjected must be calculated as nearly as possible, so that the necessary amount of material may be allowed. Usually the exact calculation of these stresses is impossible, owing to irregularity of shape and distribution of force. Here experience helps to decide the dimensions necessary to allow for all possible contingencies.

In many machines, particularly those operating at high speeds, a considerable amount of stress is produced by the weight of the moving parts themselves, different kinds of movement producing different kinds of stress. A great deal of trouble is caused by "out-of-balance" forces. If a wheel is out of balance, and rotates at a high speed, the centrifugal force of its "unbalance" is the same as that of the weight whirled round on the end of a string.

This is notably the case in the driving wheels of a locomotive, when the various cranks, coupling rods, etc., constitute large out-of-balance masses. If steps were not taken to balance these, their effect might become so pronounced at high speeds as to lift those wheels off the rails at each revolution. In any case very great strain would be put on the axles, bearings and rails due to this " hammer-blow " as it is called. Moreover, the adhesion between the driving wheels and the rails would be seriously reduced during a part of each revolution, and slipping might occur.

" Balancing " is achieved by adding weights of such magnitude and position as to counteract the effect of the out-of-balance masses. Again, the reciprocating motion of pistons and piston rods on each side of the engine tends to cause the locomotive to " nose " from side to side as it travels along. (The connecting rods of course have both reciprocating and rotational motion, and must be balanced as nearly as possible in both ways.) The unsteady and unsafe movement due to these forces is serious in a locomotive, but is also of importance in stationary engines. Foundations, engine frames, and the moving parts themselves may be subjected to severe stresses through improper balancing. This applies to all moving machinery, and the problem becomes more important as the speed and weights increase.

SOME PROBLEMS WHICH FACE THE DESIGNER

ROTATING shafts are subject to a phenomenon of their own. No shaft can ever be exactly balanced and, under the actions of its own weight and external forces, is always bent very slightly, with the result that its centre of gravity is out of line to a slight extent. Owing to rotation and this lack of straightness of the shaft, centrifugal forces are set up. These may increase the deflection of the shaft still further. At certain speeds this increasing deflection becomes dangerous, and if the shaft is run at this speed for long, it will bend further and further and finally break. This is known as the " whirling of shafts," and all shafts have " critical speeds " at which this occurs. In the design of turbines and similar machinery, particular care must be taken to ensure that this critical speed is nowhere near the normal speed of operation.

Another problem occurs in turbines where the blades are fixed on wheels mounted on the turbine shaft. These wheels are in the nature of rotating discs. Every particle of metal in a rotating disc is subject to centrifugal force, and the result is that, while rotating, there is a tendency for the wheel to burst and fly in all directions. At the high speeds at which turbines operate, great care is necessary in the design of these wheels, the problem being aggravated by the fact that merely increasing their thickness only increases the bursting tendency to a like extent. It may be of interest to note here that, if a disc has a hole in its centre, however infinitesimally small the hole be in diameter, the internal stress produced by rotation is exactly twice that in a solid disc with no central hole.

These are a few typical instances of difficulties occurring in the design of moving machinery. Everywhere problems of this and other descriptions arise, and in each case careful design is necessary to eliminate their effects. Even stationary parts are by no means so simple as they may seem and allowance must be made for the expansion and contraction of cylinders, frames, etc., due to heat (a steam turbine may increase $\frac{1}{2}$ inch in length when running, and contract again when cooling after being shut down).

From all this it will be realised that the various machines whose action has been described in previous sections are in reality highly complex creations, and something of the designer's task may be appreciated. Each part which is subjected to any force must be carefully determined, and the effect of all possible influences foreseen.

Finally everything must be designed in such a way that its manufacture prevents as little difficulty as possible. Here the necessity arises for all engineers to have had practical workshop experience, to enable them to know what is practicable and what is not in the actual manufacture. Otherwise drawings might show holes, nuts and bolts, machined surfaces, etc., in quite impossible places where no tool could reach. If one were to believe the workmen in the factory, few engineers are sufficiently intelligent in this way—but then no workman has ever had much faith in any engineer!

THE TASK FULFILLED : BUILDING THE FINISHED MACHINE

AFTER the designer and draughtsman have put their ideas on paper, and drawings and full particulars of an engine or machine are available, the next step is to secure the raw materials. Castings or forgings are made, steel ordered up, and all the various items obtained. It is for the machine shop to finish these roughly shaped parts, and send them out accurately and completely machined, ready for the final assembly and testing of the engine as a whole. Needless to say this part of the factory is very important, as on the accuracy of its work depend the proper fitting together and correct functioning of all the various parts when assembled together.

In its turn, accuracy of machining is impossible without an adequate supply of exact measuring instruments, tools, etc. The tool stores contain any special tools which may be required. Gauges for measuring the diameter of shafts and bearings, distances between machined surfaces, all those instruments necessary to make the finished part an exact reproduction of the drawing must be available. Ordinary " foot-rules " are not sufficient ; these gauges must be capable of measuring clearly the thousandth part of an inch. In their turn these workshops measuring gauges must be kept accurate, and periodically checked. For this purpose optical instruments are used, measuring distances by the reflection of a ray of light, and capable of detecting a difference of one millionth of an inch between the workshop gauge and a standard gauge with which it is compared.

The factory itself must be " designed," just as each of its products. It must be conceived and laid out as a whole, the relation of the departments to each other being considered and allowed for, and the most efficient arrangement of the different plants arranged. In other words, the factory must work as a " team," each section playing its part and working in conjunction with the others.

The arrangement depends on the product, its size, nature, and the quantity manufactured. A factory producing a few large turbo-generator sets a year, each different from the others, is of necessity very different from one turning out thousands of small identical products every week. On broad lines, however, the essential features are the same. The handling of material must be reduced to a minimum, as this is great waste of time and labour. For this reason the material should if possible " flow " straight through the workshop, entering one end as raw material and emerging from the other as the finished product. By this means the distance to be covered by each part between the various stages of manufacture is kept as short as possible.

Adequate means for handling and transportation must be provided. A turbine factory must have large powerful cranes. A mass-production factory making small articles, on the other hand, will rely on travelling belts and conveyors for transport, cranes not being necessary. Reduction in the time of manufacture must also be effected wherever possible. To this end the most efficient machine tools must be installed.

The cost of these, however, must be balanced against the financial saving resulting from their use. Only where this warrants their purchase should they be employed.

We are in an age of rationalisation and planning in industry. The whole process of manufacture of a new product must be visualised, adapted to the conditions and layout of the factory, and the machine tools available. The production must then be very carefully planned to ensure a smooth output of component parts, with no delays in one section which would slow down the production of the entire factory.

MAKING ONE HUNDRED THOUSAND MOTOR-CARS

ONE of the best examples of a large mass-produced article to-day is the popular motor-car. For the manufacture of several cars a minute the highest development of factory organisation and equipment is necessary. A car is such a complicated mechanism, each main component involves so many accurate parts, that without this organisation it would be impossible to produce the necessary quality or quantity. When it is said that a shortage of one particular small item may hold up the production of the entire factory, something of the problem will be realised.

The construction of a car is split up into various sections. The engine, axles, chassis, body, etc., are each made separately, and finally all assembled together on the main assembly line. The rough scheme of manufacture is shown in Fig. 84. At the left-hand end the various raw materials, forgings, castings, etc., enter. They proceed down the various lines in the machine shops, travelling from one machine tool to the next, and finally leaving the machine shop completely machined. They then go to the appropriate assembly lines, where the axles, chassis, engines, etc., are each made up completely. At right angles to the end of these "sub-assembly" lines runs the main assembly line on which each chassis as it arrives is fitted with axles, engines and other parts and finally drives off under its own power.

Extensive use is made of conveyors for all purposes. Parts after one machining operation are placed on a constantly moving conveyor which carries them to the next machine. Details are added to the engines as they move imperceptibly along on a conveyor. The chassis are built up on a moving platform like a very slow horizontal "moving staircase." At one end of this platform a chassis is taken from the chassis

line. To it is added a back axle. By the time this is finished
it has moved to the front axle line and one of these is now
added. From these to the engine line where the engine is
installed and so on. Finally by the time the chassis reaches
the other end of the conveyor it has been completely assembled, and the finished car is filled with petrol and driven
off. When the factory is in full production material seldom
touches the floor or is allowed to rest except when being
machined. On the assembly lines pneumatic and electric
tools and spanners are suspended from above ready to be
pulled down when needed.

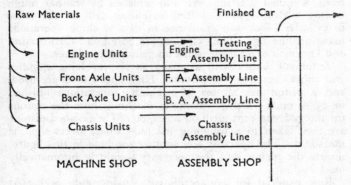

*84. How the factory is arranged for the large-scale
production of motor-cars. Conveyors are largely used
to move the work along the lines.*

The great object of all this is to achieve a steady smooth
production and to eliminate all waste of time and unnecessary
handling and moving about. Conveyors are used for transport,
for reception and collection of parts from presses and automatic tools, for the removal of " swarf " (or superfluous
metal machined off the various parts) and for supply and
outlet of unfinished and finished parts for each worker. Great
accuracy is required, as the conveyor allows no time for
delay due to faulty manufacture, filing, scraping, etc.

THE MACHINE TOOL MULTITUDE IN ACTION

BEGINNING with the foundry, where cylinder blocks and
crankcases are cast, here too conveyors are in use. Instead
of ladles of metal being brought to the moulds, the moulds

themselves are carried on a conveyor to the pouring pot and there filled with molten metal. Slowly they travel along, cooling at the same time, until they come to the " shake-out " point, where the now solid casting is turned out from the mould.

The cylinder blocks are machined in continuous, automatic milling machines. A large cylinder vertical table revolves between four cutters two on each side. As many as seven blocks are located in " fixtures " on each side of the table, which slowly rotates, bringing each block round under first a " roughing " cutter, then a " finishing " cutter. As each block is milled it is removed and replaced by another rough casting. Multi-spindle drilling machines drill all the holes in cylinder block and crankcase in two or three operations using drilling jigs. The cylinders are bored and then ground and honed to exact dimensions on grinding machines.

Automatic lathes with as many as six revolving spindles and chucks machine the pistons. High speed tools are used, and a piston has all major machining operations finished in 25 seconds. Other automatic machines bore the pistons for the gudgeon pins, drill oil holes, etc. The finished pistons are then taken to a weighing machine where overweight is measured. The operator sets another machine to this figure, inserts the piston, and the necessary weight is automatically machined off.

Raw material for connecting-rods, axles, etc., is heated for forging in an electric furnace at a temperature over 2,000° F. From there it is taken to the drop hammers and forged, the drop-forgings being heat-treated in another electric furnace through which they are slowly carried by a conveyor. Milling, broaching, and drilling machines complete the machining operations on the connecting rod, and the white metal bearing is cast in. This is then bored with a high speed tool to an accuracy within one ten-thousandth of an inch.

The crank shaft of a modern motor car engine is probably the most important unit of the entire machine, since on its accuracy depends largely the proper functioning of the engine. The drop forgings are roughly turned in lathes and then taken to special crankshaft grinding and honing machines. Here the crank pins and bearings are ground and honed to a very high finish, the maximum error allowed being about ·00025 of an inch. During the grinding operation the diameters are shown on gauges graduated to read 1/100,000 of an inch. For the final operation the crankshaft must be taken to a balancing machine. In this it rotates on four rollers, and the machine indicates where it is out of balance and to what extent. The operator finds from a table how much metal must be removed, and this is done by drilling.

If the body is to be made of steel as is usually the case, very expensive presses form steel sheets into the various sections. These are held in place in jigs and welded together in automatic welding machines. The body is then placed on a conveyor, goes through various painting operations and emerges at the main assembly line, ready to be lifted on to the chassis.

Besides the main items referred to above, hundreds of small parts are necessary for the finished car. Some of these secondary items may be bought from firms specialising in their manufacture. The rest are produced in shops where there are rows and rows of lathes, drills and other machines, automatic and non-automatic, turning out hundreds of small motor car parts every day.

Only a few of the more important operations have been mentioned—many more machines are necessary. Automatic lathes, turret and capstan lathes, boring, drilling, milling, grinding and many other machines are all essential for the modern motor-car. For the efficient operation of all these tools, a very complete tool room is necessary, where a full supply of all the necessary tools, cutters, etc., is kept and maintained in good condition. Very accurate gauges and measuring instruments are necessary for checking dimensions at various stages throughout the whole manufacture of the various parts.

THE MEN WHO MAKE THE MACHINES

A FACTORY contains all classes of men, ranging from the General Manager to the unskilled labourer who sweeps the floors of the workshops. Many departments exist side by side, each contributing its share in the production of the factory's goods, but differing widely from each other in the nature of the work they perform. The men who work in each are trained for that work, it is their trade. Years of apprenticeship are necessary before they can be regarded as fully-fledged moulders, machine operators, fitters or draughtsmen.

The designing engineers must go through their technical

training. This is largely derived from text books, but no engineer will go far without practical experience to back up his theoretical knowledge. In the same way the workmen, foremen, superintendents must all know their job thoroughly, and only years of experience can help them to do so. Consequently as a general rule each man is largely specialised, he has no time to become qualified at more than one trade. A machine operator could not make a good casting ; a moulder could not perform the fitter's job ; nor has a fitter the necessary experience for the rapid production of accurate work on machine tools.

Besides these departments actually engaged in production, there are several others equally necessary. Skilled workmen are required for the Tool Room, where special tools are made and kept in good condition. Probably a laboratory is maintained for experimental research work on products of the future. A transport section deals with all handling of materials and is responsible for cranes, mobile trucks, etc. Production and planning departments are necessary to follow the progress of work through the factory, making sure that it is up to schedule, and overcoming delays. Rate-fixers decide the payment for the various operations in the factory and machine shop. Then of course there is the Sales Department, and general office for the normal routine office work of a large organisation.

So it is that each factory includes in its staff a host of different trades. Fitters, machine operators, moulders, patternmakers, clerks, rate fixers, production clerks, experimental engineers, designers, draughtsmen, carpenters, and many more. Many thousand men may be employed by a large firm each with his particular function and all of them must be organised into one great production machine. In spite of the number of employees, complete and close control over every phase of the factory's activities must be possible. The various departments are independent of each other, but work in conjunction with each other and are all responsible to the same final authority. The whole vast organisation must be completely disciplined and under the ultimate control of one man.

AN ARMY SEVERAL THOUSAND STRONG

THE factory is nothing less than an army several thousand strong, devoted not to destruction, however, but to creation. It is subject to discipline in a similar way, and has its own " officers " and " N.C.O's." In the military sphere, the orders and decisions of the general travel through colonels, majors, captains, sergeants, corporals and finally reach the private soldier. All these intermediaries are necessary to link up the actual " operating force," the rank and file, with the authority in command. It is a sort of pyramid organisation at the apex of which stands the commander-in-chief. From him spread out the " lines of authority " to his colonels,

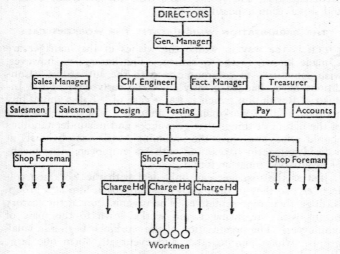

85. The organisation of personnel in a modern machine factory.

from them to their subordinates, and so on down to the lowest ranks who form the base and solid mass of the pyramid. A factory must be organised for its business of production in the same way. Fig. 85 shows how the supreme authority of the Directors is conveyed down the lines to the various heads of departments : the Sales Manager, Chief Engineer, Works Manager, and Treasurer. Each of these is in charge of his own department, and further lines of authority go from him to each man in it.

In the case of the works or factory manager, he is responsible for the whole of the actual production of the factory—he controls foundry, machine shops, assembly shops, stores, tool-room, etc. Each of these is under a " shop foreman " who answers to the factory manager. Finally the workmen in the shop are divided into several sections each under a " charge hand " who is responsible to the shop foreman.

The lowest ranks of this industrial army are thus under the complete control of the directors. By organisation and sub-division of this nature, the whole of the great mass of work-men in a large factory are disciplined and allotted to their particular jobs, and at the same time the necessary control and supervision is possible.

THE ORGANISATION WHICH STATES THE WORKER'S CASE

SUCH is the way in which the wishes of the manager are made known to the workmen. The latter also, however, wish sometimes to communicate with the authorities. Con-ditions have changed greatly since the early days of the In-dustrial Revolution, when it was a case of " Kill a mule, buy another. Kill a workman, hire another." Nevertheless it is in the nature of things that grievances and misunderstandings should arise, and since the individual worker is obviously at a disadvantage in bargaining with his employer, other means of negotiation must be found.

Just as the manager can only deal with the workmen col-lectively, so they in their turn must approach him as a group, through their representative. The organisation of the factory begins with the manager and works down to the mass of employees. The organisation of the workmen begins in small groups, which join together and eventually form one large Trade Union.

Slowly in the past men in the various trades made contact with those employed in similar work elsewhere. Each trade organised itself, until today we have the different great Trade Unions, representing those of that calling irrespective of the firm by which they are employed. The National Union of Railwaymen, the Amalgamated Engineers Union, the Trans-port and General Workers Union, and such are all established institutions. Each Union has its " branch secretaries " in the various manufacturing districts, who represent its members in each locality. They report to the Union Headquarters, which controls the activities of its members throughout the country and acts for the trade as a whole.

All workshops of " Trade Union " factories have their shop committees and shop stewards, chosen as their representatives by the men themselves. To them all grievances and disputes are brought for consideration and any necessary action.

The shop stewards are the real leaders of the rank and file in matters affecting the day to day lives of industrial workers. They inspect Trade Union contribution cards, recruit new members, and report regularly to the local branch secretary on matters requiring official attention. They are empowered to negotiate with their immediate superiors on matters of minor importance, but for major disputes they must report to the local branch of the Union from which really they derive their power. The branch secretary may then approach the management in matters of a purely local nature but all questions of policy must be referred to the headquarters of the Union. If it be a matter affecting the trade as a whole, the Trade Union then negotiates with the " Employers' Federation," each representing their membership as a whole, and possessing full responsibility to act and decide for them.

The manager cannot deal with his employees individually but must control them through his superintendents, foremen, and charge hands, so individual workers have no power alone but must stand together and voice their demands through shop stewards, and, if necessary, branch secretaries and Trade Union leaders. Finally of course members of all Trade Unions throughout the country join together and are represented by the Trades Union Congress. This speaks for all Trade Union Labour as one mass.

In the huge organisation of to-day the " personal touch " is lost. The worker cannot feel that he is dealing with a man who employs him, but a soulless institution. That personal contact and give-and-take between the old " master-craftsman " and his apprentices which so helped mutual understanding is thus impossible. This being so, good will in industry is all the more vital, as without it the efficiency and spirit of the factory is very low. Success and mutual satisfaction can only be achieved by managers and superintendents who lead the men, and do not drive them, as was the case in the dark days of industry.

THE GREAT CHEMICAL INDUSTRIES

by H. T. F. Rhodes, Dip.Inst.C.(Lyons), Member of the Institute of Engineering Inspection (Chem.), Editor of " The Chemical Practitioner."

*I*T was Lord Kelvin who said that he never understood the principles of an invention until he had seen a model of it. For the chemical engineer the principles upon which his models are constructed exist for him ready made. Nearly all chemical engineering plant has its prototype in the laboratory. It is the task of the engineer to interpret these models in terms of production in large quantities, to translate the fragile glass of the scientist—his beakers, retorts, funnels and test-tubes—into the huge metal vats, pressure chambers, boilers and machinery of the chemical industry.

The processes of the laboratory are, in miniature, the replicas of the large-scale operation ; boiling, cooling, filtering, distilling, crystallizing, extracting, precipitating—all have their special problems for the engineer. It is these processes that we shall consider first in the pages which follow, with many interesting side-lights on their adaptation to modern requirements. Then follows an account of the inspection and testing of the materials the engineer uses, and finally a description of some of the great industries which have arisen at the call of the chemical engineer —fertilisers from the air, dyes, artificial silk, the Bakelite industry, petrol from coal—producers of the million necessities and luxuries which man is making at the demand of modern civilisation.

The chemist in the laboratory, if he wishes to weigh anything, uses his sensitive balance, but in the works, where weighing is no less important, it is a question of dealing with tons, not with grammes and minute fractions of grammes. In England it is still the custom to weigh in hundredweights and tons, but on the Continent the same measure is used for large- and small-scale operations. The working unit for the laboratory is the gramme ; for the large-scale operation, the kilo, which is one thousand grammes.

For large-scale operations, a lever balance has to be used. It consists of a platform which is connected with a system of levers so arranged that the platform only requires a tenth or even a hundredth of the actual weight to counterbalance it.

These lever balances have specially adjusted weights, minia-ture tons and hundredweights which correspond to the true weight. To record pounds and ounces there is an arm with a small weight which moves along its length. This arm is divided up, each division corresponding to an ounce or some other fraction of a pound.

Balances of this type are made to carry ten tons or more. The best models are sensitive to three to four ounces, that is to say, to about a ten-thousandth of a ton. This is the same order of sensitiveness as the laboratory balance. For weighing comparatively small quantities, the scales are most suitable, and they have been constructed to carry as much as a ton, although for such weights the modern lever balance is more convenient.

In the laboratory, liquids are measured in graduated glass vessels. The cubic centimetre and the litre, one thousand cubic centimetres, are always used. On a large scale, liquids cannot conveniently be measured by laboratory methods. Very large vessels can never be made of glass, and the ordinary metal tank cannot be graduated in such a way as to be easily read. This difficulty is often overcome by the attachment of a glass gauge which runs from the bottom to the top of the tank. Against this a scale is fixed graduated in gallons. There is now, however, both in weighing and measuring, a tendency to make use of the metric system. The large-scale unit of weight is, as we have said, the kilo. The large-scale unit of volume is the hecto, which corresponds to 100,000 cubic centimetres or 100 litres.

Probably the oldest method of ascertaining the quantity of liquid in a vessel is by the use of a dip stick. This is merely a long piece of wood marked in inches which records the height of the liquid in the vessel. The stick is dry when it is dipped and the wet line determines the height of the liquid. This method, which is very accurate, is still much employed, notably in breweries. The volume of liquid which a vessel will contain is calculated by estimating its cubic capacity in gallons and relying on the fact that a cubic foot of water is equal to 6·25 gallons.

It is often essential to determine the relation between the weight of a liquid and its volume. A cubic foot of sulphuric acid weighs more than a cubic foot of water ; a cubic foot of alcohol weighs less. If we know the specific gravity of the given liquid, that is, the ratio between the weights of equal volumes of the liquid and water, the relation between volume and weight of the liquid can be calculated.

To determine specific gravity an old but efficient instrument is used in the works : the aerometer. It is a float which rises or falls according to the specific gravity of the liquid in which it is placed. The top of this float is a glass or metal column divided into degrees corresponding to specific gravity. When the specific gravity is determined the calculation is simple. If a liquid is one and one-quarter times as " heavy " as water a given volume will weigh one and one-quarter times as much as the same volume of water. Conversely, if the liquid is " lighter " it will weigh less. The Twaddell aerometer is generally used in this country for liquids heavier than water ; the Baumé for liquids lighter than water.

TAKING THE TEMPERATURE AT RED AND WHITE HEAT

NEXT in importance among measuring instruments is the thermometer. In this instance there is no difference between the instrument used in the laboratory and in the works, except that for safety's sake the works thermometer is generally encased in metal. But where high temperatures have to be measured, instruments known as pyrometers are used. They operate on rather a different principle. One type relies upon the fact that a given metal expands when heated to different temperatures to a definite extent which does not vary. This expansion is recorded through a lever system upon a dial which records the expansion in terms of temperature.

There are also electrical methods of recording temperature. One of them relies on the fact that the electrical resistance of a metal to a current depends upon the temperature. It follows that the measurement of the resistance of a metallic wire is an index of the temperature of the medium in which it is placed, but instead of recording the resistance in ohms, the dial records the corresponding degrees of temperature. The other type of electrical thermometer depends upon the fact that if the junction of two different metals is heated, an electric pressure is set up. This is manifested as an electric current if the other ends of the metal strips are joined to an ammeter which measures the current produced. By selecting a suitable pair of metals which give currents proportional to the temperature of their junction, the dial of the ammeter can be calibrated to register temperatures instead of currents, and a sensitive pyrometer suitable for measuring very high temperatures is obtained. Thermometers, whether for normal or high temperature work, have to be checked frequently. A faulty instrument will often give a great deal of trouble.

There are simpler methods of measuring high temperatures approximately. The fusion points of a number of chemical salts are quite definite. A salt such as potassium nitrate fuses at 329° C. If it is required approximately to record this temperature, a small quantity is placed in an iron spoon and introduced into the furnace. If it melts, the temperature is at least 329° or in excess of it. By the use of a series of salts of known fusion points a fairly accurate idea of temperature can be obtained.

BOILING LIQUID IN TONS AT A TIME

IF the chemist wishes to heat or boil a liquid in the laboratory, he generally carries out the operation in a glass beaker or flask. When a beaker is used, a glass rod is employed for stirring, or the beaker or flask is shaken with a rotary movement. But the chemist has only to deal with, at most, a litre (about a quart) of liquid at a time. The chemical engineer is concerned with perhaps five hundred or a thousand gallons, and the problems of heating the large containing vessel and stirring its contents must be solved.

The obvious method of a fire underneath might suggest itself ; and this is indeed one which is still employed with suitable modifications. The question of efficiency has to be considered, and the conservation of heat which would otherwise be lost by radiation. Heat must be applied to as large an area of the vessel as possible. For this reason, the vessel rests as a rule on a brick pillar and is enclosed within a brickwork frame which contains the furnace. The hot free gases pass around and under the pot and finally escape through a flue to the chimney. A considerable amount of heat is conserved in this way but, unless two or three units are at work, the efficiency is not very high.

In modern practice heating and boiling with steam is much more common, since the efficiency is much higher. Steam-jacketed vessels are very common adjuncts of the chemical works. There are many modifications, but essentially they consist of vessels which have a surrounding jacket with a cock at the top to admit the steam and one near the bottom to allow the escape of waste steam and water. The steam has to be regulated in such a way that only so much is admitted as will condense in the jacket, in order to avoid waste of power. Precautions also have to be taken to prevent the radiation of heat from the metallic surface of the containing vessel. The method generally used is that of insulation with some material such as an asbestos composition, the conductivity of which is very low.

Steam when under pressure is hotter than boiling water. It can be superheated, and can attain a temperature as high as 400° C., which is four times the temperature of boiling water.

FLAMES WHICH BURN UNDER WATER

ENGINEERS, and particularly chemical engineers, have always been searching for a method in which all the heat generated could be utilised. As long ago as 1880 attempts were made to produce a burner which would burn under water. As a result of these early attempts the Brunler submerged flame burner was patented in 1923. It is a burner which uses a mixture of oil fuel and air, which is enclosed in a special steam-generating annex of the boiler itself or other vessel to be heated. Water is admitted into this chamber, and coming into actual contact with the flame, is volatilised, and passes back into the boiler. The efficiency of this method of heating is very high, in the neighbourhood of 96%. The disadvantages are that the products of the combustion of the flame pass into the material to be heated.

In principle the vessel used for boiling liquids under great pressures is not an elaborate piece of apparatus. It is known as an autoclave and consists of a metal vessel which carries a tightly-fitting lid which can be firmly secured to the body of the vessel by means of iron clamps. The boiler is fitted with a safety valve which " blows off " when the pressure corresponding to the counter-pressure it exerts is attained. Autoclaves can be constructed to resist a pressure of ten tons to the square inch. These are, of course, constructed of high-grade steel which has been very carefully tested. The object of pressure boiling is to bring about certain reactions which would not take place at ordinary atmospheric pressure.

MAKING SUGAR AND ALCOHOL FROM SAWDUST

A CASE in point is the hydrolysis of sawdust, which can be utilised on a large scale for the production of alcohol. (Hydrolysis is the decomposition of a substance by the water into another substance or substances different from the original compound.)   All kinds of wood and paper consist essentially of a substance known as cellulose, which is chemically allied to starch and to the sugars.   It has been known for a very long time that when starch is treated with acids and the mixture boiled, the starch is hydrolysed and sugars are produced which upon fermentation can be converted into alcohol.

It was later discovered that although cellulose was hydrolysed much less readily, something of the same kind could be done with it.   But the temperature of boiling water was not sufficient.   The mixture had to be heated under pressure —in order to bring about the reaction.   When this pressure boiling is carried out with sulphuric acid a certain percentage of the sugar, dextrose, is produced.   This, upon fermentation with yeast, produces alcohol.

The efficiency of this process is not very high, and for this reason it has not been greatly utilised, but very great improvements have been made in it recently, and it is quite probable that in the near future a great deal of our alcohol will be made from sawdust and paper.

There are a very large number of chemical processes which entail pressure boiling.   Another notable example is the preparation of fatty acids used for making candles.   Hydrolysis by means of pressure boiling is not always necessary in this case, but it is quite frequently used.   The fat from which the fatty acid is to be produced is mixed with such a base as lime in solution in water, and the mixture is heated in an autoclave at a pressure between eight and fifteen atmospheres.   The products of this hydrolysis are glycerine and the calcium (or lime) salts of the required fatty acids.

The glycerine dissolves in the solution which is drawn off and the glycerine is recovered from it.   Acid is added to set free the fatty acids from their combination with the calcium. The fats float like an oil on the surface of the liquid and can thus be separated from it.

Autoclaves are not necessarily made of steel.   Those intended for comparatively low pressure may be constructed of copper.   The material of their construction is often a great problem for the chemical engineer.   One of his great difficulties is the corrosive effect of many chemical substances upon metal.   The chemist in the laboratory can always, or nearly always, use glass.   In the vast majority of cases this is entirely impracticable in large-scale operations.   There are a number of chemical reactions which would have considerable industrial importance if it were possible to find vessels composed of a suitable material in which to conduct them.

KEEPING THE LIQUID MOVING

THE boiling of liquids is bound up with the question of their agitation. Anyone who doubts this need only attempt to make a small quantity of soap by boiling together an alkali of some sort and a soap-making oil. Without strong agitation, the whole mixture will froth over. This is, of course, not true of all chemical reactions, but in a large number of cases agitation is necessary for one reason or another.

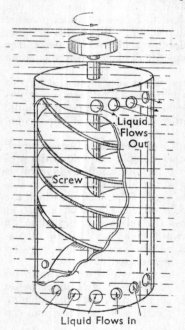

The commonest form of agitator is a shaft passing from top to bottom of the vessel fixed in a footstep bearing at the bottom and passing through another bearing at the top. Arms are fixed at right angles so that when the shaft revolves under power the liquid is swirled round. This is the simplest method of agitation and is much employed, particularly in breweries. It is not, however, efficient for all purposes, and it is quite useless for viscous liquids.

A much more efficient method of agitation is a stirrer, the basis of which is the Archimedian screw (Fig. 86). This revolves within a metal cylinder which is pierced with holes. The liquid is thus sucked into this cylinder through the holes, which are in the lower part of it, and drawn up through the top. Circulation therefore proceeds from the centre and the

86. A mechanical stirrer which, by rotation of the Archimedian screw, keeps large quantities of liquid in constant motion.

bottom upwards, and is much more complete than in the other method. It is also more economical of power. There are many other methods such as the use of revolving paddles, but the two mentioned are the most important.

COOLING AND DRYING WITH CHEMICALS

COOLING and refrigeration are very largely chemical operations. Before refrigerating machinery was invented the use of ice was an expensive and inefficient method of refrigeration. The principle of all refrigeration apparatus is the same. When a volatile liquid evaporates, it absorbs a large amount of heat either from the atmosphere or from any other medium with which it is in contact. A good example of this phenomenon is freezing with ether, which is a highly volatile liquid. If ether is sprayed upon the skin, a feeling of intense cold is experienced and frost will appear on the surface of the skin, caused by the rapid withdrawal of heat. Ether can be used as a local anæsthetic on account of this property.

One of the earliest forms of refrigerator was that which utilised ammonia gas. (Ordinary " ammonia " as bought from the chemist is a solution of ammonia gas in water.) " Anhydrous " (that is, water-free) ammonia gas is pumped into a condenser which is surrounded by cold water. Under the influence of the pressure and the low temperature, the gas liquefies. The liquid gas flows out of the condenser into the refrigerator where the pressure is greatly reduced by the pump, which is generally a double-action pressure-suction instrument. The liquid gas evaporates rapidly and thus absorbs heat from the liquid, usually brine, which is present in the refrigerator. Temperatures in some cases as low as $-20°$ C. can be attained in an efficient plant of this type, which is still extensively used. The action of the refrigerator is, of course, continuous. The ammonia gas is alternately compressed and allowed to evaporate by the action of the pump.

TURNING A GAS INTO SNOW

OF recent years carbon dioxide has become a favourite refrigerating agent. It will be obvious that by liquefaction and evaporation it can be utilized in a plant which works on the same principle as that already described. But carbon dioxide is now often frozen and compressed into blocks of " snow." It is in fact often called carbon dioxide snow. This snow can be, and frequently is, used in exactly the same way as ice. A small fragment dropped into a relatively enormous quantity of liquid will greatly reduce the temperature.

Sulphur dioxide is another gas which can be employed in a plant very similar to that used for ammonia. The advantages of using sulphur dioxide are that it requires less pressure for liquefaction than either ammonia or carbon dioxide. There are, however, many disadvantages. It is, for example highly corrosive to metals, and the odour is suffocating, so that any leakage in the plant is a great annoyance. Carbon dioxide has practically no corrosive action, and it is odourless. Leakage in the apparatus would have to be serious before a quantity dangerous to life escaped into the atmosphere.

The uses of cooling and refrigeration in chemical reactions are very numerous. There is always a tendency when a chemical reaction takes place for the temperature of the mixture to increase. It is not always necessary or even desirable for the chemical engineer to check this, but in some cases irreparable damage is done if temperatures run too high. A good illustration is the case of alcoholic fermentation.

When a solution of must (grape juice), wort (extract of malt) or a sugar solution is fermented with yeast, the action is at first extremely violent, and the temperature may rise as high as blood heat (100° F.). If the fermenting liquor is not cooled, the results may be disastrous. The enzymes, bio-chemical substances which cause the fermentation to take place, are very sensitive to temperature. They work best at about 25° C. or 78° F., the temperature of a hot summer day. If this is exceeded, the fermentation may cease before all the sugar has been converted into alcohol. In such cases the fermented liquor is likely to sour.

The apparatus used for cooling is a system of attemperating tubes. These are merely tubes arranged in the form of a coil through which cold water is circulated continuously. Since as we have seen cold water at a temperature close to its freezing point can very easily be produced in the refrigerator, the control of temperature is quite a simple matter.

GETTING TO THE BOTTOM OF THE TEMPERATURE SCALE: LIQUID AIR

THERE are, of course, operations which require much lower temperatures, and the preparation of liquid gases is one of them. In order to liquefy a gas a low temperature and considerable pressure are generally necessary. Further, the lower the temperature can be forced, the less is the pressure required for ultimate liquefaction. If therefore a low temperature can be attained easily, economy can be effected.

The Claude process for the liquefaction of air is an example

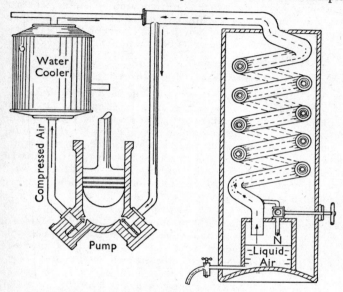

87. An early form of Linde's apparatus for liquefying air. Compressed air cools as it expands from the nozzle N and returns through the outside tube of the worm, cooling the incoming air. It is then re-compressed and under the progressive cooling and pressure it finally liquefies.

of this. Air under a pressure of 40 atmospheres [1] passes into an expansion machine and so round the outside of the tubes of the liquefier. By reason of its expansion there is, as in the case of other gases, a pronounced cooling effect. At the same time, air under a pressure of 40 atmospheres is passing through the liquefying tubes, which have been cooled to −140° C. by the passage of the expanded air. At this temperature and pressure, the air liquefies and is

[1] An "atmosphere," the normal pressure of air on the earth, is about 14·7 pounds per square inch.

run off from a cock at the base of the liquefier. In the Linde process, the air which is itself being liquefied is, by a process of successive compressions and expansions, used to reduce the temperature to the point at which fresh air entering the apparatus can be liquefied.

It will now be clear that all refrigeration apparatus, whether moderate or extreme cooling effects are required, relies upon the same principle. When a liquid evaporates it absorbs heat, and upon the speed of its evaporation depends the degree of its cooling effect.

" DRYING WEATHER " MADE TO ORDER

DRYING on a large scale is one of the most complicated problems which faces the chemical engineer. It is not until comparatively recently that attempts have been made to solve it. In the laboratory the chemist dries his compounds either by heating them in a water oven or by vacuum dessication (i.e. by drying in a closed vessel in which the air is at a reduced pressure and with the help of substances such as sulphuric acid or calcium chloride, which rapidly absorb moisture from the air).

A good example of the classical large-scale methods is the drying of glue. Glue after purification and concentration is a jelly-like substance of about the same consistency as a table jelly. It is an extremely difficult matter to deprive a substance of that kind, of its moisture. The original method of drying it was merely to cut the jelly into slabs of suitable size, and to leave them exposed to the open air to dry. A roof, of course, had to be built to protect the glue from the rain. Even in a dry climate this process was extremely lengthy ; and it was also very uncertain. If the glue was exposed to the sun, it melted, whilst on the other hand if it dried too quickly, cracks appeared in it. The manufacturer was entirely at the mercy of the weather.

When nature is capricious there is no alternative but to fall back upon artifice. If the weather is changeable the obvious remedy is to create one's own. Of recent years this problem has been solved with a considerable measure of success. It has been possible to devise methods and plant which automatically supply an atmosphere of any given temperature and degree of humidity. We are concerned here, however, merely with the creation of an atmosphere which will prove to be suitable for drying purposes.

If the air in contact with a moist substance is quite dry it can exert no pressure of aqueous vapour. The moist substance will, however, have a vapour tension due to the water present, so that the water will continue to evaporate until there is equilibrium between the vapour tension of the substance, and that of the surrounding atmosphere.

In practice therefore, the method of drying on a large scale is to pass a current of dry air heated to a suitable temperature over the substance to be dried. This is in effect a refinement of the hot-water oven principle ; it is, however, definitely a refinement to heat the air independently of the substance to be dried. The use of hot air is of value because as the temperature of the air rises, it is able to take up a greater percentage of water.

The principle of the dryer is simple. It consists essentially of an iron chamber containing trays which are perforated to allow of the passage of the hot air. Below is the source of heat and above this a distributor. A flue of some sort is connected with the source of heat to allow the combustion products to escape. In its simplest form a fan for circulation is not used. Air is displaced automatically by the entry of cold air as the hot air rises.

DRYING UNDER DIFFICULTIES : THE VACUUM DESICCATOR

As in the laboratory, it is sometimes necessary to dry in vacuo or under reduced pressure, and in many cases even if it is not necessary, it may be more economical. The large-scale vacuum desiccator (so to call it) differs somewhat in construction from the laboratory type ; it is a hot-air oven and vacuum desiccator combined. A vacuum dryer consists of an iron chamber fitted with trays as in the case of the other dryer. It has to be absolutely air-tight and its door is thus lined with rubber and fastened with screws and butterfly nuts. The top of the dryer is fitted with a suction pump which draws off the vapour, and it is also fitted with a pressure gauge. With this apparatus, the trays themselves are jackets through which hot water or steam can be made to circulate, so that we have in this dryer almost an exact counterpart of the hot-water oven except that the dryer works under reduced pressure.

Dryers working under reduced pressure are particularly useful for the removal of volatile solvents such as alcohol, benzene and petroleum ether. These liquids which should evaporate more readily than water are liable to play strange tricks. It is the old refrigeration difficulty. Heat is absorbed during the evaporation and in consequence the liquid cools. The evaporation is thus greatly retarded. In some cases where a solvent is being evaporated from treacly substances, a point is reached when it will no longer evaporate by itself. In such examples evaporation with reduction of pressure is the only economical method to employ.

As in the laboratory, so in the large-scale operation, the stability of the substance to be dried is the first consideration. Heating it, at any rate to a high temperature, may thus be out of the question. In such instances the alternative is drying under a pressure reduced as much as is practicable.

Scientific methods of drying enormously increase efficiency in manufacture and reduce its cost. A good example of this is the manufacture of soap. Six or seven days used to be necessary in order to dry the soap sufficiently ; the process can now be completed in almost as many minutes by passing the soap on an endless belt through a hot-air chamber.

There is another very interesting method of drying, also applicable to soap, to which no allusion has so far been made. It relies upon a chemical reaction, and not upon physical methods. Many years ago it was discovered that the only method to make soap-powder was to add a large quantity of soda-ash to the soap mixture. The reason of the drying effect was not then understood. Soda-ash is anhydrous (water-free) sodium carbonate ; and sodium carbonate has a property shared with many other salts of being able to absorb water by combining with it to form crystals.

Salts which have this property do not become moist by absorbing this water. In the example of the soap powder, therefore, the effect of the addition of the soda-ash is to attract the water away from the soap to combine with the sodium carbonate.

Substances which act in this way are known as " dehydrating agents," and they have very important applications in practice. Anhydrous substances of this kind all take up water with great avidity, and are therefore used for ridding non-aqueous liquids of admixture with water. An example is the dehydration of alcohol. By fractional distillation it is not possible to produce alcohol of a greater strength than about 96%. In order to " dry " it completely it must be treated with some dehydrating agent and redistilled. Lime or dry caustic potash, both powerful dehydrating agents, are often used for this purpose. The lime or potash is added to the alcohol and it is allowed to stand for some time. The alcohol is then re-distilled, and the pure anhydrous product passes over. Where absolute purity is necessary, however, the alcohol may have to be treated with metallic sodium which vigorously reacts with the water and removes the last traces.

SEPARATING SOLIDS AND LIQUIDS

THE separation of solids from liquids is as fundamental in the large-scale operation as it is in the laboratory, but the apparatus employed does not greatly resemble the small-scale apparatus. In the works, however, as in the laboratory, filtration is not used where methods of decantation [1] can be applied. This latter can, of course, only be done when the solid separates easily from the liquid and lies at the bottom of the vessel. Siphons for large-scale operations are generally made of metal and fitted with a float which automatically regulates them.

Large-scale filters are in general of two types : those which operate under reduced pressure, and those which operate under increased pressure. A filter working under reduced pressure is generally in the form of a cylinder capable of being tightly closed with an inlet pipe at the top and an outlet at the bottom. The cylinder is divided by a tray-like partition which is perforated and on which the filtering medium rests. When the pressure is reduced by means of a suction pump, the liquid to be filtered is drawn through. This apparatus is exactly on the same principle as the Gooch filter and pump used in the laboratory.

THE MODERN FILTER PRESS

THE filter press has now for many years replaced the re-duced pressure filters for the large majority of filtration operations. All filter presses consist of a number of frames, which when in use carry filtering cloth. These frames fit upon two parallel rods so that they can slide in either direc-tion. At one end, the press has a rigid end ; the other end of the press can be adjusted by means of a screw so that the system of frames can be tightly pressed together. An outflow

[1] In decantation the solid material is allowed to settle and the liquor poured off, the process being repeated during the course of several washings with water.

tap is attached to each frame, and there is a funnel pipe at the head of the press which is the main inlet.

The material to be filtered is forced through the filter press with a pump. As soon as all the liquid and solid matter has passed in, the movable end of the press is screwed up, and the remaining liquid is expressed. There is a further advantage in the filter press that the filtered material can be washed. Water can be run in after the first pressing, and the process can be repeated as often as is necessary.

The filter press is of great value not only for dealing with the solid precipitate but with the filtrate. Very serious losses may occur if the liquid held by the precipitate is not recovered. An example is the yeast residue after wine fermentation. The yeast holds a large quantity of liquid containing alcohol. The yeast is therefore passed through a filter press not on account of the yeast, but for the purpose of expressing the alcohol-bearing liquid.

There are other methods of filtration of considerable practical importance which relate in particular to those liquids from which every trace of solid matter must be removed. The filtration of beer and wine are again cases in point. Absolute brilliancy in the filtrate is essential. For this purpose filters are used which are built on the same principle as the filter press so far as the use of perforated trays are concerned, but no squeezing pressure is applied.

The liquid to be filtered is forced through the filter with a pump in the same way, but the filtering medium is specially prepared pulp. This is packed between the trays so that the liquid has to pass through very thick layers of the material. Such filters are very efficient. Even where the solution is only slightly cloudy it emerges completely brilliant after filtration.

TRAPPING DISEASE GERMS BY FILTRATION

WE now have to consider the very interesting problem of ultra-filtration which has great practical importance for the bacteriologist. Essentially the method of preparing an antitoxic serum is as follows : The bacteria which produce a given disease are artificially cultivated in a pure state. The medium upon which they are grown is frequently broth (meat extract). The germ in the process of development produces a toxin which is the actual cause of the disease. This toxin is injected into the blood of an animal, which subsequently shows symptoms of the disease. By repeated injections, however, the animal produces a serum, a constituent of the blood, which fights the disease, and makes the animal immune from further attack. The antitoxic serum of this animal when injected into the human subject, will alleviate and finally actually cure the disease to which the serum corresponds.

After the cultivating medium has developed its maximum concentration of toxin, it has to be filtered to remove the bacteria which in a liquid medium forms a heavy crust on the surface of the liquid. But ordinary filtration is of no use. The toxin must be absolutely sterile, that is to say, entirely free from bacteria. The apparatus used for the purpose is known as the " Berkefeld Filter." It consists of unglazed porcelain of a special kind made in the form of a large test-tube. It is enclosed in a metal cylinder to protect it and to protect the substance being filtered from contact with the air. The liquid to be filtered is forced through it with pressure. Liquids filtered in this way emerge absolutely sterile.

The clogging of filters is one of the many anxieties of the chemical engineer who has to study very closely the physical condition of the liquid he is filtering. The uninitiated might think that in the use of the filter press, for example, the greater the pressure used in forcing the liquid into the press, the more satisfactory the result. That conclusion is quite wrong. What happens in such a case is that ultra-microscopic particles are forced into the filtering material, and prevent even the liquid passing through it. A clogged filter in the laboratory can give a great deal of trouble ; a clogged filter press of large dimensions is a really serious matter.

WHIRLING AWAY THE UNWANTED LIQUID

THERE is another process midway between filtration and drying which is of great interest to the chemical engineer. In the laboratory the chemist will often place crystals in a glass funnel for the purpose of draining them from the mother liquor. Alternatively some chemists place the crystals in a muslin bag attached to a piece of string and " whirl " them.

This is a very elementary method of applying the principles of centrifugal force. In large-scale operations " centrifuges " are often of great use. The essential form of the " hydro-extractor," as it is often called, is a cage of cylindrical form which revolves within a case of the same shape but larger in size. This larger vessel is provided with an outlet through which any separated liquid may drain. The wet substance is placed in the cage which is rotated, and the liquid is thus separated from the solid matter. Separation by this method can, of course, only be used when the particles of the substance are large. It is most suitable for crystalline solids.

But centrifugal methods can be and are applied for other than crystalline solids. Very fine solids can be centrifuged in filter bags which hold the precipitate and allow the liquid to pass through. Centrifugal methods are used in cases where the solid is so fine that it is in suspension in the liquid and thus cannot be easily separated from it.

Solids separate from liquids when " whirled " because there is a tendency for anything travelling in a circle to fly out at a tangent. If the speed of rotation is increased ten times, the force is increased a hundred times. In general, therefore, the faster the whirling the more rapid and complete the separation, but many precautions are necessary in practice. At high speeds the centrifugal force is very great and may lead to accidents due to fracture of the rotating parts. Secondly the actual result, even if there is no accident, may be unsatisfactory if the speed is too high owing to the particles being forced into the interstices of the bag so that the filter is clogged.

In the foregoing methods of separation, mechanical power in some form must be employed, but this power is incidental, the composition of the substance itself being the first consideration. The chemical engineer has to understand the composition and reactions of the substances he is dealing with, in order to decide by what mechanical methods it may be effected.

THE RETORT : ANCIENT SYMBOL OF ALCHEMY

WE now come to consider the most ancient of all chemical and chemical engineering processes, namely distillation. Long before the chemical engineer was ever heard of, there were men who practised the art of distillation. It is known alike to civilised and savage people, and both separative distillation (in which no change of composition occurs) and destructive distillation (which involves the decomposition of the material distilled) have been practised from very early times.

The date at which the Chinese first began to make their famous ink, now commonly known as Indian ink, has not been ascertained : but it seems to have involved a process of destructive distillation. That is to say, the oils from which the carbon to make the ink was produced were burnt in the presence of a limited supply of air. The smoke from the ignition was sublimed in the cool part of the retort, the deposit being mainly very finely divided carbon, which formed the basis then, and does still, of the intense black pigment of Indian ink. While this process of destructive distillation is hardly comparable, chemically, with, for example, the destructive distillation of coal, the actual technique is the same.

As an example of separative distillation, the rectification (that is, the refining or purifying by distillation) of alcohol is also a very ancient art. Alcoholic distillation dates from very primitive times, and it is, indeed, probably one of the oldest of the civilised arts. Nor can it be said that the primitive apparatus lacked ingenuity. Scientific method and knowledge has greatly improved the technique of distillation, but fundamentally both process and apparatus are the same.

For the alchemist the retort has a mystical significance. This is not surprising when we remember that one of its functions is to *concentrate*. The alchemist knew how a scented body could, by distillation, produce an essence many times more highly perfumed. Thus to augment the essential characteristics of a given substance became a process of mystical significance. The very term " essence " which is still commonly used to describe distilled products of certain kinds originally bore a philosophic meaning.

It is perhaps for this reason that the retort has come to be the popular symbol of the laboratory, despite the fact that it is very rarely used in the modern work-shop of the chemist. Curiously enough, however, it is still employed on a large scale and, in its essential parts, it does not differ from the traditional forms. The essential parts are a flask-like vessel with a long neck which is bent to make a more or less acute angle with the body. The matter to be heated is placed in the flask-like body and the vapours are partially cooled in the long neck. In all cases where the distillation of liquid is in question, the retort is connected with a condenser, a tube surrounded with a jacket through which cold water flows. It is to stretch the point of analogy somewhat to suggest that modern distilling apparatus are generally of this actual *shape*, but they do essentially consist of the vessel, the neck, and the condenser.

AN AGE-OLD INDUSTRY : THE DISTILLATION OF ALCOHOL

OF the two distinct classes of distillation, separative and destructive, the former has a very wide application in the production of alcohol for drinking and other purposes. The methods, however, by which it is carried out so greatly affect the taste of the product of distillation, whisky or brandy for example, that it is important to consider in some detail the various methods in use.

The simplest form of still is often regarded as the best for brandy. Ordinary distillation allows not only the ordinary alcohol to pass over, but higher alcohols, aldehydes and ketones which give the product its characteristic flavour and bouquet. It is for this reason that the so-called " pot " still, a type which has been used for thousands of years, is even now in use in some places in Scotland, Ireland and on the Continent. Sometimes rectifying devices are introduced between the still and the condenser. The disadvantage of this method is that several separate distillations are necessary to produce spirit of sufficient strength.

From the point of view of the chemical engineer this method is impossible. Distillation and rectification must take place at the same time. But it is important to remember that from a *chemical* point of view the old-fashioned method is sound, since it takes into consideration the products which affect the taste of the alcohol. In all modern plants, however, continuous distillation is a necessity owing to the very low efficiency of the ordinary distillation apparatus.

HOW THE DISTILLING PLANT WORKS

DISTILLATION and rectification can be carried out at the same time by means of apparatus specially constructed for that purpose. The method is an elaboration of the rectifying column of the laboratory, and continuous distilling plant instead of employing a simple condenser is fitted with an analyser, a rectifier and a refrigerator. The analyser consists of a chamber divided into sections by a number of copper plates (Fig. 88).

These are fitted with a valve to regulate pressure and also with a small pipe one end of which projects about an inch above the copper plate while the other end dips into a cup on the plate below. Each copper plate carries these attachments, the pipes being on opposite sides of the alternate plates. The rectifier is also fitted with copper plates and tubes together with piping through which the liquid to be rectified is conveyed.

In working, the analyser is filled with steam which passes upwards and is carried to the base of the rectifier by a connecting pipe. The liquid (wash) to be rectified is now pumped through the coils of the rectifier, passing from top to bottom. It is, of course, heated and the surrounding steam cooled by interchange of heat.

The heated " wash " containing alcohol then passes to the top of the analyser through a connecting pipe. What now happens is this. The steam, as we have seen, is *ascending* in the analyser, passing through small holes in the plates. The wash entering the top of the analyser cannot pass through the holes which only allow the passage of the steam. The wash therefore collects on the plates and passes *downwards* through the small

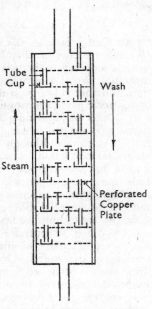

88. *The analyser of the Coffey still, which is used to produce alcohol suitable for drinking purposes.*

pipes. As it flows down, at all stages in contact with the steam, the steam extracts the alcohol from the liquid in the form, of course, of vapour. This vapour with its alcoholic contents passes out of the top of the analyser.

It returns to the rectifier through another pipe. Here the condition is that the steam-filled part of the rectifier has given up some of its heat to the wash passing through the coils. This part of the rectifier is therefore cooler and the alcohol-steam mixture is partially condensed. But the water condenses more readily than the alcohol so that a liquid weaker and weaker in alcohol passes downwards through the pipes of the rectifier, a vapour richer and richer in alcohol passes *upwards*. It escapes at the top of the rectifier and passes thence to a condenser. Practically a complete separation of water and alcohol is effected by this means.

STILLS—ANCIENT AND MODERN

THE Coffey Still, as this type is called, is one of the earliest achievements of chemical engineering. It was invented in 1831 long before the title chemical engineer had any precise meaning. But it is nevertheless a chemical engineering invention. Further it is a good illustration of an early development of scientific principles applied to a very ancient art.

It is also an interesting fact that Coffey stills of the traditional type are still in use, and that they have not been modified in essentials although there have been, of course, many elaborations of detail. The principle in all continuous distillation is that of the Coffey still. The Saville Still has a more elaborate system of plates in the analyser and rectifier, designed to achieve greater efficiency of analysis and rectification, but there is no essential difference in construction. The modern stills also are of improved pattern in that analyser and rectifier are combined structurally in one column, which increases the power efficiency of the plant, although the principle of working is unchanged. Originally the Coffey still could produce alcohol of 80–90% strength contaminated with a considerable amount of fusel oil. Filtration through charcoal was accordingly necessary to purify the spirit. Modern systems of rectification make this unnecessary.

But this question of filtration through charcoal is mentioned here on account of its significance for chemical engineering in another but a related connection. Many coloured solutions, for example, can be decolorised by filtration through specially-prepared " activated " charcoal which is said to *adsorb* the particles which colour the solution. This interesting property is due to the extreme minuteness of the particles of the carbon itself which act as nuclei on which the colour particles congregate. Coloured liquids such as crude solutions of sugar can be decolorised in this way, and many of the impurities removed.

The principle of adsorption has very important applications in chemical engineering practice. Not only can ultra-microscopic particles be adsorbed from liquid, but certain adsorption agents can adsorb gas and vapours. An extremely interesting application of the method which also involves distillation is concerned with solvent recovery.

TIDYING UP THE WASTE : SOLVENT RECOVERY

SOLVENT recovery is a very important matter from the economic point of view. Solvents are in general highly volatile liquids which are used for a variety of purposes such as extraction of oils and fats, dry cleaning, in " dope " and in cellulose lacquers. The problem is that, owing to their great volatility, large quantities are lost through direct evaporation into the atmosphere. The question arising is the possibility of recovering this solvent as it evaporates.

The problem has been solved, and the solution is one of the triumphs of chemical engineering. Like many other important inventions, the principle is simple. In the neighbourhood of the apparatus where the solvent is escaping, the opening of an aspirating system is placed. This consists of a pipe or system of interconnected pipes to which suction can be applied by the inclusion of a fan. The further end of the aspirator is connected with adsorbers which contain specially prepared activated carbon. When the suction is applied, the evaporating vapours are drawn through the pipes into the adsorbers, the vapours are there adsorbed by the activated carbon which is capable of taking up a very large quantity of the solvent.

When the adsorption is finished, the aspiration is shut off, and the adsorbers are ready for discharge. These vessels are of metal made in the form of a cylinder. There is an inlet connected with the aspirator, and an outlet which leads to a condenser. The activated carbon is then heated to drive off the solvent in the form of vapour. This is recondensed and collected in the receiver in the same way as in ordinary distillation.

The method of heating is an important element in the process. In the centre of the adsorbers there is a system of tubes heated by steam. Fans are so arranged within the cylinders that heated air is made to circulate through the activated carbon. This ensures uniform heating, obtainable in no other way, and the complete discharge of the adsorbed solvent.

This system has a very large number of applications and among them is the recovery of alcohol lost in fermentation. A fermenting liquid loses alcohol with the carbon dioxide gas which is evolved, and to deal with this alcohol-bearing gas, a modification of this form of solvent recovery apparatus has been devised. The method is complicated by the fact that the vapour contains water as well as alcohol, but the principle of adsorption is, of course, the same, no new principle of any kind being involved.

Activated carbon has to be very carefully prepared, since its efficiency as an adsorption agent depends upon the method of combustion of the material used to produce the carbon. A particular form of carbon much used for solvent recovery and for the recovery of alcohol in particular, is a substance manufactured in France known as " Acticarbone." Activated carbons vary very much in their efficiency as adsorption agents and different types of carbon have to be used according to the type of material to be adsorbed.

DESTROYING IN ORDER TO CREATE: DESTRUCTIVE DISTILLATION

WHILE the apparatus employed is of the same general type, destructive distillation differs entirely in principle from separation distillation. When a mixture of alcohol and water is heated and its vapours condensed, no chemical change takes place in the material distilled or in the distillate. It is simply a matter of separation of two liquids from each other. Destructive distillation always involves a change of chemical state in the material distilled, so that the distillate differs, and generally differs profoundly, in chemical composition from the original substance.

Probably one of the oldest forms of destructive distillation is the distillation of wood. It is of exceptional interest because the scientific methods of distillation grew out of a very old art, charcoal burning. Before the chemical nature of the reaction was understood, charcoal burning was utilised merely for the sake of the charcoal. An unscientific age did not realise that the most important product was not the charcoal but the vapours which escaped into the atmosphere and were lost.

But it was discovered by laboratory methods that these vapours, some of which are gaseous, and some of which can be condensed, were of great value. They consist of tar, acetic acid (wood vinegar), acetic anhydride, methyl alcohol (wood alcohol), and gases such as carbon dioxide, carbon monoxide, methane (marsh gas), and hydrogen.

The apparatus used for the distillation of wood is an iron retort, more generally a pair of retorts heated by means of a fire. An interesting point about the heating is that the gases finally given off, the carbon monoxide, methane, and hydrogen, can be burned. They are thus conducted back by means of a pipe into the furnace and are burned as fuel, so that the distillation itself supplies much of its own heat requirements.

The temperature of the process is a very important matter. According to whether the wood is heated quickly at a high temperature, or slowly at a lower temperature, so the composition of the distillate varies. If the temperature is high, and the retorts small, much gas is produced, less charcoal, and less acetic acid and tar. If the temperature is lower and the retort large, greater quantities of acid and charcoal are produced and less gas.

This is a very pretty problem both in science and economics. It is one of those examples in which the very essence of chemical engineering might be said to be summed up. In the first place, there is the chemical problem which is very complex. The temperature, the speed of heating, the size of the retort, the nature and composition of the wood, all have a profound effect upon the products of distillation. These questions have been studied in the laboratory and are thoroughly understood by the chemical engineer.

Without describing the reaction in detail, destructive distillation in general involves chemical changes technically known as " cracking." In detail, cracking is among the most complex of chemical reactions, but in general the word exactly describes the principle. It is the breaking down by heat of a complex substance into a number of other substances which are less complex.

Wood, for example, consists mainly of cellulose, the formula of which is $(C_6H_{10}O_5)_n$ which means that six atoms of carbon, ten atoms of hydrogen and five atoms of oxygen are associated together, and that this complex molecule is linked with others like it, although the number thus associated is not certainly known and is therefore represented by the letter n. Although recent researches have thrown a great deal of light on its composition, it must suffice to say that it is very complex.

But the compounds resulting from its distillation are much simpler. The formula of methyl alcohol is CH_3OH, that of acetic acid CH_3COOH, methane is CH_4, while carbon monoxide and carbon dioxide are respectively CO and CO_2. It is evident that these products are simpler in composition than the original cellulose, though they consist of the same elements. This form of degradation, as it is often called, is the principle of cracking. The scientific problem is so to control the temperature and other conditions that consistent results can be obtained in every case.

CHANGING THE CONDITIONS TO OBTAIN NEW PRODUCTS

THIS control of conditions has also an economic aspect. We have already seen that if the temperature is high, there is high yield of gas and lower yield of acetic acid and tar. If the temperature is lower, the conditions are reversed. It becomes a question of deciding how much gas is required to assist in heating the retort, and what is the maximum amount of other products which can be produced consistent with economical heating. More generally there is the obvious economic advantage that from wood, which is cheap and plentiful, valuable products can be obtained by destructive distillation.

The charcoal left as a residue in the retort, apart from its use as fuel, for gunpowder, and as a purifier, is the basis of many grades of activated carbon. The method of the preparation of Acticarbone, for example, is a further ignition of the charcoal under carefully regulated conditions in an oxidising atmosphere. This purifies the carbon and leaves it in a suitable physical condition to make it effective as an adsorption agent. The wood tar is also again redistilled, using fractionating apparatus very much on the principle of the Coffey Still. Tar oils, pitch, and turpentine are obtained by this process.

The most important process, however, is the treatment of the crude wood vinegar. This consists mainly of a mixture of acetic acid and methyl alcohol. These are separated by passing the liquor, as it distils, through lime in water. The acetic acid combines with the lime, while the methyl alcohol passes on and is condensed and rectified. The acetic acid combined with the lime (calcium acetate) is the source of pure acetic acid and acetone, but in 1912 the Feuerbach process,[1] which will be considered later, was developed for the production of acetone. Acetone is, however, still produced by the distillation of wood. The most important products are, however, from a commercial point of view, the methyl alcohol and the acetic acid. Both substances are very important industrially.

[1] See page 364.

A GREAT MODERN INDUSTRY: THE DISTILLATION OF COAL

IT used to be said of England, and for that matter of the Continent, that the introduction of coal gas did more to make the city streets safe for civilisation than hundreds of years' legislation. And the statement is quite true, since there is no question that crimes of robbery with violence, committed by footpads who took advantage of the dark streets, lost almost all their terrors for peaceful citizens after 1813. It was in this year that Murdock practically applied in the streets of London one of the most famous discoveries of modern civilisation, the destructive distillation of coal to produce coal gas.

In principle the method is exactly the same as that employed for the distillation of wood. The essential products of the distillation are coke, tar, an aqueous liquid and gas. Even now extremely little is known regarding the chemical composition of coal. The most recent researches of Bone and Armstrong seem to suggest that it consists mainly of a highly complex substance related to benzene, but substances of a resinous character are also present in it, and derivatives of cellulose. Coal also contains nitrogen and sulphur. In any case, a great deal more is known about its distillation products than about coal itself. The most important of these products is coal gas, which consists mainly of hydrogen and methane with some carbon monoxide. It is further contaminated with many evil-smelling compounds of which sulphuretted hydrogen is one. Before efficient methods of purification became available, the citizens at the beginning of the nineteenth century must have endured a good deal.

Although the plant is more complicated than the distilling apparatus of the laboratory, there is no essential modification in the gas retort. It consists of a series of chambers in which the coal is heated, with pipes corresponding to the neck, to conduct away the gas. It is also fitted with an outlet for liquid products.

The purification of the gas is a most essential part of the operation. Much of the tar and moisture is removed by condensation first in hydraulic mains and afterwards in air condensers, and sometimes it is finally cooled to complete the condensation. The next process is the washing of the gas by its passage over wetted coke. Finally the gas passes through chemical purifiers containing iron oxide and lime to remove sulphuretted hydrogen, carbon dioxide and other impurities.

This very briefly is the principle of the production of coal gas. It will have been noted that this first operation is more elaborate than in the distillation of wood since the gas, instead of being burnt crude to feed the furnace, is used for other purposes.

COAL-TAR : THE "STONE THE BUILDERS REJECTED"

WHEN we consider coal-tar, we are at once in the region of the greatest triumphs of modern industrial chemistry and chemical engineering. Originally the by-products of the distillation of coal were merely regarded as a nuisance to the manufacturers of coal gas, who had to get rid of them, and to the users of the gas, who were offended at their odour. Coal-tar, of course, always had its uses, but it was not until the chemist and the chemical engineer began to distil coal-tar, as they had distilled coal, that there was produced, among many other things, that variety of dyestuffs that has done so much to change the face of the modern world.

Again the operation of distilling coal-tar is destructive. The principal products of the distillation are benzene, toluene, xylene, naphthalene, anthracene, phenol and cresol. These compounds are all more complex than those produced by the distillation of wood, but they are, all the same, degradation products of the extremely complex coal-tar, the constitution of which is not known.

The first distillation process for coal-tar is carried out in the traditional form of still, the retort with the long neck attached to a coiled tube which is cooled by immersion in a tank of water (Fig. 89). As the distillation proceeds, however, the coil has to be heated with hot water, which takes the place of the former cold water, because the substances passing over solidify if they are overcooled. Below the still is a tank in which the fractions are collected. In this distillation also, the final fractions have to be distilled under reduced pressure in order to assist the distillation of the heavier oils.

The whole distillation consists of four fractions known as the light, middle, heavy and anthracene oils. These are again subjected to fractionation separately, and as a result, benzene, toluene, and xylene are separated. These are all solvents of very great value and of wide industrial application. The still used for this purpose is of a type similar to the Saville. Although the temperature at which these distillations are carried out is higher than for alcoholic liquids, the same principle of separation applies. The lighter fractions ascend and are thus separated from the heavier fractions.

In dealing with the middle oils, we are introduced to a very interesting modification of the process of distillation, since these oils contain large quantities of naphthalene. This is a solid substance which separates out from the oil on standing.

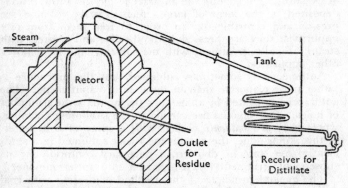

89. *Distilling coal-tar to obtain by-products in the manufacture of coal gas. The more volatile products are cooled in the tank ; later hot water is used in the tank to prevent solidification of the heavier oils. The heaviest fractions are distilled under reduced pressure.*

It is not possible to distil a solid substance, but it is possible to *sublime* it. The process of sublimation is to heat the solid so that it vaporises, and to conduct the vapours into a large chamber which is cool. As a result, the vapours are redeposited on the sides of the chamber in their original solid form. Just as in distillation and in recrystallisation, the sublimed solid is purer than the original substance.

FURTHER PURIFICATION OF COAL-TAR : THE BY-PRODUCTS EMERGE

ADDITIONAL methods of purification are, however, necessary. The naphthalene has to be recrystallised as well. Petroleum is the solvent used, and it is heated with the naphthalene under a reflex condenser, that is to say, a condenser is fixed to the heating apparatus to prevent the escape of the petroleum, which is condensed, and drops back into the crystallizing vessel. The naphthalene is finally dried centrifugally, and forms beautiful white crystalline plates. The heavy oils consist mainly of creosote, which is invaluable for the preservation of wood.

The anthracene oils are the most important of all, because they are the source of alizarin, which is the base of a group of dyestuffs. On cooling the anthracene oil, the anthracene is deposited in the form of large green crystals. These are pressed and centrifuged. In order to free them from oily impurities, they are pressed hydraulically, and treated with steam. Finally, treatment with the solvent naphtha removes other impurities.

Anthracene is sometimes sublimed, but the procedure is rather more elaborate than in the case of naphthalene. The anthracene is heated in a chamber perforated with a number of holes. The vapours are carried to the subliming chamber, where they are *suddenly* chilled with a spray of cold water. If this is not done, the anthracene is not sublimed in a sufficiently fine state of division, a necessary condition for its subsequent treatment and conversion into anthraquinone.

The general principle of this method of dealing with coal will now be clear. It will also be evident that the entire success of the operation depends upon the technique of distillation. The coal has to be distilled in order to obtain gas. The by-products have to be redistilled, for the purpose of separation and cracking.

Benzene and anthracene are the two most important by-products of coal distillation. Both are the basis of valuable dyes, benzene through aniline, and anthracene through anthraquinone. In the production of aniline, nitrobenzene has first to be prepared from benzene. This is carried out by treating benzene with a mixture of nitric and sulphuric acids. It is a good example of a reaction in which the temperature must be most carefully regulated and energetic agitation employed. The mixture is first kept down to below blood heat and it is later allowed to rise somewhat above it. This question of temperature is vital because if it rises too high a different compound, dinitrobenzene, is formed. Further, the reaction is dangerous since with too high a temperature the mixture may fire.

The second operation is the *reduction* of the nitrobenzene. Roughly speaking, reduction replaces some or all of the oxygen in a compound by hydrogen ; in this case, nitrobenzene, whose formula is $C_6H_5NO_2$, is converted into aniline, whose formula is $C_6H_5NH_2$. The reduction is carried out by mixing the nitrobenzene with hydrochloric acid and iron in a retort fitted with a condenser. Hydrogen is generated which replaces the oxygen, and as a result of it aniline and nitrobenzene distil over, and are continuously returned to the retort until the reaction is complete. This operation can also be very dangerous. When it becomes too violent, explosions can, and have often been known to take place.

We have thus arrived, after a series of processes involving distillation at most stages, at the formation of a number of compounds upon which the greater part of the huge structure of the organic chemical industries is based. From aniline and anthracene the whole dyestuff industry has been evolved, while drugs and plastics also find their genesis in the products of coal-tar.

This principle of cracking finds many applications outside the sphere of the distillation of coal. The cracking of oils in general has large and increasing applications in industry. The great importance of the application of this process to the treatment of oils is its ability to separate the lighter from the heavier fractions, the lighter oils being in great demand for petrol and oil-driven engines.

In principle, the cracking process consists in heating the crude oil in a distilling apparatus until the lighter fractions have passed over. Successive fractions are returned to the still, which is heated to a higher temperature so that a further cracking is achieved. This is continued until nothing remains but a residue of tar and heavy oils. Many elaborations of the simple still have been devised. In one process, the oil is vaporised in a chamber consisting of a series of tubes heated to a suitable temperature. The cracked vapour is then cooled in a condenser and collected.

CATALYSTS : THE SPONSORS OF CHEMICAL CHANGE

BEFORE considering further modifications of the cracking process something must be said regarding the interesting question of " catalysts." A catalyst is a substance which, when present only in relatively minute quantity, will bring about a reaction which cannot otherwise be induced to take place. This in itself might not appear surprising if it were not for the fact that the catalyst itself apparently remains unchanged. It is not certain that this is, in fact, the case. Possibly the catalyst may undergo a temporary change or series of changes and then return to its original form. On the other hand, its effect may be purely physical. It is, however, generally held that the real effect of the catalyst is to accelerate a reaction which would take place in any case if given time ; but the reaction without the catalyst may be so slow as to be, for all practical purposes, no reaction at all.

If hydrogen and oxygen are mixed in a vessel they may be left in contact indefinitely without interaction taking place. Introduce a little " platinum black " (finely divided platinum) into the vessel, and there will be an explosion. Acting catalytically, the platinum black has caused the hydrogen and oxygen to combine with the formation of water (H_2O).

An interesting practical application of this catalytic effect is a certain form of gas lighter. This contains a small quantity of platinum black. When this is held over an open gas burner, it brings about combination between the hydrogen of the gas and the oxygen of the air, so that a flame is produced and the gas lights. There is no explosion because the gas has not reached a sufficient concentration in the atmosphere of the room. It would be extremely dangerous if a lighter of this type were left in a room where the gas had accidentally been left on. When the required concentration of gas was attained, an explosion would occur as inevitably as if a match were lit in the room.

These catalysts have now a very wide application in industry, but we will first consider an early application in connection with the matter we have discussed, the cracking of petroleum vapour. The process consisted in the heating of a mixture of petroleum and water in a chamber fitted with red-hot iron. This was supposed to act as a catalytic agent. The oil and aqueous vapours were conducted to a fractionating column and then condensed and collected. By this means it was claimed that a very high yield of light spirit was obtained. In this process, it is probable that not only the petroleum but the water was cracked, and that the hydrogen produced assisted in the production of the lighter oil. We shall consider this later.

An interesting modern development is the cracking of ammonia by passing it at a temperature of 600° C. over a catalyst, the nature of which is still a commercial secret. The hydrogen obtained by this means (ammonia consists of nitrogen and hydrogen) contains a high percentage of nitrogen which cannot readily be separated from it. It is believed, however, that this method will be developed to have wide industrial application in the future.

HOW HYDROGENATION IMPROVES UPON "CLASSICAL" REDUCTION

BUT it is impossible to consider the technique of oil-cracking apart from what is known as "hydrogenation." Hydrogenation is, in effect, the process of reduction which has already been described.[1] It effects the introduction of more hydrogen into certain compounds, so that, for example, petrol and high-grade oils can be produced from the crude products of coal carbonisation more effectively than by simple cracking, and often when cracking alone would not produce the required result.

Hydrogenation is a refined method of reduction, and it consists in mixing hydrogen gas with the product to be refined in the presence of a catalyst. In classical reduction processes where no catalyst is used, the hydrogen, to be effective, must actually be generated in the presence of the substance to be treated. This involves the use of a strong acid and some metal such as iron or zinc. In practice this is not always simple. From a chemical engineering point of view it is easier and generally more effective to pass the gas into the required vessel containing the vapour or other matter to be treated in the presence of a catalyst.

The reduction of nitrobenzene to aniline which has been described is an example. It will not be long before the old method of reduction gives place entirely to the hydrogenation of nitrobenzene, thus reducing the cost, trouble, and even to some extent the risk, of an operation which can still be scheduled as "dangerous."

Apart from its applications in this connection, hydrogenation is employed for the hardening of certain fats. In one process the hydrogenation is carried out under pressure in an auto-clave.[2] A further important application is the hydrogenation of all kinds of fuel and the application of the process to certain phenols which produce emulsifying agents.

[1] See p. 317.   [2] See p. 292.

THE EFFICIENT USE OF COAL : LOW-TEMPERATURE CARBONISATION

WE now have to consider a modification of the distillation of coal which, while it has not yet attained great industrial importance, is the fuel industry, par excellence, of the future : the low-temperature carbonisation of coal. There is no doubt at all that the use of coal as fuel is no longer an economic proposition, for it has long been recognised that nothing is more wasteful than a coal fire. It is being steadily replaced by oil, of which enormous supplies are available, thanks to modern methods of treatment which have been described. The day of coal as fuel is undoubtedly over unless more economical means of utilizing it are made available so that it can compete with oil in the industrial field. Proceeding a step further, we realise that our indirect method of utilizing coal in the form of gas is uneconomic in practice, unless some new method of producing the gas can be found, whereby so much of the energy of the coal which would be wasted by the old method can be successfully used.

Roughly speaking, low-temperature carbonisation has three main objects : the production of fuel burnt as coal which shall be equally efficient for the heating purposes, and shall be practically free from sulphur, and smokeless ; the production of phenolic bodies which by cracking can be converted into petrol and Diesel oils in sufficient quantities to produce liquid fuel at an economic price ; and the production of coal gas.

It is not true to say that low-temperature carbonisation is not being utilized commercially at all. Most people have heard of " Coalite " even if they have not used it. Coalite is essentially a product of one of those low-temperature processes which is actually in operation. It is claimed that by this method, 4,000 cubic feet of high grade gas are produced, 14 cwt. of Coalite, 18–20 gallons of crude oil and 2–3½ gallons of petrol per ton of coal treated. The crude oils are said to be amenable to cracking for the production of good petrol and other high-grade fuel oils.

There are many processes which are being tried out on a large-scale experimental or semi-industrial basis. There is the Wissner, the K.S.G., the Plassman and the McEwen Runge among many others. At Ashby-de-la-Zouche a small low-temperature carbonisation plant is at work. Even if complete details were available, and they are not, space would not allow of a description of all these processes, but at the same time some allusion to the general principle lying behind all of them is necessary.

The old method of producing gas was founded more or less upon the principle of " letting it rip," but as soon as it was discovered that certain constituents passed over at certain temperatures, the principle, at least, of scientific carbonisation was established. One of the main features of all low-temperature carbonisation methods is the rigid control of temperature. In the Julius-Pintsch process, for example, the temperature is between 1,000° F. and 1,250° F. In the Wissner process it does not exceed 600° F. In the K.S.G. process the temperature is from 925° F. to 1,025° F.

The next question is the method of applying the heat. This varies very greatly. In some cases the heat is applied externally in the classical manner, but in general this method is too crude. Air heated to a definite temperature is used in some cases. There is a method which employs superheated coal gas. A certain Italian process utilizes superheated steam; in another, the coal is heated over a bath of molten lead, the temperature of which is rigidly regulated. It is these refinements of temperature control which so profoundly affect the nature of the resulting products.

A third matter of great importance is the physical state of the coal itself during the process of heating. It may be in lumps or in powder or it may be agitated in a variety of ways. In the McEwen-Runge process, pulverised coal is passed through a long cylinder, which is heated to the required temperature. In the Piron-Caracristi process, the coal is contained in conveyors which travel across the heated bath. As in many other chemical operations, the physical conditions under which the action takes place have a great effect on the final products.

THE FUTURE OF LOW-TEMPERATURE CARBONISATION

MANY new developments in and modifications of the process of low-temperature carbonisation are possible and will probably be utilised in the future. Up to now, there has not been much work done on the distillation of coal under reduced pressure. It will be remembered that the object of heating, and distillation which involves heating, under reduced pressure is that the substance so treated can be volatilised at a lower temperature if the pressure is reduced.

It is interesting to consider why low-temperature carbonisation should give more satisfactory results than the classical methods of distillation. Having regard to the highly complex composition of coal, the reactions which take place when it is heated, are only partially understood, but there are certain effects of low-temperature carbonisation which are quite clear. It avoids a premature cracking of the products of distillation and therefore renders the subsequent heat treatment a process which can be much more readily controlled. Apart from this, low-temperature distillation gives a good yield of petrol, a hydrocarbon of low boiling point. For this reason, the products of the distillation have a high value, and in terms of power, represent an enormously increased efficiency as compared with that of the original coal.

A large coal distillation plant might be described as the paradise of the chemical engineer. There is no operation which requires more careful regulation nor a closer under-standing of the reactions which are going on within the apparatus. On the other hand, there are the mechanical problems controlling the change of physical state of the sub-stance treated so as to ensure the most satisfactory results.

There is another matter which is of considerable interest. Since the technique of low-temperature carbonisation is already fairly well understood, it might well be asked why it has not been more widely adopted. There is, technically speaking, nothing whatever to prevent the application of low-temperature carbonisation on a much larger scale than obtains at present. It has been shown to be an economically sound method of dealing with coal. By no means all the problems have been solved, but there is a good case for its introduction on a much larger scale in direct connection with coal mining itself.

It must be remembered, however, that the successful application of science to industry depends, at present, upon whether it is more profitable to exploit a new scientific dis-covery, or to obstruct its exploitation. On the face of it, it would appear that the former course must always be the more successful, but experience has shown us that opinion is not unanimous in this matter. This again raises the question of whose interest scientific invention ought to further, and under what social regime technical achievement is likely to receive the fullest recognition.

Without expressing any opinion regarding the solution of

these problems, it will be sufficient if those interested in applied science will realise that they exist, and will endeavour to find a solution for themselves. The technologist is not merely a specialist, he is a part of the highly technical structure of modern society ; and in the material sense he is, in fact, the skeleton of that structure itself. He can no longer consider his work out of relation to its application in the society in which he lives. A new coal distillation process is invented, and at once international rivalry with a foreign oil-exporting power creeps higher. In another country miners' wages will be forced to a lower level. This is an example of the social and economic consequences necessarily attendant upon technical discovery. The interaction between technical and social problems is a matter which cannot be ignored by the technician without peril to himself and the society of which he forms a part.

EVAPORATING : CRYSTALLISING : PRECIPITATING

EVAPORATION, which is a simpler operation than distilling, need not detain us very long. Essentially there is no difference in method between that used in the laboratory and in the works, but, the question of efficiency has to be considered since the heat required to evaporate, for example, a solution of some substance in water is the principal charge against the operation. It is for this reason that unlike the laboratory evaporation it is generally carried out under reduced pressure.

If the pressure of the atmosphere is reduced, the boiling point of a liquid is invariably lowered. From the point of view of economics this is important. With a moderate reduction of pressure for example, the boiling point of water can be reduced from 100° to 50° C. If the vacuum can be produced at lower cost than the amount of fuel required to raise the liquid through that extra fifty degrees, it is obvious that an economy has been effected. Now in general it is true that it is more economical to reduce pressure than to raise temperature. The vacuum pan is therefore a commonplace of the works where evaporation has to be carried out.

There are often other very good reasons for evaporation under reduced pressure. The solution being evaporated may be unstable when boiled under normal pressure. All sorts of precautions have to be taken to avoid this. The steam coil, for instance, is generally used for heating ; and accidents may happen. Although, roughly speaking, at a given pressure a liquid cannot be heated above certain temperatures, if the steam passing through it is too hot, the vessel itself may become superheated. The liquid or the substance dissolved in it may thus be decomposed.

Further the liquid itself may become superheated in some circumstances and thus " bump." Most people who have boiled water in a glass vessel will know what " bumping " is. The liquid boils quietly and then suddenly appears to cease

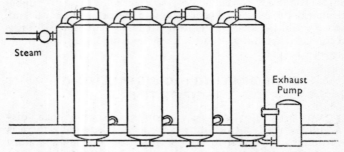

90. The multiple heat evaporator which economises heat by using the steam, cooled during the evaporation process taking place in one vessel, to heat the next.

boiling. Suddenly the normal boiling effect will recommence but with great violence so that some of the water may be thrown out of the vessel. On a large scale the effect is somewhat less violent but it may give considerable trouble.

The principal problem of evaporation is the economic utilisation of heat. Steam, as we have said, is commonly used, and with it often the " multiple-effect " system (Fig. 90). In this method the steam given off by one vessel is conducted through pipes to heat a second, third, or more vessels. In many cases this is the more economical method of heating but not in all.

With evaporation as with other methods which require heat, certain units are the basis of the calculations used in connection with the heat applied. The principal one is the British Thermal Unit. This is the amount of heat required to raise 1 pound of water through 1° Fahrenheit. The Continental unit is the metric unit. Both in England and on the Continent this unit is called the *Calorie*, though this term should strictly be reserved for the metric unit. The metric calorie is the quantity of heat required to raise 1 gramme of water through 1° Centigrade. The great calorie or kilocalorie is the amount of heat required to raise 1 kilogramme of water through 1° Centigrade. Since 1° Fahrenheit equals $\frac{5}{9}$ of a degree Centigrade and 1 kilogramme equals 2·2 pounds, the British Thermal Unit equals 0·252 kilocalories.

The quantity of heat in terms of calories required to raise water and other liquids to a given temperature is of course known. It is thus possible to calculate the calories required for a given operation and express them in terms of steam at a given pressure. This is an essential part of the economics of any heating operation.

But a second and almost equally important point is the heat lost from a given vessel by radiation. This can also be calculated on the basis of radiation from every square metre of the surface of the vessel. The radiation, of course, varies with the material of which the vessel is made.

In practice wherever possible vessels have to be " heat-insulated " to reduce radiation to the minimum. Asbestos is commonly used for this purpose. The question of the amount of heat which can be utilised in any given operation is often of first-rate importance. It may make just the difference required to turn a loss into a profit.

It is for this reason that the submerged flame which we have already described is so interesting to the chemical engineer. The efficiency is extremely high. But the disadvantage is that the products of the combustion of the flame pass into the liquid which is being heated. This in many cases brings about chemical changes which adversely affect the solutions which have to be evaporated. It is for this reason that it has not up to now been greatly employed for evaporation.

CRYSTALLISATION IN THE MANUFACTURE OF SUGAR

WHAT is the most common aim of evaporation ? While it may be merely for the purposes of concentration, it is very frequently intended to effect *crystallisation*. In order to illustrate the uses of crystallisation we could not do better than describe the operation in relation to a substance we use every day, namely sugar. It might be thought that so cheap and universal a commodity must be simple to manufacture, but in fact the production of sugar involves highly technical operations, particularly in connection with its crystallisation.

The problem is that the juice containing the sugar is primarily in a very liquid state and a high degree of evaporation is necessary to crystallise it. The classical methods for the evaporation of sugar juice involved the use of open pans heated directly by fire. As a result the sugar was *caramelised* to a great extent, invert sugar (honey sugar) was formed, and the cost of heating was relatively high. The first improvement was the use of steam and this was followed by the " multiple effect " system which is very economical for this kind of evaporation. Reduced pressure and the " multiple effect " are commonly used together.

The first vessel is heated with steam, and the steam from the evaporating solution is conducted on to heat the next vessel and so on. An exhaust pump is connected with the final vessel so that the last stages of the evaporation are carried out under reduced pressure. As it concentrates the syrup passes from vessel to vessel, and, under increasing concentration it is subjected to decreasing pressure. There are two advantages in this method. In the first place the heat is utilised with great efficiency. In the second place the reduction of pressure in the final stages minimises the decomposition and darkening of the syrup.

Syrup of a certain concentration is obtained by this boiling, but evaporation to the crystallisation stage requires further heating with further reduction of pressure. As the syrup evaporates its boiling-point becomes higher and without thoroughly efficient vacuum pans, great damage would be done to the product.

The crystallisation of the sugar is a very important technical problem. This boiling to the " grain " stage is intended to effect crystallisation of a uniform kind, and to produce crystals of a type which will not give trouble in the subsequent centrifuging. One of the difficulties which arise may be the formation of small crystals which clog up the apparatus.

The preliminary operation has to be carried out in two stages. After the syrup has been concentrated to a certain thickness, small crystals tend to separate as the syrup stands. It is then heated, so that the small crystals go into solution first. As the concentration continues under the second heating the larger crystals remain undissolved, and a further crop are deposited also of large size. This is the key to the whole process at this point. Conditions of pressure and therefore of temperature have to be adjusted so as to ensure that small crystals shall not be formed. Unless the operation is very carefully controlled the small crystals tend to reform. They are sometimes called the *false grain*.

GETTING THE PERFECT CRYSTAL

THE bulk of the crystallisation takes place, however, when the syrup cools. For this purpose it is transferred to vessels which may be opened or closed. A crystalliser is often used which is made in the form of a cylinder. These crystallisers are always fitted with some form of agitating apparatus. Alternatively the cylindrical vessel can be rotated. *Crystallisation in motion*, as it is called, is generally regarded as the most satisfactory method.

The object of this elaborate method of crystallisation is the formation of crystals of sufficient and uniform size. In principle the aim is to produce as a preliminary crystals of large size round which the new crystals collect as around a nucleus. If the *false grain* is formed at any step in the operation this object is defeated.

In considering the next step in crystallisation we are again introduced to the centrifuge. It is of the general type which has already been described. The object of the centrifuging is preliminary separation of the crystals from the mother liquor. This separation is not complete and the crystals have to be washed with water which is applied in the form of a fine spray. Some of the sugar is, of course, dissolved in the washing water. This is one of the problems of the sugar industry and indeed a problem of industrial crystallisation altogether. In order to purify by crystallisation, and to purify the crystals when they are obtained considerable loss seems to be inevitable. The " mother liquor " from which the crystals are obtained always contains a quantity of the substance remaining in solution, and washing methods also always remove not only the impurities but considerable amounts of the substance to be purified also.

Another source of great trouble and loss is the presence of substances which interfere with the crystallisation of the sugar. Mineral salts present in the juice have a very serious effect. The reason for this is not clearly understood. But the matter is very important and raw sugar is always sold on the basis of its " crystallisable sugar."

CASTING A SUBSTANCE OUT OF SOLUTION : PRECIPITATION

WHEN we come to consider the treatment of the molasses, the residues from the previous operations, the reader has to be introduced to a new principle : that of precipitation, which depends in principle upon so changing the nature of the substances in solution that the one to be separated becomes insoluble in water, when it can be removed by evaporation, filtration or decantation. In separating sugar from molasses, a chemical reaction is made to occur by adding a salt of calcium, barium or strontium. Cane sugar has the formula $C_{12}H_{22}O_{11}$. Calcium, strontium and barium hydrates are respectively $Ca(OH)_2$, $Ba(OH)_2$, and $Sr(OH)_2$. If we represent either the calcium, barium or strontium as R the general form of the equation is as follows :

$$2R(OH)_2 + C_{12}H_{22}O_{11} = C_{12}H_{22}O_{11}2RO + 2H_2O$$
The hydrate + sugar = the saccharate + water

It will be noted that while the hydrate has changed its composition the sugar molecule has remained unchanged. The new compound is, however, insoluble, and the sugar is thus precipitated in the form of this basic sucrate or saccharate as it is called. This precipitate is rapidly filtered. It is then suspended in water, and treated with carbon dioxide gas. Carbon dioxide combines with the barium, calcium or strontium, as the case may be, to form the insoluble carbonate. The sugar is thus again set free purified from other substances which previously contaminated it.

SOFTENING WATER : THE PREVENTION OF BOILER SCALE

AN extremely interesting example of precipitation involving a mutual change in the substances in solution, to form new compounds, is the technique for the softening of water. There is probably no chemical process of greater importance industrially than this. Steam raising still remains, ultimately, the basis of a large part of our industrial power, and with steam raising, boilers are inevitably associated.

The efficiency of a boiler depends, more than anything else, upon the water used to feed it. If it is *hard*, that is to say, if it contains relatively large quantities of calcium and magnesium, particularly in the form of carbonates, then when the water is boiled these salts are precipitated, the calcium carbonate at once and some of the magnesium carbonate with the passage of time. This is the well-known *boiler scale,* which can be found in any kettle. The effect of this *boiler scale* (which is often so hard that it cannot be removed without heavy hammers and cold chisels) is enormously to reduce the efficiency of the boiler. The object of softening the water is to prevent the formation of this scale.

In order to do this, the calcium and magnesium must be removed from the water. There is a variety of methods for effecting this. The calcium and magnesium are present in the water in the form of the bicarbonates. If the water is treated with lime these salts are converted into magnesium and calcium carbonate. Practically all the calcium carbonate —being insoluble—is precipitated. The magnesium is further acted upon by the lime forming the insoluble magnesium hydrate and calcium carbonate, so that the magnesium is also precipitated. This process, the oldest, was first advocated in 1841, and it was in use in 1884. The chemical equations are as follows :

(1)
$$Ca(HCO_3)_2 + Ca(OH)_2 = 2CaCO_3 + 2H_2O$$

calcium bicarbonate + lime = normal calcium carbonate + water

$$Mg(HCO_3)_2 + Ca(OH)_2 = CaCO_3 + MgCO_3 + 2H_2O$$

magnesium bicarbonate + lime = normal calcium carbonate + magnesium carbonate + water

(2)
$$MgCO_3 + Ca(OH)_2 = Mg(OH)_2 + CaCO_3$$

magnesium carbonate + lime = magnesium hydrate + normal calcium carbonate

But this method deals only with the carbonate. Other salts of calcium may be, and generally are, present, such as calcium sulphate. If the water is treated also with sodium carbonate the calcium sulphate is converted into calcium carbonate.

Of recent years a highly interesting method of softening has been widely introduced, known as the Permutit Process. Like many others it is an artificial adaptation of natural technique. It was discovered many years ago that certain waters were naturally softened by percolation through mineral strata known as zeolites. These substances are complex silicates which have the property of exchanging part of their base with the base of the water with which they came in contact.

E.   11*

Calcium and magnesium, for example, can thus be removed from water which is treated with sodium permutit so that the permutit captures the calcium and magnesium, and the sodium passes to the water.

This method is extremely simple, and it is very economical by reason of the peculiar property of the permutit of exchanging its base, but otherwise remaining unaffected. Water is merely passed through the permutit as through a filter, and is softened as it passes. After a time the sodium permutit becomes completely changed to calcium and magnesium permutit, but to regenerate it it is merely necessary to pass through the permutit filter a solution of salt (sodium chloride). The reaction works both ways. Calcium permutit exchanges with sodium quite as readily as does sodium permutit with calcium. By this simple method the permutit is regenerated and can be used over and over again.

The Permutit Process is one of the triumphs of chemical engineering, particularly on account of the great simplicity of its operation. In other water-softening plant the operation is much more elaborate since precipitation and filtration are necessary, and various automatic devices have to be introduced to control the quantity of softening reagent being added as the water passes through the plant. These devices can be the source of a good deal of trouble. In devising the Permutit Process, chemical engineering achieved what is one of its principle aims, that of making a chemical reaction carry out as much work as possible.

These examples of precipitation methods give a general idea of how the principle is applied in large scale operations. There are, of course, many others, but all alike rely upon the mixing of two substances to produce an insoluble substance which is removed from its menstruum either by filtration settling or passage through a filterpress in the manner which has been described.

USING A SOLVENT AGAIN AND AGAIN

SOLIDS are separated from solids, and particularly oils from fats, by the extraction method, which consists in using a solvent, applied several times, to dissolve one constituent of the mixture, leaving the other untouched. It is important to remember that in large scale extraction one of the methods used is never applied in the laboratory : the extraction of oil by pressure. Nor need we do more than notice it here since the apparatus employed involves, as a rule, purely mechanical problems.

One of the questions involved in connection with extraction with volatile solvents concerns the danger of fire and explosion. Most volatile solvents for oils are highly inflammable. There is one remarkable exception : carbon tetrachloride. Not only is this solvent non-inflammable : it is even used for extinguishing fire.

Two methods of extraction are commonly in use, the hot

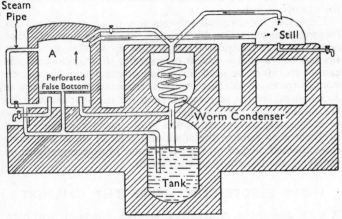

91. The hot method of separating solids by dissolving one constituent with a solvent applied again and again. The solvent is superheated, its vapour passes upwards through the material to be extracted (contained in A) and is then recondensed to start the cycle again.

and cold extraction. The principle of the cold extraction is very simple. Material to be extracted is placed in a cylindrical vessel fitted with outlets and inlets. The solvent to be used is pumped in at the bottom of the vessel, and when it is full is left in contact with the material to be extracted for a short time. There is usually a battery of vessels and the solvent passes from one to the other. The solvent remaining in contact with the extracted material is driven off with steam, recondensed in the ordinary way and used again.

The hot method of extraction is the more interesting technically. Essentially the plant consists of receiver containing the solvent which passes to a superheater where it is vaporised. The vapour passes to the extractor which contains the material from which the fat is to be removed. Extraction of the fat is effected in this chamber and the fat passes to the bottom of the extractor dissolved in that part of the solvent which is condensed there.   The vapour passes out of the extractor to the condenser where it is liquefied and returned to the original receiver, whence it passes once more to the superheater.   The process is thus continuous.   This apparatus is much used for the extraction of bones.   It is economical in the use of solvent.

Extraction by chemical solvents is a much more thorough method than extraction by pressure, but it has one great disadvantage.   It has proved impossible up to now to remove the last traces of the solvent completely.   Extraction methods cannot therefore be used for edible oils and fats, since even minute traces of solvents impart a nauseous taste.   There is a considerable field of research both for the chemist and the chemical engineer in this direction.   From the point of view of economics, solvent extraction is obviously superior.   The problem is to remove the smell and taste in some way from the extracted oils, or on the other hand to devise methods of removing the last traces of the solvent.

HOW ELECTRICITY HELPS THE CHEMIST

WE now have to consider another chemical operation which has an ever widening field of application in industry : electrolysis.   Electrolysis is one of those operations peculiar in the sense that it was applied in some directions commercially before it was developed in the laboratory. Before the chemist began to estimate the quantity of a given metal in a mixture by electrolysis, silver plating was being practised on a commercial scale.   Even coiners knew how to utilise it as far back as 1870.   It has now many other applications besides the electro-deposition of metals, and we shall consider these presently, but since the electro-deposition of metals is the oldest industrially, we will consider this first.

Theoretically any metal can be electrically deposited from a solution of its salts.   But in practice the metal either cannot be deposited in sufficient quantity, or it may be deposited in such a condition as to make it commercially useless.   Unless the method can be applied either to plate a metallic or other surface with a smooth bright coating, or to deposit the required metal in the form of sheet which can be stripped off the electrode, the process is of no use commercially.

Many metals, however, can be, and are deposited on a large scale in a satisfactory manner. The first of these was, as we have indicated, silver. Copper seems to have been the next to be developed; zinc, iron, chromium, nickel, tin and lead are others which are amenable to electrolysis. This does not mean that these processes are in all cases being worked to any great extent, but copper, nickel, silver, and more recently chromium, are well established industrially.

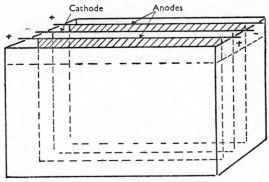

92. *The essentials of an electroplating tank. This form contains a central cathode and two anodes.*

From the mechanical point of view, electro-deposition presents no very difficult problem; it is in fact a domain almost entirely reserved for the chemist and the chemical engineer. Essentially the apparatus consists of a tank to contain the solution to be electrolysed and the electrodes, anode and cathode, secured on opposite sides of it, insulated, of course, in respect of the tank so that contact can be established only through the solution (Fig. 92). These are, naturally, connected positively and negatively with the source of electrical power.

This is the simplest arrangement, but in some cases the metal has to be deposited upon a *rotating* cathode. In this case the cathode is cylindrical and is surrounded by the anode in place of mere opposition of the two plates. Mechanically this slightly complicates the plant, but it obviously involves no special difficulty.

The problem involved in all methods of electrolysis is the production of a deposit which shall be in every way equal to the production of metal in the form required by any other process. It is useless if a protective coating is porous, or if the metal has not the necessary tensile strength, or if it has faults or impurities.

METALS WHICH CAN BE ELECTRO-DEPOSITED : CHROMIUM PLATING

To ensure that these conditions shall be fulfilled the most rigorous control of the composition of the electrolyte is necessary. There is no chemical reaction more delicate, nor more easily disturbed than that of electrolysis. It is indeed a remarkable fact that while a great deal is apparently known regarding the reactions that take place in any electrolyte during the passage of the current, and that they appear in principle to be simple, it is in many cases extremely difficult to obtain consistent results. The reactions may be more complex than is realised. There is no doubt at all that minute quantities of impurity in some electrolytes will profoundly affect the nature of the deposited metal, and that for reasons very difficult to ascertain a deposition process which has been working perfectly smoothly will sometimes begin to give trouble.

This is not to say that electro-deposition is unreliable in the industrial sense. The difficulties are not as great as that. Excellent electrolytic copper is produced in the form of foil or sheet. By deposition upon a cathode of the required shape, copper tubes can be produced which have the advantage of being seamless. Electrolytic zinc is frequently used as a protective coating for iron in place of galvanising. For some purposes it is much more satisfactory since a good electro-deposit of zinc is much smoother than even the best galvanising.

Lead is another metal which can be satisfactorily deposited, and lead of excellent quality and high purity can be obtained. The method has often been used for the purpose of refining lead, as well as obtaining directly utilisable deposits. In connection with lead also, there have been many interesting patents for the production of lead foil on revolving cathodes of special construction, from which the lead is stripped while the deposition is proceeding.

The position in connection with iron is very interesting. As long ago as 1910 or earlier, a plant was working in Sweden which produced iron tubes of considerable length and thickness. But for technical and probably economic reasons the deposition of iron has not, up to now, prospered commercially. The advantages would be very great if it were possible to produce iron tubes by deposition, since the expense of welding is eliminated. But at the present moment the deposits obtained are unreliable and the metal often has to be annealed in special ways so that the process ceases to be economic.

Chromium plating is now a commonplace of the household, and has, as everyone knows, widely extended application. It is only during the last seven years that this form of electro-deposition has been made a commercial success, and there is still plenty of room for improvement in the processes in use. It is, however, the most interesting recent development in the technology of electro-metallurgy.

We now have to consider other applications of electricity to the chemical industries. The most interesting of these is the electrolysis of fused salts. This has great interest theoretically as well as practically, since the fact that a fused salt can be electrolysed shows that ionization can take place without the presence of water as a medium of solution. Aluminium, calcium, magnesium, sodium and potassium can be produced commercially in this way.

The principle is to heat the salts to their melting point and to electrolyse them, generally between carbon electrodes. In the case of aluminium, the metal separates and falls to the bottom of the fusion pot where it is drawn off in a molten condition by means of a tap. Calcium separates in a solid condition, as does magnesium. Sodium and potassium float on the surface of the electrolyte and are drawn off at the top by means of a tap.

These processes are rapidly gaining great industrial importance. The older methods for the production of metals from their salts involve more or less complicated processes and consequently high costs of production.

PRODUCING GASES BY ELECTROLYSIS

WE must also consider the production of gases by electrolysis. Where large quantities of oxygen, for example, are required, we have already the process of fractionating liquid air. But the gas so obtained is not pure. Its purity seldom exceeds 97%. Electrolytic oxygen, on the other hand, can be produced of a purity of 99·3%. Electrolytic oxygen can be produced by the electrolysis of water. Hydrogen is produced also, the oxygen at the anode and the hydrogen at the cathode. The hydrogen is of high purity and therefore particularly suitable for the hydrogenation of fats.

But the most important application of electrolysis to the production of a gas is the electrolytic process for chlorine. It is among the earliest of applications of electrolysis to industry. The first process for the production of electrolytic chlorine, the Griesheim Diaphragm Process, was first operated in 1890. The principle is the same both in the classical and the more modern methods : a solution of common salt in water, which is, of course, very cheap, is electrolysed. Chlorine appears at the anode, and sodium, which is converted by the action of the water into sodium hydrate, at the cathode.

The process is not as simple as this in operation, since secondary products such as sodium hypochlorite are formed which seriously retard the electrolysis. In practice that is overcome by the use of the diaphragm, which is simply a porous partition which prevents the diffusion of the soda and the consequent secondary reaction. A second method is the use of a mercury cathode which forms an alloy with the sodium. In this method not only are the secondary reactions prevented, but the metallic sodium can be recovered.

There are many other applications of electrolysis to industry, but these, namely, the production of metallic deposits, the electrolysis of fused salts, and the electrolytic preparation of gases represent the most important.

INSPECTING AND TESTING THE MATERIALS USED

CHEMICAL analysis is an extraordinarily important factor in the examination of materials. Thus the chemical engineer is frequently concerned with the problem of the strength of materials, particularly so in relation to their resistance to chemical reagents. The composition of metals and alloys has a great bearing upon their resistance to corrosive action.

This is well illustrated by the example of metallic *couples*. When two metals are in contact and both are suspended in water or in a moist atmosphere what is known as galvanic action takes place. In other words, the couple becomes an electric cell. The result is that severe corrosion will take place in one of the metals. This corrosion will be much more serious than if the metals alone were exposed to moisture or water. Different metallic couples react differently in this respect. Again, the nature of the liquid in contact with the metals affects the corrosive conditions.

The nature of the alloys used for different operations has therefore to be very carefully watched by the chemical engineer working in collaboration with the chemist. An alloy is a mixture of two or more metals and these, of course, may act as a galvanic couple producing a strong corrosive effect. It depends upon the metals combined in the alloy, and the nature of the liquid with which they are in contact. Secondly, impurities in metals may, obviously, have the same effect, and some metals even when present in minute quantities may seriously lower the resistance of the metal to the various agents of corrosion.

This is as good an illustration as any of the relation between the work of the analytical laboratory and the question of chemical engineering inspection. The analytical chemist makes the analysis, but in conjunction with the chemical engineer he also has to interpret it. It is not sufficient to know the composition of the material which is being inspected. What is much more important is to discover how given conditions will affect it, and why.

This, of course, applies to other questions besides corrosion. The actual strength of materials is greatly affected by their composition. Here again the analytical laboratory must be consulted. Traces of impurities in some metals affect their strength enormously. A good example is the presence of antimony in lead. Relatively minute traces of this impurity will render the lead so brittle as to make it useless.

These examples serve to show how chemical composition and physical properties are closely allied. One of the problems of inspection is to determine from the data of the analytical laboratory the suitability of a given material for a given purpose.

But there is a technique belonging to inspection which is distinct from, even if it is related to, chemical analysis. In chemical, as in other branches of engineering, the practical test of the material will often give information obtainable in no other way. The testing of the materials has been enormously developed since the War.

ANOTHER METHOD OF TESTING : MAKING MODELS

ROUGHLY the tests are of two kinds : the testing on a small scale of materials under conditions as closely resembling the large-scale operation as possible ; the use of physical methods, X-rays, microscope, and photography for the examination of materials.

As an example of the first method we might again consider the question of corrosion. Essentially the method of testing is to place the corroding agent in contact with the material to be tested. A piece of iron, for example, coated with zinc, might be suspended in a vessel containing salt solution. The metal is then left in contact with the solution for given periods of time and its corrosive effect is examined. One of the simplest methods of finding out if any corrosion has taken place is to weigh the piece of metal before and after immersion in the salt solution. If there is loss of weight then there has been corrosive action. Here is a practical test of what will happen if an iron tank coated with zinc is filled with salt solution.

This sounds very simple indeed, but in practice the inspector has many difficulties. It is these difficulties which are bound up with the technology of inspection. The mere suspension of a piece of metal in a given solution, and the results of such a test are not necessarily equivalent to what will happen on a large scale. The problem is, in any given case, to reproduce the large-scale conditions as nearly as possible. Otherwise the tests may be useless.

This is often extremely difficult, but tests can generally be designed to fit the special case. We will give one instance. It is chosen because it illustrates a general principle. Size and quantity very much affect reactions of this kind. If a piece of metal three inches square is immersed in a given volume of liquid, and if another piece three feet square is immersed in a relatively larger volume of liquid, it does not follow that the corrosion will be the same. The reason is that, actually, many other factors, such as speed in change of temperature, which depends upon size, affect the test. There are also others which it is not possible to allow for. But it is possible to ascertain by experiment what kind of differences result from varying the sizes and quantities in the same test. By this means an estimation can be made of the relation between the small-scale and large-scale behaviour of a given material.

Numerous tests relating to corrosion and similar phenomena have been rigidly standardised so that the conditions under which the tests are performed are as constant as possible. In the case of many materials specifications are laid down which include corrosion tests of this kind, and the material must survive these tests before it is accepted.

This, however, is only one aspect of the test. It is often essential to find out the cause of corrosion and if possible how to prevent it. Inspection is not only important from the point of view of those who are going to use the material ; the makers of it also have to make use of this kind of control.

Causes are generally more difficult to investigate than effects. In investigations of this kind the microscope and other physical instruments have to be used to supplement the work of the analyst. Inspection literally means a visual examination ; but it is a visual examination in which the naked eye has to be assisted so that it can see clearly.

THE WARP AND WOOF OF METALS

IT is for this reason that what is known as metallography has become of such great importance as a part of the technology of inspection. Metallography consists in taking photographs of the metallic surfaces through the microscope. Metals and alloys have a definite structure which is invisible to the naked eye but which has a profound effect upon their durability. Under magnification the structure shows up very clearly. Long study and experience have shown that certain structures are connected with certain characteristics in the metal. Photographs of this kind are, therefore, pictures which show the strength or weakness of the material in question.

To take the example of a pure metal, it has been found that the structure is crystalline, just as, say, common salt is crystalline. Crystals are due to an orderly arrangement of the atoms themselves. They are, as it were, arranged in an often repeated pattern which does not vary. The metallic surface might be likened to a wallpaper with a pattern consisting of the same forms repeated over and over again. The unit of the pattern is, of course, so minute that it cannot be seen even with the most powerful microscope ; but its *results* are evident enough. If the original units are symmetrical, then large groups of them will be symmetrical ; the visible structure of the metal under the microscope will be satisfactory, and the strength of the metal good.

But if the metal has been unsatisfactorily treated when forged, hammered, or annealed, the crystals may be broken or deformed. They cease to be arranged in an orderly fashion in relation to each other. The result is that the strength of the metal suffers severely.

Such conditions are shown up very clearly by the microscope in conjunction with the camera. Skilled metallurgists are often able to tell merely by the inspection of the photomicrographs what the physical properties of the metal being examined are likely to be.

CONSIDERING METALS AS FROZEN LIQUIDS

THIS method, if it is important for the examination of pure metals, is even more useful for the examination of alloys. As time goes on, the use of alloys in industry becomes more and more important. At this point we need only cite the example of steel. Steel is still the most important of all alloys. The best-known and earliest are the various forms of carbon steel. According to the quantity of carbon present, the form of it which is added to the metal, the cooling, and the annealing, so will the steel vary. There are now, of course, many other kinds of steels, such as alloys with nickel, manganese, chromium and vanadium. These all have different properties and are in use for different purposes. In these examples also, the conditions under which the alloys are made profoundly affect the strength of the resulting metal, and great care has to be taken in their preparation.

The metallurgist looks at alloys from quite a different point of view from the ordinary one. We are accustomed to think of metals as hard solids ; the metallurgist regards them as frozen *liquids*. There is a very good reason for this. Most of the important reactions which take place when metals are mixed together occur when they are molten. It is obvious that mixture is not possible except when the metals are in a liquid state. When we remember this, it is easy to see that a mixture of molten metals may react just as chemical substances react together. This very often happens. The strength and hardness of alloys frequently depend upon the fact that the metals actually combine and are not merely mixed.

The combination, however, is not generally so definite as in the ordinary chemical reaction. But alloys have not the same properties as the individual metals, so that they cannot be merely mixtures. For this reason alloys are generally supposed to be what are known as *solid solutions*. A solution is different from a mere mixture. Sugar will dissolve in water up to a certain point, but sugar can be mixed with any proportion of, say, custard powder. It is the same with alloys. Only a certain proportion of one metal can be in solid solution in the other. There is a very interesting property of certain metals when mixed which demonstrates this fact. When in a molten condition they apparently mix freely together in all proportions. But as the mixture cools one or other of the metals separates out. When the mixture attains a certain proportion of the two metals it remains constant and homogeneous. This is called an *eutectic*.

Alloys are not necessarily solid solutions. In many cases there is a definite combination of the metals. Just as some chemical salts actually combine with the liquid in which they are dissolved, so the one metal may actually be in combination with the other.

ALLOYS : COMPOUNDS : MIXTURES

NOR are alloys always mixtures of two metals only. Malleable iron, steel and cast iron are alloys of iron with carbon. When carbon is mixed with molten iron, part of the carbon separates as graphite, part remains as iron carbide known as *cementite*, part is a solid solution of some of the iron carbide in the iron known as *martensite*. This is a very good example of what may happen in the case of alloys generally. There is, in this instance, the iron itself, a combination of iron with carbon, and a solid solution of some of the combined iron in the iron itself.

The reaction which takes place, the proportions of the solid solutions and the formation of eutectics vitally affect the nature of the alloy, its strength and general durability. Insignificant changes in these conditions brought about by temperature, speed of cooling, mechanical working of the metal, and annealing may entirely alter the resulting alloy.

A definite relation exists between the crystalline structure of the alloy and its composition. It is the function of metallography to show up the structure of the material under examination, and interpret that structure in terms of composition, and thus of strength. We will give a résumé of the method employed.

The microscopic examination of a highly polished metallic surface tells the metallurgist nothing. All metals and alloys appear homogeneous in these circumstances. But when a metal is to be examined it has first to be prepared by polishing. The process has to be carried out very thoroughly. There must be no scratches on the surface at all. This result is achieved by rubbing the surface with jewellers' rouge. More and more finely divided rouge is used for each successive polishing until the surface is free from even microscopic scratches.

BRINGING THE METAL'S STRUCTURE TO LIGHT

THIS is only the first part of the process. After polishing, the metallic surface has to be *etched*. Etching is the most important part of the whole process. It consists in treating the surface with the etching material, which is generally a weak acid. The result is that the surface of the metal is etched in the form of a pattern. The crystals which form the surface of the metal are, according to their disposition and composition, more or less attacked by the etching acid. At certain definite points, therefore, the acid will mark the metal and etch it out in the form of a design. This design will be the same for alloys of the same composition, but if the composition varies even to a slight degree, the etched pattern will vary.

Very beautiful photomicrographs of etched metallic surfaces can often be produced. The etched surface may show markings of intricate shape but regularly disposed over the surface in the form of a network, the size of the meshes, as it were, being approximately the same, and the shape more or less uniform. On the other hand, there may be two or more inter-related patterns corresponding to different types of crystal structure, but still arranged in a typical order.

The photograph of an etched surface will often tell the metallurgist much more than can any analysis of the material under consideration. Indeed, an analysis of an alloy does not generally give a great deal of information. The analyst can tell what the constituents of the material are but he cannot always give an opinion as to how they are combined in the original material.

Metallography, on the other hand, not only gives an indication of the composition by revealing the shape and size of the crystals, but also it shows up, as no other method of examination can, the actual structure of the surface. The surface structure is more important and determinant of strength than the composition itself—the manner in which the crystals are arranged and their degree of cohesion being one of the first considerations where durability is concerned.

This is a very important example of inspection as it bears directly upon the problem of the strength of materials. There are, of course, numerous mechanical tests for strength which have to be applied. But this method of metallurgical inspection is actually able to predict, with more or less accuracy, what the strength of a given piece of metal will be, its hardness, and even its powers of resistance to corrosion.

DETECTING FAULTY PRODUCTION IN METALS

METALLURGICAL inspection can, however, do more than this. It is able not only to predict the probable condition of the metal, but to suggest the reasons why it came to be in that state. Often, too, the metallurgist may be able to propose, as a result of his examination, suitable changes in the method of treating the metal, so that its quality may be improved. He may find, for example, by an examination of the photomicrographs, a surface condition which suggests that the alloy has been cooled too quickly. This has altered the eutectic point and profoundly affected the condition of the metal. Decrease in the rate of cooling may put the matter entirely right.

Metallography is also extensively used in connection with the electro-deposition of metals. Deposits of this kind are generally examined as they are, without polishing or etching. A great deal of work has been done upon the relation between the structure of the deposited metal and the chemical solution from which the deposit is produced. We have already indicated that small changes in chemical solution greatly affect the condition of the metal deposited from it. Conversely, an examination of a deposit with the microscope may reveal what is wrong with the solution.

It will now be obvious that although metallography is a matter for the laboratory, it is quite a different technique from that of analytical chemistry. Analysis relies upon indirect methods of detecting the presence and quantity of given constituents in any substance. The use of the microscope and other optical instruments involves direct observation of the material examined, and an interpretation of the thing seen. The examiner is relying, in this case, not only upon the constituents, but upon the manner in which they are disposed throughout the material. This has a great bearing upon the quality of the metal.

HOW THE ETCHING IS DONE

THE technique of etching has become highly complicated. Originally the substances used consisted merely of weak acids. Of recent years, however, many refinements have been introduced. The acid or other etching mixture may contain, as well as the etching material and water, alcohol, glycerine or acetone. The reason for this is that the degree to which the etching material affects the surface can be closely controlled according to what other constituents are present. The exact degree of etching is a matter of great importance. If the process has gone too far, or not far enough, the results may be useless. The same metallic surface too faintly or too deeply etched will appear quite different under the microscope.

Substances now used in etching are not necessarily acids. Alkalis such as ammonia are sometimes used for etching brass, and hydrogen peroxide is another substance sometimes used for the same purpose.

The most important developments of etching probably relate to iron and steel. Iron is so extensively employed that its strength is more important than that of any other metal. Etched photomicrographs of iron show extraordinary differences in structure. Various kinds of iron and steel which do not greatly differ in chemical constitution show profound differences in the size of the grains (crystalline structure) and in their appearance. They may be of uniform size or they may vary within wide limits. They may be differently affected by the etching agent so that they are lighter and darker in shade. The boundaries between the edges of the grains may be clearly defined or, on the other hand, they may be only faintly outlined. All such details are of significance. Rightly read, they give the metallurgist and the chemical engineer very useful information relating to the properties of the metals he is examining.

TESTING THE STRENGTH OF BOMBS AND BUILDINGS

METALLOGRAPHY is in fact a method, par excellence, for obtaining information relating to the strength of materials. Its importance for us here is that fundamentally it is a question of strength interpreted in chemical terms. When the molten metals are mixed together certain more or less definite physical and chemical reactions result. Many of these reactions are known, and more is being discovered about them every day. Metallography has thrown great light upon the result of these reactions and its effect upon the quality of the metal. It is for this reason that this form of inspection has been so greatly developed in this age of metallic alloys.

There was great development of the technique of metallography during the War. It is obvious that the steel for rifles, cannon, and bombs must necessarily be submitted to the most rigid tests if severe accidents and ineffectiveness are to be avoided. This is the cause of the immense development in the technology of iron and steel inspection during the last twenty years. But, as a result of it, the lessons learned have fortunately become available for more useful purposes. In building this is the age of ferro-concrete. The strength of the steel structure of our huge modern concrete buildings is largely an achievement of the metallurgist. His inspection of the structure of the metal with the microscope goes a long way to ensure that its strength shall not fail at a critical moment.

SEEING THROUGH METALS WITH THE HELP OF X-RAYS

OF recent years many new methods for the inspection of materials have been developed. Among the most interesting is the use of X-rays. There is good reason for including this kind of examination here, since chemistry has been very largely responsible for the development in the technology of X-rays. Almost all that we know about the structure of crystals is due to the radiographical work of W. H. and W. L. Bragg. Their researches have a definite bearing upon chemical theory. X-rays thus have become part of the technical equipment of the laboratory and are being used in a number of new ways.

Strictly speaking, the use of X-rays in the examination of crystals is the most important aspect of X-ray work for the chemist. But it has only a theoretical interest for the engineer. He is concerned with materials, not with intricate fundamental research. The most practical application of X-rays in industry is the direct examination of materials for faults which exist within the structure and are invisible on the surface. X-rays will often reveal these and thus make unnecessary any other examination. In most cases, moreover, no other kind of examination would give the information required.

SAFEGUARDING THE AEROPLANE PILOT

LET us consider the example of aeroplanes. It is obvious that the aeronaut's life depends upon his craft being faultless as to the strength of the materials. A hidden worm hole in a piece of wood may cause his death. Since and during the War X-rays have been used to discover hidden worm holes in the timber used for aeroplanes. If a ray of suitable strength is used, faults of this kind show up quite clearly. The timber can then be rejected without further examination. No other method is so rapid or efficient.

Turning from the structure to the engine, faults can also be discovered in the same way. A minute crack in a piston or cylinder head will show up clearly. This is again a method which is rapid to apply and more efficient than any other.

Radiographs can also reveal many kinds of fraud. It is provided that certain parts of the wooden structure shall be solid without joints. In hidden parts an attempt is sometimes made to evade this regulation. Excellent radiographs have been taken of aeroplane spars which reveal prohibited joints with great clearness. Joint cracks and similar faults show up particularly well.

Before we continue it will be well to give a brief description of the way in which X-ray photographs are taken. The method is quite different from that employed in ordinary photography. A camera is not used, since the rays actually pass through the object to be photographed. If an ordinary photographic plate is placed in contact with semi-opaque material such as a piece of printed paper, a photograph of the printing can be obtained merely by exposing the plate and paper to the light for an appropriate time. The reason is, of course, that the light passes through the paper, but is masked by the printing, which is completely opaque to the light rays.

In the case of X-rays the same principle applies, but the X-rays will pass through material which is quite opaque to ordinary light, such as wood, metals and other material. To take an X-ray photograph, therefore, a film is enclosed in a light-tight case. This is placed close to and behind the object to be photographed. The X-rays are then directed upon the object and a radiograph is obtained.

With X-rays, as with ordinary light, the permeability depends upon the material. Different metals, for example, have different degrees of permeability. It is for this reason that radiographs can be taken. Cracks or other faults also allow the rays to pass more freely; in consequence they are revealed in the radiograph. This does not mean, of course, that an object like a bomb, which is composed of the same material in all its parts, cannot be radiographed. Where the layers of metal are thicker, that is to say, where the rays have to pass not only through the walls of the bomb, but also through the internal mechanism, there will be different degrees of permeability. Excellent radiographs of even complicated mechanism can be obtained. To take another example, all the essential mechanism of an alarm clock is revealed by a radiograph.

Successful radiography depends upon the quality of the ray and its suitability for the work in question. The "hardness" or "softness" of the ray is the most important factor. The "harder" the ray the greater its power of penetration. If the ray is too hard it may pass through the material to be radiographed so completely as to make no difference between one part and the other ; if the ray is too soft it may not penetrate any part sufficiently. "Hardness" depends upon wavelength, and this can be adjusted by suitable arrangements to obtain the required result. There are very few things which cannot be satisfactorily radiographed if the conditions are carefully standardised.

Extensive use was made of radiography for the examination of war material. As we have stated, bombs and fuses can be examined to ascertain their mechanism. Radiography was also much used for the examination of signal rockets and shells. A rocket, for example, if badly filled, shows the powder grains irregularly disposed. Without opening a single specimen, it was possible to decide if the work of filling had been properly done.

TESTING THE POWER OF EXPLOSIVES

THE technique of engineering and chemical inspection was greatly developed during the Great War. Owing to the haste with which material had to be passed or rejected, the most rapid methods compatible with efficiency had to be devised. The small scale practical test became, in this connection, one of great importance. An example was the testing of the power of explosives by exploding them in a miniature bomb in the presence of a given quantity of sand. The power of the explosion was decided by passing the sand through a series of sieves. The greater the quantity passing the finest sieve, the greater the power of the explosion.

In explosive material, the degree of fineness of the ingredients is nearly always the first test to be applied. In general, the finer the state of division, the greater the efficiency of the explosion. Sieving is the method employed. The material is passed through a series of sieves, the size of the apertures of which is known, and the quantity retained on each sieve is noted. Specifications generally require that a given material shall pass through a sieve of a given size.

The next test is sensitiveness. A given weight of the explosive is placed upon a special anvil over which a weight is swung which ultimately strikes the explosive material after a given number of movements backward and forward. This test, standardised according to the material examined, determines sensitiveness.

Other modifications are the various forms of falling weight test. These depend in principle simply upon a body of known weight falling upon an anvil from a given height. This test can clearly be an indication of the sensitiveness of the explosive material.

Recently these comparatively crude tests have been greatly refined. It must be borne in mind that an explosion is a chemical reaction. Its violence depends to a large extent upon the rate of chemical change of the explosive, and its effect upon the enormous pressure developed by the sudden evolution of large quantities of gas. For this reason a refinement of the method of examining the sensitivity is to measure the volume of gas evolved, when the material is exploded, by the falling weight or other method, in a closed apparatus. Such tests are carried out against standard explosive materials to decide their " Figure of Insensitiveness."

One of the most recent developments of this kind of inspection has been the photographing of the velocity of shock through air and other gases upon a film moving at a high speed. At the present moment these developments have not much more than an academic interest. When, however, they have been worked out sufficiently to make them easily available in practice, they will be of the greatest use for the testing of explosives.

Another test of great practical value is the temperature of

ignition. It is worth bearing in mind that mere ignition is not generally sufficient to cause an explosion. Detonation of some kind is nearly always necessary. But the detonation required may be very slight. In some cases falling dust is sufficient to produce a violent explosion.

The temperature of ignition is, however, a useful indication of the stability of the explosive. These tests are also sometimes combined with impact tests. The material to be tested is dropped from a given height into a tube heated to a given temperature and the point of explosion determined.

So far as explosives are concerned these tests are typical. Their connection with many engineering tests is almost self-evident. The intention is to reproduce on a small scale the conditions likely to arise in practice, and thus as far as possible to create a link between the laboratory and the field. The problem in connection with these tests, as with most others, is to be able to relate the small-scale test to the large-scale operation. A laboratory test which is not a consistently reliable index of what is going to happen in practice is useless, or worse than useless.

SOME GREAT ACHIEVEMENTS OF THE CHEMICAL ENGINEER

THE reader who has studied the previous sections will have realised that the achievements of chemical engineering, to some extent, speak for themselves through the medium of the fundamental processes which have been described. This does not mean that there is not a great deal more to be said. Our task is to present to the reader the final results of some of these processes. We have described, for example, the destructive distillation of coal. It is essentially a chemical engineering matter. But from the point of view of the public the final results of that primary operation are really the most important. When it is realised that as a result of modern technology coal becomes the origin of such divers things as aniline dyes, umbrella handles and modern drugs, we begin to understand how profoundly modern science has changed the face of the world in which we live.

Some years before the War, Sir William Crookes prophesied that if a method of obtaining nitrogen from the atmosphere was not perfected in the near future there would be a shortage of nitrates, which are essential as fertilizers. He pointed out that the natural supplies were not inexhaustible and that a heavy drain was being made upon them.

Very little notice was taken of his warning. It required, as a matter of fact, the threat of the World War to stimulate a successful prosecution of this problem. Germany knew that she would desperately need synthetic nitrates in the event of war, since supplies of the natural product would be cut off. In the very year in which war broke out Haber had solved all the practical details relating to his ammonia process.

Before describing this, an allusion to earlier methods will be interesting. The problem was simply this. Our atmosphere consists of a mixture of nitrogen and oxygen. The gases are not chemically combined. If the nitrogen could in some way be extracted economically the nitrate difficulty would be overcome.

Nature produces utilisable nitrogen in two ways. A thunderstorm produces nitrates and nitrites. This is due to the electrical discharge taking place in the atmosphere which causes some of the nitrogen and oxygen to combine. The second source of nitrogen is the micro-organisms which exist in the soil and are able to extract the nitrogen from the air and convert it into nitrates and nitrites. Once these natural processes were sufficient. They are entirely inadequate under present conditions.

As has often happened before, chemists working upon the problem of the fixation of atmosphere nitrogen did their best to imitate Nature. They tried to induce a mixture of nitrogen and oxygen to combine by passing electric sparks through it. Another group of bio-chemists attempted to cultivate bacteria artificially which would do under laboratory conditions what they did so efficiently in the world outside. The first method ultimately succeeded, the second has been more or less a failure.

THE THUNDERSTORM IN MINIATURE

THE first methods tried to reproduce the conditions of the thunderstorm. A mixture of nitrogen and oxygen (i.e. atmospheric air) was exposed to an electric arc fitted into a metal drum. The first results obtained were not particularly satisfactory. Only a small percentage of nitric oxide was produced. It was at this point that the chemical engineer began to investigate the problem. In order to obtain good results it was found necessary to extend the surface of the arc so that a considerable volume of air was in contact with it. Further, it was found necessary to circulate the air so that after the combination had taken place it could be quickly *cooled*. If this was not effectively done the oxides of nitrogen were again decomposed and the whole process became inefficient.

The Arc Process, as it is called, is still used to some extent. The first hint that such a thing was possible came from the English chemist Cavendish, who had observed in 1784 that oxides of nitrogen were produced when electric sparks were passed through air. In 1897 Lord Rayleigh actually prepared nitric acid by this method and showed that the process could be economically applied.

But it was not until 1916 that anything like a commercially practicable process was worked out. This was largely due to the solving of the chemical engineering problem. The working conditions had to be so arranged that consistent efficiency could be expected of the plant.

The arc process is still extensively worked in Norway, where cheap water power is available. The works at Rjukan expend some 380,000 horse-power in connection with this process. The method has been largely superseded elsewhere on account of power expenditure. Where this is cheap and plentiful it can still be satisfactorily worked.

THE FAMOUS PROCESS DISCOVERED BY HABER

THE Haber Process has now largely superseded earlier methods for the fixation of nitrogen. The circumstances under which it was brought to perfection have a grim sort of romance. It is an open question whether Haber's discovery of a really practicable method of combining nitrogen and hydrogen precipitated the European War, or if the War, or at least the imminence of it, inspired Haber finally to complete a work he had begun at least as far back as 1905. However this may be, it is a fact that the independence of Germany in the matter of the production of nitric acid made it possible for her to continue hostilities which otherwise would have been abandoned much sooner, perhaps even after twelve months.

The Haber Process depends upon the direct union of hydrogen and nitrogen under pressure in the presence of a catalyst. It will be remembered that a catalyst is a substance which, present in minute amount and remaining unchanged, induces or accelerates a chemical reaction which would not otherwise take place. The principal work done in connection with this process was the search for a suitable catalyst. Metals such as osmium were tried, uranium oxide and other compounds of uranium. Experiments were made with pure iron and finally with mixtures of metals and oxides. A catalyst the basis of which is nickel is now generally employed.

By the use of the catalyst and of pressure, nitrogen and hydrogen have thus been induced to combine in such quantities as to make the process profitable commercially. While the basis of this process is largely a chemical reaction, very elaborate chemical engineering problems are involved. Although the temperature required is much lower than with the arc process, the reacting gases have to be heated, and they have to be mixed under pressure. Conditions of temperature and pressure very greatly affect the efficiency of the process, and a great deal of the research carried out has in consequence been directed to the chemical engineering problems involved.

ADAPTING THE PRESSURE TO HELP COMBINATION

THESE problems are of particular interest in the case of the Claude Process at present being worked out at Montereau, near Fontainebleu. In this method of union between hydrogen and nitrogen very high pressures are used. In some cases these attain nine hundred to one thousand atmospheres. The object of applying this enormous pressure is to increase the efficiency of the reaction. Ammonia of a strength of 20% is said to be produced by this method. It is particularly at these high ranges that the relation between temperature and pressure and their effect upon the efficiency of the reaction becomes important. Ultimately the matter turns upon economics. This is the real motive for the highly elaborate studies made by chemical engineers concerning the velocity of reactions under different conditions of temperature and pressure on a large scale.

Various other methods for the fixation of atmosphere nitrogen in one form or another are in existence. Of these the only one of importance is the Cyanamide Process. This method relies upon the fact that calcium carbide, a substance well known to all those who use acetylene lamps, will combine with nitrogen to produce calcium cyanamide.

$$CaC_2 + N_2 = CaCN_2 + C$$

(calcium carbide) + (nitrogen) = (calcium cyanamide) + (carbon)

The calcium cyanamide under treatment with pressure steam is decomposed and ammonia is liberated.

$$CaCN_2 + 3H_2O = CaCO_3 + 2NH_3$$

(calcium cyanamide) + (water) = (calcium carbonate) + (ammonia)

This process involves some extremely interesting problems from a chemical engineering point of view. The reaction has been studied very carefully and it has been found that at every temperature there is a fixed pressure equilibrium for nitrogen. In practice this means that the rate of absorption of the nitrogen is proportional to the pressure. In regard to temperature it was found that the use of certain substances as fluxes made it possible to lower the temperature without affecting the absorption of nitrogen by the calcium carbide.

It is easy to see the practical importance of these discoveries. The lowering of temperature and the adjustment of pressure so as to obtain the maximum yield meant a great saving in cost of production. This is one of the most important aspects of chemical engineering research which has to adapt the laboratory method to the large-scale operation and make the plant work economically.

THE ATMOSPHERE AN INEXHAUSTIBLE MINE

SIR WILLIAM CROOKES did not exaggerate the dangers of a nitrate shortage. The original source of nitrogenous fertilising material was *guano*, large deposits of which used to be found in Peru. Guano is formed from the excreta and decayed bodies of sea-fowl. These deposits have collected over hundreds of years. Owing to the dryness of the climate the guano became highly desiccated, so that all its nitrogen was retained. Under the influence of moisture it would have been converted into ammonia, and the nitrogen would have been lost. The dry substance, however, was an excellent fertiliser but there was not enough of it. The deposits originally amounted to only 10,000,000 tons. They were quickly exhausted.

The natural sodium nitrate deposits of Chile were then utilised. These are much more extensive. But they amount only to some 250,000,000 tons. With the possibility of opening new beds, as yet untouched, the deposits might last for 200 years. But that is only at the present rate of consumption. It might be quadrupled, for the needs of modern civilisation for a particular commodity sometimes leap in an unexpected and sensational fashion. That would mean that in fifty years we should have no fertilisers for wheat and other essential food-stuffs.

The fixation of atmospheric nitrogen removed this real menace to civilization. As far as we know the atmosphere is inexhaustible, so that there is now an unlimited supply of nitrates. Further, it is cheaper to produce ammonia and nitric acid synthetically (from which nitrates in the most suitable form can be readily prepared) than to mine the nitrates direct.

ALL THE COLOURS OF THE RAINBOW

THE discovery and development of aniline dyes has been another revolution which science has brought about. Aniline dyes and artificial silk have done more to break down social barriers than legislation, however enlightened, would have achieved in two hundred years. Before the discovery of aniline dyes natural dyestuffs were expensive and comparatively scarce. The extreme drabness of the nineteenth century was a matter of necessity rather than choice.

In order to indicate the place of chemical engineering in the technology of aniline dyes we cannot do better than consider how a typical dye is produced. Coal, it will be remembered, when destructively distilled produced, among other products, benzene. From benzene, nitrobenzene is produced by treatment with a mixture of nitric and sulphuric acids. This in itself involves careful attention from the chemical engineer. While the reaction is proceeding the mixture must be stirred efficiently and cooled, or very serious accidents may result from spontaneous ignition. Further, the agitation and temperature have to be controlled carefully in order to ensure that the reaction shall take place as rapidly and completely as possible.

Again, we must stress the economics of the process and its relation to chemical engineering. The acid used for the

reaction is not wasted.   After the nitrobenzene has been
formed, a certain excess of acid remains. This is regenerated
by allowing it to pass in a cascade down a series of porcelain
vessels heated with hot air. During the reaction much of the
nitric acid escapes in the form of nitrous fumes. These fumes
are collected and condensed and thus used to make nitric
acid.

Nitrobenzene is an oil which is lighter than water and
separates sharply from the water medium. The separators
are therefore merely vessels funnel-shaped at the bottom,
with a tap. The water layer is run off and the tap closed
before the nitrobenzene escapes. Practically complete separation results.

The next step is the *reduction* of the nitrobenzene to produce
aniline. This has already been briefly described but we will
consider the apparatus used in a little more detail.   The
principle is that of distillation. An iron container fitted with
a steam pipe and agitator is used for the reaction. This container is connected with a condenser to cool the aniline vapours.
Its outlet is connected with a second vessel which receives
the condensed aniline. This crude distillate is, however,
mixed with water from which it must be separated. The
aniline is accordingly pumped into separating tanks where it
is allowed to stand for about twenty-four hours. Like nitrobenzene, aniline is an oil which separates from water. Below
the settling tanks is a vessel to which high pressure can be
applied. The aniline is finally run into this " high-pressure
egg " whence it is blown into a second distillation tank.

Aniline has to be finally purified by distillation under
reduced pressure. This is the only method by which it can
be separated from impurities. The plant consists of a vacuum
pan fitted with steam coils to heat the aniline. A pipe conducts
the vapours to the condenser. This is connected with the
receivers for the aniline oil. The principle is the same as in
the previous distillation apparatus, with an important difference.
The receivers are fitted with pipes which are connected with
a vacuum pump which exhausts the air from the apparatus.

This vacuum distillation is a very important part of the
operation. A mixture of aniline and water first distills over.
This is returned to the settling tanks for a second separation.
The second fraction contains aniline and benzene. If the
original nitrobenzene has been properly made there should
not be a great deal of this impurity. This mixture must be

redistilled to separate the benzene and aniline. The third fraction consists of practically pure aniline.

It is important to realise how closely all these processes are interrelated. If the original nitrobenzene has been carefully made a great deal of trouble will be avoided in the preparation and distillation of the aniline. The first distillation operation in which the aniline is actually prepared is run continuously with the second vacuum distillation. We begin with benzene, and complete the process with pure aniline.

THE FOUNDATION OF DYESTUFFS

ANILINE is the basis of an enormous number of important dye-stuffs. " Aniline salts," for example, is a compound of aniline with hydrochloric acid. This substance is extensively used for the production of aniline black, magenta, and other dyes. Again, aniline, when treated with sulphuric acid yields a substance known as suphanilic acid. This is an intermediate compound from which a large number of dye-stuffs are produced. A Methyl orange, a Resorcin yellow, an Anthracene brown, a Columbia green are a few of the more important.

On the basis of these comparatively simple reactions, large numbers of new compounds covering almost the whole range of colour can be produced. There are, of course, many more complicated reactions by which other dyes are built up on the basis of aniline.

From an economic point of view one of the best illustrations of the value of aniline is the production of indigo. This is one of the most important commercial dyes, although there are now other blues which compete with it. Natural indigo has, however, been almost entirely replaced by the artificial product. It is much cheaper and equal in quality to the natural dye.

In one of the most important processes indigo is made directly from aniline. An intermediate product known as phenylglycine is produced, a second known as indoxyl from which the indigo is produced. This process begins with benzene, which is nitrated to produce nitrobenzene. From this aniline is made by the method described. The aniline is treated first with chloracetic acid and then with soda and a substance known as sodamide. Indoxyl results, from which the indigo is produced. Indigo is thus produced indirectly from coal.

As a result of these discoveries, the cultivation of plants producing natural indigo has been greatly reduced. The supply of indigo which was once definitely limited even at full production is now able to meet any demand made upon it.

From the spectacular point of view, the success of the modern dye-stuff industry is one of the greatest achievements of science applied to industry.   Synthetic dye-stuffs have entirely changed the face of modern civilisation. Well within living memory, clothing and fabrics which were not very expensive were either extremely drab, or they were garishly and badly dyed. It is now possible not only to produce fast dyes at an economical price, but artificial colours in almost any required shade. For a long time after the synthetic dye-stuffs industry became established it was still necessary to use natural dye-stuffs if certain delicate shades were required. Artificial dyes are, however, now rapidly replacing the natural products and they will soon replace them altogether.

PLASTIC MOULDINGS : THE BAKELITE INDUSTRY

ANOTHER remarkable discovery to the industrial perfection of which chemical engineering has contributed a good deal, is the artificial resin and plastic industry. " Bakelite " is now a well-known name and its uses are manifold. It is used for electrical fittings, strap handles in buses and the underground railways, aeroplane propellers, ash trays, umbrella handles, cups, saucers and plates, and its uses are being extended every day.

In 1871 a chemist named Backland discovered that when phenol and other similar substances were mixed with substances known as aldehydes they reacted to produce compounds which were plastic when hot. On cooling they set hard to form a mass which greatly resembled vulcanite. The great importance of this discovery was realised at once, but it is not until comparatively recently that the industrial processes have been perfected.

Phenol is a product obtained from coal. It is commonly called carbolic acid. Formaldehyde, the well-known antiseptic, produces, when mixed with it, a resin of the Bakelite type. The formalin and carbolic acid are mixed together in an iron digester, which is a closed vessel heated by steam. In one modification of the process a catalyst is used and the temperature employed is comparatively low, below the boiling point of water. In the other method, no catalyst is used, but the temperature and pressure are higher.

Very accurate control of the reaction is necessary, or the resulting product will be useless. The resins are very complex substances or mixtures of substances which are profoundly affected by the temperature and pressure, the nature of the impurities in the reacting substances and the method of agitating the mixture. Particular care has to be paid to the temperature which is liable, in a high-temperature process, to rise sharply and thus injure the resulting product. The resin when hot is a clear liquid which is run into pans to cool. It then sets hard to the consistency of the well-known Bakelite.

" Fillers," as they are called, are also mixed with the resin. These may consist of asbestos, wood, pumice stone, starch or various chemicals, metallic oxides, all in fine powder, which give the resin a particular colour and consistency. Again, by the use of different aldehydes and derivatives of phenol, a considerable range of resins can be produced in imitation of amber, horn, ebonite and celluloid. Another interesting use for these resins is the impregnation of wood with the heated product so as to give it a highly lacquered finish.

Two of the most important characteristics of these resins are their insulating properties and their non-inflamability. It is for this reason that they have come so much into use for electrical fittings. Bakelite is, in fact, rapidly replacing all other materials for this purpose.

THE RELATION BETWEEN DYES AND PLASTICS

THE process for the production of synthetic resins might appear to be simple. In fact, the large-scale difficulties are considerable owing to the consistency of the resin produced, and the gross changes liable to take place in it due to apparently insignificant changes in the conditions of manufacture. It is for this reason that the chemical engineer by the design of plant specially adapted for the processes in question has been able to carry the production of synthetic resins from the laboratory to the industrial stage. Specialised applications of the methods of heating and cooling, and above all, efficiency in mechanical agitation has made the large-scale operation possible. With resins, as with dyes, the perfection of the industrial process has been in the hands of the chemical engineer.

There might at first appear to be no essential connection between dyes and artificial resins, but indirectly they are related. We have already explained that chemical engineering processes have a wide application in connection with destructive distillation. Of all destructive distillation processes that of coal tar is the most important. Through benzene it is the source of aniline for dyes ; through phenol (carbolic acid) it is the source of artificial resins. To use a popular expression, the products of coal and coal tar are members of the same family tree. From coal tar an immense variety of products are obtained which finally become, as we have said, dyes, electrical fittings, umbrella handles, ash trays and cups and saucers.

It is the fundamental process of destructive distillation upon which all subsequent success depends. In the last analysis, it is these primary achievements which give chemical engineering its great significance in modern industry.

LIVING ORGANISMS FOR RAW MATERIAL

THERE is a branch of the fermentation industries which rather surprisingly owes a good deal to chemical engineering : the artificial cultivation of yeasts and micro-organisms used in industrial processes. It might be thought that the bio-chemist, as he is called, would be able to dispense with the services of the chemical engineer. In fact, what might be described as the mass-production of micro-organisms is very largely a problem of chemical engineering.

There are a large number of moulds, yeasts and micro-organisms which bring about profound chemical changes in many substances. The bio-chemist is a laboratory worker who studies these organisms and discovers how they may be used in practice to bring about given changes in given substances. Two well-known examples are the conversion of sugar into alcohol by means of yeast and the production of vinegar by the action of acetic acid bacteria.

Originally these processes, which are very ancient, were very crudely performed. No attempt was made to purify the fermenting agent, and the whole process was left more or less to nature. This is all being altered. The scientific man controls the processes of nature in the laboratory and causes even micro-organisms to carry out their work under his control.

It was the great French scientist, Pasteur, who discovered that alcoholic fermentation was produced by yeast cells, or more strictly, by substances known as enzymes which they produce. He further discovered that yeasts and other organisms belong to different races, and that yeasts themselves are divided up into different families.

This discovery was of immense significance, and the whole of the modern fermentation industry is built upon it. The results obtained by fermentation used to vary enormously. Wine, beer, and other alcoholic liquids would go sour, develop an unpleasant taste, or re-ferment when the fermentation was supposed to be at an end. Pasteur found that these irregularities were due to the development of foreign organisms, in some cases bacteria, in others families of yeast of a different type from that which induced the original, or " true " fermentation. Yeasts and other organisms fly about in the atmosphere, settle, and where the medium is suitable, produce fermentation. On the other hand, they may be mixed with the yeast used to bring the original fermentation about, and thus cause trouble at some stage in the operation.

The remedy suggested by Pasteur and greatly developed since his time, was the preparation of pure races of yeast. We will briefly describe the fundamental principles of the process for the preparation of these pure cultures as they are called.

STOCK-BREEDING UNDER THE MICROSCOPE

YEAST consists of minute cells which are only visible under a microscope. These cells reproduce by "budding." A second cell grows out of the first, and finally separates from it. This process is repeated indefinitely so long as the yeast is living and active. The result is that from a single cell any required quantity of yeast can be produced.

The principle of producing pure yeast is therefore quite simple. A single yeast cell must be allowed to propagate in a suitable medium from which every other kind of living organism has been removed. It is obvious that in this way the resulting culture must be pure.

In practice the procedure is rather elaborate. A microscope " count " has to be made of the number of yeast cells present in a given quantity of the liquid from which the pure yeast is to be prepared. A small drop, the exact volume of which is known, is placed on a glass microscopic slide. It is then covered with a small circle of glass which is marked with a number of minute squares of known area. When this is examined under the microscope, the yeast cells appear under the ruled squares. It is thus possible to count the number of cells over a given area of the glass slide. Since the area of the glass slide is known, and the volume of the drop, it is possible to calculate the number of yeast cells in the drop itself.

Now when this is known, it is possible to add water to a given quantity of the liquid containing the yeast cells, and to measure out a quantity of this diluted liquid containing the yeast cells, so that the quantity taken contains a single cell. The liquid containing this single cell is transferred to a sugar solution or other liquid in which the yeast will grow. The cell multiplies, and thus produces a *culture* of pure yeast.

Different species of yeast produce enzymes more or less effective for the work in hand. Distillery yeasts are different from brewery yeasts, and wine yeasts are again of a different type. Even different classes of beer and wine yeasts exist suitable for the fermentation of various kinds of wine and beer.

The process of separating yeasts is interesting. A culture suspected to contain a number of different yeasts is grown on a special medium on what is known as a *Petrie Dish*. This is a shallow glass vessel with a cover. The medium lies in a thin layer over the bottom. When the medium is inoculated with the yeast culture and allowed to stand at a suitable temperature the various yeasts grow separately in different *colonies*, which take the form of small nodules scattered over the surface of the medium. Specimens can be taken from each of these. They can be cultivated in a larger vessel, and the most suitable yeast chosen. This does not mean that a further cultivation from the single cell is not necessary. The colonies are not absolutely pure, so that afterwards resort must be had to single cell cultivation.

This in very brief outline is the method used for the cultivation of pure yeast. In detail the technique is too elaborate to be fully described, but the principle should be clear. Yeasts can be separated by cultivation in colonies. They are further purified by cultivation from a single cell.

THE MASS PRODUCTION OF PURE YEAST

WE are here principally concerned with the mass production of yeast. It is in this connection that the engineering problems arise. Three names are closely associated with this problem : Hansen, Jörgensen and Lindner.

We must first explain that the vital question in connection with pure yeast is that of *sterilisation*. Air, liquid, apparatus or anything else which comes in contact with the yeast culture from beginning to end must be *sterile*. That is to say, it must be free from foreign organisms. It is only necessary to enter any good brewery or winery to realise this. A properly run brewery or winery is literally as clean as an operating theatre. Where pure yeast is cultivated this condition is even more rigorously observed. In connection with the plant itself the problem is so to construct it as to make impossible contamination from within or without.

The first and simplest of these plants was one constructed by Lindner. It consists essentially of a vessel capable of being heated by steam. This contains the medium, wort (extract of malt), must (grape juice), or specially prepared sugar solution in which the yeast is cultivated. The vessel is connected with another container with two outlets, one connected with the first vessel and the other with a suction pump. This is the receptacle for the yeast culture. The first vessel also has two openings. One is connected with the yeast container ; the other admits air.

But the air admitted has to be purified. Before it enters the apparatus at all it passes through cotton wool filters to remove all foreign bodies. The air is, of course, sucked through the apparatus by means of the pump. No air is admitted except through this filter, the apparatus being otherwise completely enclosed.

In working, the medium (wort, must, or sugar solution) is first sterilised by boiling. It is then allowed to cool, and by the application of pressure, yeast is transferred to the sterile wort. The fermentation proceeds in the presence of sterile air so that contamination is impossible.

This is the principle more or less elaborated, upon which all pure yeast is produced. A plant designed by Hansen, the author of a famous book, *The Management of Pure Yeast*, gives a continual supply of pure yeast for a year or even more. The whole apparatus is closed except to admit sterile air heated and filtered in the manner described. It can be sterilised by high pressure steam. The outlets by which the pure yeast is drawn off are fitted with special valves that make it impossible either for the yeast drawn off to be contaminated or for any foreign organisms to enter the plant.

EFFICIENT BREWING: HOW SCIENCE DISPLACES RULE-OF-THUMB

THE perfection of these methods for the production of pure yeast has had the most profound effect upon the fermentation industries. The old rule-of-thumb methods of fermentation have practically disappeared. Even twenty years ago, a technical man in charge of a fermentation process could never be certain of the time that a given fermentation would take. In the case of beer there might be differences of days, in the case of wines sometimes weeks.

In really large scale operations irregularities of this kind mean the loss of large sums of money. Although other factors affect the result, difficulties of this kind generally arise through faults in the yeast. To-day it is possible to predict almost within an hour or two the time which will be required to ferment a given liquid.

Nor is this the most important consideration. Wine, beer, and other alcoholic liquors which are improperly fermented readily go bad, or become, at least, unpalatable. This has often been the source of great loss. Originally small breweries used always to allow for a percentage of " returns," and sometimes for a surprisingly high percentage, too. Returns in the modern brewery due to sourness or unpalatability are so rare as to be an event. Faults of this kind were almost always found to be due to faults in the yeast, which were produced through contamination brought about by the unscientific methods of cultivation in use.

AN IMPORTANT SOLVENT PRODUCED BY FERMENTATION

THE modern fermentation industries do not only include the production of alcohol for drinking or as industrial spirit. One of the most recent and significant developments is the formation of acetone by fermentation. Acetone is a very important solvent, and it was extensively employed during the World War. Originally, acetone was produced by the distillation of wood, but the supply obtainable by this method was inadequate.

It was in 1912 that a bio-chemist named Feuerbach discovered a micro-organism which, by fermentation, converted starch into acetone. This discovery was developed by Feuerbach himself and two collaborators named Strange and Weizmann and the process at once promised great importance for the future.

The greater part of the acetone now available is produced by the Feuerbach process. Essentially starchy matter from potato or other material is inoculated with " Feuerbach's Bacillus." Acetone and alcohols are produced. The acetone is separated from the other constituents by fractional distillation in a still of the Coffey type.

We need not enter into the chemical engineering problems involved in detail. The production of pure cultures of the micro-organisms involve the same kind of problems as those arising in the case of yeast. Fractional distillation has been described in some detail already. It will be sufficient to say that the production of acetone by this method is quite as much an achievement of the chemical engineer as any other process described.

Acetone is of great and increasing importance. Since it was used as a solvent in connection with explosives, the War could not have been continued if the supply had given out. It is the basis for the production of chloroform and iodoform, and of a number of synthetic drugs. Its widest application is now probably as a solvent for the plastics and resins whose uses are developing so rapidly.

OIL FROM COAL : SOME DETAILS OF HYDROGENATION

TURNING from alcohol and acetone to edible and other oils and fats the question of hydrogenation, to which a brief allusion has already been made, has come into great prominence of recent years. As we have already explained hydrogenation consists in introducing more hydrogen into various kinds of oils so that the change in composition profoundly affects their properties. Fuel oils of low grade are, for example, greatly improved in quality. Edible oils are *hardened* so that they can be used for margarine. Evil smelling oils can be deodorized, a fact of great economic significance in modern industry.

The method of hydrogenating oils is to treat them with hydrogen gas in the presence of a nickel catalyst. This has already been explained. We will now consider the chemical engineering problem. The most important requirement is that the hydrogen should come into the closest possible contact with the oil. In one process the oil is mixed with hydrogen in an autoclave which is fitted with agitators.

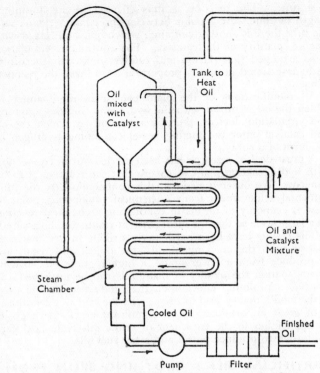

93. *The essentials of the process of hydrogenating heavy and impure oils. The process has several applications and is an important step in the production of petrol from coal. The hydrogen is pumped upwards through the plant, the reaction taking place in the heated U-tubes.*

More recently, however, another method has been devised. The oil passes from a tank down a tube bent in the form of a series of U's (Fig. 93). This tube is heated by means of a steam jacket. The oil is pumped through the tank and passes continuously through the tube, the cooler, and the filter. The hydrogenation takes place in the *tubes* and not in the tank. The pumps are so arranged that the hydrogen is pumped upwards while the oil passes downwards. By this means the hydrogen comes into contact with small quantities of oil at a time. The reaction is thus effected in the minimum length of time. At a point between the container tank and the tube there is another container which holds oil mixed with a large quantity of the catalyst. The continuous circulation is so arranged that the oil and catalyst mix with the oil to be hydrogenated in such a proportion as to make the reaction efficient.

All modifications of the plant consist in the manner in which the oil is mixed with the hydrogen. Besides agitating and circulation devices, there is a method by which the oil and catalyst enter the mixing vessel containing hydrogen in the form of a spray.

A great deal of research has been carried out in connection with hydrogenation plant to ensure that the reaction shall be efficient. We observe again in this connection that the fundamental achievement from a chemical engineering point of view is economy of means in conducting a chemical reaction on a large scale so that the most efficient results can be assured.

The results have been particularly striking in this instance. Just as with the cracking of oils, the object and result are to produce from a lower grade, a higher grade oil, so with hydrogenation the quality of many oils can be improved. It has had a profound effect upon the production of fats used in the food industry, and its use as we have said as a deodoriser is of great importance. Most significant of all, perhaps, is its application to the treatment of crude oils from coal carbonisation to produce petrol and other fuel oils.

ARTIFICIAL SILK : CLOTHING SPUN FROM CELLULOSE

CLOTHING also owes a great deal to the achievements of chemical engineering. Artificial silk has created a revolution in the matter of clothing among civilised peoples. The Viscose and the Acetate Processes are now the most important. There are also the Cellulose Nitrate and Cuprammonium Processes.

Viscose was discovered by C. F. Cross, of Cross and Bevan, on April 29th, 1892.[1] He discovered that when cellulose (paper, wood, or other cellular fibre) was acted upon by soda and carbon disulphide a viscid substance which he called Viscose was produced. The Viscose when mixed with am-

---

[1] Cross also initiated the Nitrate and Acetate Processes.

monium chloride was reconverted to cellulose, but in a new form. It becomes artificial silk. Paper, wood, cotton, and silk all consist of cellulose. The fundamental importance of Cross's discovery was that he found how to convert the commoner kinds of cellulose into that modification which could previously only be produced in small quantities, and therefore at considerable expense, by the silk worm.

In the Nitrate Process, the cellulose is first converted into cellulose nitrate, a dangerously explosive compound. This cellulose nitrate is denitrated and the cellulose is redeposited. In the Cuprammonium Process the cellulose is dissolved in a mixture of copper sulphate and ammonia. The cellulose is redeposited by treatment with sulphuric acid.

The Acetate Process differs in producing a cellulose acetate which is itself a form of artificial silk. The cellulose is treated with acetic anhydride and acetic acid which forms the acetate. It is finally mixed with ammonium chloride ; after the treatment it takes on the characteristic bright lustre of artificial silk.

THE PROBLEM OF SPINNING THE "SILK" INTO THREADS

THE vital problem in connection with artificial silk is that of spinning, that is to say, its production in the form of fine threads. In all cases the preliminary treatment converts the cellulose into a viscid liquid. This liquid is squirted through minute holes so that it emerges in the form of long fine threads. The final treatment follows which converts it into artificial silk proper.

The principle is quite simple, but its practical application has involved the solution of the most elaborate chemical engineering problems. Chief of these has been the production of a thread of sufficient fineness. Real silk has a thickness of only 0·01 to 0·02 millimetres. Artificial silk is never less than 0·03 millimetres. There is a further difficulty that the strength of artificial silk does not equal that of the natural variety. The fine-spun artificial threads are thus deficient in strength. It is for this reason that artificial silk does not wear so well as natural silk.

Enormous improvements have, however, been made in artificial silk of recent years. These have resulted mainly from improvements in the design of the spinning nozzles. But the spinning technique does not, in itself, affect the strength of the silk. This depends upon the general efficiency of the reaction itself. Control of temperature and pressure, and of the quality of the materials employed for the reaction greatly affect the physical properties of the viscid intermediate product from which the silk is made. Improvements in the design of artificial silk plant are continually being made. With artificial silk as with other chemical processes, the chemical engineer has completed the work which the laboratory began.

CHEMICAL ENGINEERING TO-DAY AND TO-MORROW

A N endeavour has been made in this review first to show the wide field covered by the achievements of chemical engineering, and secondly to give an outline of some processes which have not previously been considered. We have seen that without the technique of chemical engineering we should have no artificial fertilisers, no dyes, no artificial silk. The great Bakelite industry would not be in existence. Again, the future fuel of the world is undoubtedly oil. It is not an exaggeration to suggest that the future of our industrial civilisation largely depends upon efficient methods of utilising fuel oils of one kind or another. Here again chemical engineering is to the fore. Both in " cracking " and hydrogenation we observe processes which have revolutionised the question of the utilisation of fuel. Material which would once have been regarded as useless for driving an engine can now be treated in such a way as to make it a substitute for high grade oil.

It should be evident indeed that it is particularly in the sphere of fuel technology that chemical engineering has so secure a footing. The low-temperature carbonisation of coal is another aspect of the solution of the great fuel problem, and the aim of applied science to make natural resources go as far as possible. One of the outstanding features of the old-fashioned rule-of-thumb methods was their extreme wastefulness. The use of a coal fire, 75% of the efficiency of which is lost, is an example.

We considered, also, the fermentation industries and the contribution which chemical engineering has made to their efficiency. It is appropriate to remark here that the alcohol produced by fermentation is not necessarily for human consumption in the form of alcoholic liquor. Large quantities of industrial alcohol are produced by the same general methods for use as solvent and for fuel. Its use in industry is very widespread since it is essential to the manufacture of ether, chloroform, aniline dyes, explosives, artificial silks, soap, photographic materials, paints, resins, lacquers, and polishes—to name but a few of its uses in industrial processes.

In terms of human requirements we observe that fuel, food, clothing, and ornament all depend in some way upon the work of the chemical engineer, and as the efficiency of his technique increases there becomes available to mankind an increasing volume of necessities and luxuries.

The original thesis should, however, be borne in mind. Those achievements of chemical engineering ultimately rely upon the fundamental processes originally described—boiling, cooling, evaporation, distillation, crystallisation, precipitation, electrolysis, filtration. On a last analysis the work of the chemical engineer must be considered in relation to the work of the laboratory. The plant that he designs and modifies for this purpose or that is related to laboratory apparatus as the model is related to the full-size machine.

The essential difference in function between the model and the full-size plant turns to a large extent upon economic consideration. In preliminary laboratory investigations the question of cost is not considered. The first thing to find out is if the process can be made to work at all. The laboratory has achieved many things which have not yet been practically applied, simply because the economic difficulties have not been overcome. It is here that the chemical engineer enters the field. In every process which has been described, economical working is a paramount consideration. It is one of the greatest achievements of chemical engineering that it secures not only technical efficiency in a given process as far as the reaction is concerned, but that it devises means by which the process can be worked in the most economical way. Many instances have been given in connection with the processes described.

In conclusion, we might consider the future of chemical engineering. It is a branch of applied science still more or less in its infancy. And it is very interesting to consider how many laboratory successes which have been abandoned and forgotten might now be the basis of flourishing industries, if at the time of the discovery chemical engineering had reached even its present stage of development. In considering the question of the fixation of atmospheric nitrogen we must remember that it was not technically developed for thirty years. The discovery itself might have been, for all practical purposes, forgotten, had it not been for the desperate need for solving the problem which arose at the beginning of the present century. Many other processes for which the need is less urgent, but which would be of the greatest value to mankind have not been developed for this reason.

SOME GLIMPSES OF THE FUTURE

THE result of the development of chemical engineering has been that, to-day, as soon as a laboratory process which appears promising is worked out on a laboratory scale, a study of the large-scale problems is begun at once. Large-scale research goes hand in hand with laboratory work. A laboratory success may literally become a successful industry within six months.

We might consider finally an example in which chemical engineering may develop laboratory research with results of great significance to industry and mankind.

One of the most interesting branches of organic chemistry is the production of chemical compounds from their elements, that is to say that, given hydrogen, oxygen, and carbon, it should be possible to combine them to produce chemical compounds. An example of this is the research being carried out at present in Liverpool by Professor Baly and his collaborators. It has been found possible to produce carbohydrates by the combination of carbon dioxide and water. This means that from a gas and water two substances very widely distributed in nature, sugars and possibly even cellulose—sugar for food and cellulose for silk—could be produced as it were from the air.

In the laboratory, sugars have been produced in this way. This reaction is merely one of a general type by which the laboratory is finding means of building up commodities essential to mankind, independently of nature, but it is a considerable step from the laboratory to the large-scale operation in an instance of this kind. Again the need has not yet arisen for producing sugars or other carbohydrates in this way. The natural supplies suffice. But it does not follow that this will always be so, or that it may not be possible to produce food and clothing literally in the laboratory more economically than they can be produced by nature. It is the chemical engineer who will be finally responsible for the large-scale developments of laboratory products of this kind.

MAN'S GREATEST SERVANT: ELECTRICITY IN HARNESS

by E. O. TAYLOR, B.Sc., A.C.G.I., D.I.C., Associate Member of the Institute of Electrical Engineers, Associate of the American Institute of Electrical Engineers.

ALTHOUGH electrical engineering is one of the newest branches of engineering it has grown so rapidly that it is already of equal, if not greater, importance than some of the older branches of the subject. Electrical engineering covers the generation of electrical energy in power stations, that is, the conversion of the mechanical energy of the steam or water turbine, into electrical energy, the transmission of this energy to the consumers, and the uses to which it may be put for heating, lighting, driving machinery and the numerous other industrial and domestic purposes for which electric currents may be applied ; added to this there is also its use in the transmission of speech and music by telephone and wireless, and in television, which promises shortly to become as ordinary a feature of everyday life as we now regard broadcasting.

Before commencing to study the behaviour of electric currents and the way in which they can perform the various functions mentioned above, it is necessary to have some idea of what an electric current really is. To obtain this we must first consider how the various substances with which we have to deal are made up. All such substances, whether solid, liquid or gas, are made up of atoms which are very, very small particles of the substance, and each one of which is so small as to be quite invisible even with a powerful microscope. Each of these atoms is made up of even smaller particles, namely a nucleus and a certain number of electrons ; every atom contains one nucleus but may contain different numbers of electrons, for instance, an atom of copper contains a nucleus and 63 electrons, while an atom of hydrogen contains a nucleus and only one electron.

When a lot of atoms are combined to form a large piece of a substance, such as a piece of copper wire, there are always a number of free electrons not attached to any particular atoms and free to move about. Now these free electrons can be made to move along the wire in one direction by applying an electric pressure between its two ends—an electric pressure which may be produced by an electric generator or by a battery. Exactly how this is done will be described later. In this way a continual flow of free electrons is maintained in one direction along the wire constituting what is called an electric current. The size of the current depends on the number of electrons which pass any special point in the wire in a certain time. Thus, the unit of current, the ampère, represents a flow of 6·3 million million million (6·3 × 10^{18}) electrons past one point in one second. An instrument which measures the current is called an ampère-meter, or more commonly, an ammeter.

The force which causes the electrons to move, that is, produces a flow of current, is usually measured in volts by an instrument called a voltmeter, and instead of speaking of electric pressure, engineers usually speak of voltage.

Some substances have very many more free electrons than others and these electrons can move about more easily so that it does not require much pressure to send a fairly large current through a wire of such a substance. In other substances there are very few free electrons, and they cannot easily move about, so that a given voltage or pressure will produce only a very small current, in many cases so small as to be negligible for ordinary purposes. This property of substances which governs the ease with which currents may be made to pass through them is called " resistance " and is measured in " ohms." If we have a piece of wire with a difference of electric pressure of 1 volt between its ends and it is found by means of an ammeter that this pressure is producing a current of 1 ampère flowing through it, then that wire is said to have a resistance of 1 ohm.

Now there is a definite law connecting the current, the electric pressure or voltage applied and the resistance of the medium through which the current passes. It is that the current, measured in ampères is equal to the voltage, measured in volts, divided by the resistance, measured in ohms. Expressed mathematically, using I to represent the number of ampères of current, V the number of volts of electrical pressure and R the number of ohms of resistance,

$$I = \frac{V}{R} \quad or \quad V = IR \quad or \quad R = \frac{V}{I}.$$

This is known as Ohm's Law, taking its name, as does the unit of resistance, from G. S. Ohm, who first performed the experiments to prove its truth.

Substances which offer a low resistance to the flow of current are called " conductors." All metals fall into this category but some are better conductors than others. The best conductors, that is, those having the lowest resistance, are gold, silver, copper and aluminium. The two former are, of course, too expensive for ordinary use, but copper and aluminium are very widely used in electrical engineering.

Materials which offer a very high resistance to the flow of current, and in fact pass practically no current at all are called " insulators " or " insulating materials," and into this category come practically all non-metallic substances. Porcelain, mica, rubber, bakelite, paper, and oils are largely used in electrical engineering when it is desired to prevent current flowing in a certain path. For instance, the ordinary electric wire used for suspending electric lamps consists of a conductor of copper surrounded by rubber and cotton insulating materials to prevent the current escaping from the wire.

It may still be difficult for the reader to visualise what is meant by electric current, pressure and resistance so that a comparison between an electric circuit and a water circuit may be helpful, in which the flow of electric current in conductors is compared to the flow of water in pipes. Suppose we have a water circuit consisting of a pump and a circuit of pipes. In order to get a given flow of water (measured in gallons per second) round the circuit, the pump will have to generate a certain pressure of water ; the amount of this pressure will depend on the resistance to the flow of water offered by the pipes, this resistance being due to friction of the water on the sides of the pipes, the effect of the corners, etc. This water circuit may now be compared to the electric circuit in which we have an electric generator taking the place of the pump and generating an electric pressure instead of a pressure of water ; this electric pressure causes a flow of current round the circuit (measured in ampères) instead of the flow of water caused by the pump ; the electric circuit offers a resistance (measured in ohms) to the flow of current just as the pipes offer a resistance to the flow of water. The walls of the pipe keep the water in its proper place and prevent its leaking away and the insulating material round the wire in the electric circuit similarly keeps the current from leaking away.

THE TWO KINDS OF CURRENT FLOW : DIRECT AND ALTERNATING

IF the current is flowing continuously round the circuit in the same direction, in a similar way to that in which water flows round an ordinary hot-water circulating system, then we have what is called a direct or continuous current. In any source of such a current, such as a battery or generator, the terminal which is at the higher electrical pressure is called the positive terminal, while the other terminal is called the negative terminal. It is the accepted convention in dealing with electric current that the current flows *from* the positive terminal *to* the negative, but it must be remembered that the electrons themselves are charged negatively and therefore flow *towards* the positive terminal. Electron flow is therefore *opposite* to the assumed direction of the current—a confusion which arose because the electron was not discovered until the convention was well established.

It is possible to employ currents which, instead of always flowing in the same direction, flow first for a short time in one direction and then for an equal length of time in the other ; the electrons constituting such a current do not therefore actually move round the circuit in a steady stream, but the number passing any point in a certain time reaches a maximum, gradually falls off to zero, and then reaches the same maximum in the other direction, and so on. A current which behaves in this way is called an alternating current and such currents are, in practice, used more than direct currents. With an alternating current the time during which it is flowing in one direction plus the time during which it is flowing in the other direction, that is, the time for one complete cycle of operations, is called a " period," and is always a very small fraction of a second. The number of periods per second is called the " frequency " and is stated in " cycles per second."

For ordinary purposes such as heating and lighting, driving of motors and so on, the frequency of the alternating currents employed is nearly always 50 cycles per second in this and other European countries ; in America frequencies of 25 or 60 cycles per second are employed. For certain purposes it is necessary to use currents at lower frequencies, for instance, the electric railways of Germany and Switzerland employ currents at $16\frac{2}{3}$ cycles per second ; radio telegraphy and medical uses of electricity, however, require currents at frequencies of hundreds of thousands of cycles per second. Alternating currents, no matter what the frequency, are measured in ampères just like a direct current, one ampère of alternating current producing the same heating effect in an electric radiator or the same lighting effect from an electric lamp as one ampère of direct current. Similarly the alternating electrical pressures which produce these alternating currents are measured in volts.

Having thus explained what is meant when we speak of an electric current we can proceed to see how these currents can be produced by electric generators and batteries and how they can be used for heating, lighting, and the driving of various forms of machinery.

ANCIENT MAGNETISM, ELECTRICITY'S SHADOW

IT has been known from the very earliest times that a certain mineral, found largely in Magnesia in Asia Minor, possessed strange properties, namely, that two pieces of it would attract each other and would also attract pieces of iron ; another and even more important property is the fact that if a piece of the mineral is suspended freely by string or cotton it will always turn so that one end of it points towards the North.

If a piece of iron is placed near to one of these magnetic stones or " lodestones," the iron itself will exhibit similar properties to those of the lodestone—the iron is then said to be magnetised and when in this state it is called a magnet. Ordinary soft iron loses its magnetic properties as soon as the lodestone is removed, but a piece of harder iron or steel will retain them and it is then called a permanent magnet. If a permanent magnet be suspended freely it will be found that one end will always point towards the North just as with the lodestone; this end is called the North pole of the magnet and is generally marked with an N or some other distinguishing mark. The other end of the magnet will, of course, point towards the South, and is called the South pole. Permanent magnets are generally made in the form of a bar magnet or a horseshoe magnet (see Fig. 95) ; the actual making could be carried out by bringing the properly shaped piece of iron near to or touching the lodestone as described above, but actually magnets can be made much more easily and strongly by means of an electric current. Experiments show that the North pole of one magnet and the South pole of another will attract each other, but that two North poles or two South poles will repel each other.

USING A CURRENT TO CREATE A MAGNET

IN the year 1820, Hans Oersted of Copenhagen discovered that an electric current exhibited similar properties to those of a magnet, namely that a small magnet placed near the wire carrying the current was attracted or repelled. In 1825 this discovery was taken a step further by Sturgeon of Woolwich, who wound the wire round a piece of soft iron and then passed a current through it ; he found that when the current was flowing the iron was magnetised and behaved in the same way as an ordinary bar magnet only the effect was very much stronger. When the current was switched off the magnetism all disappeared. This device was called an electromagnet and, as the magnetism can be switched on and off at will, it is obviously a more valuable sort of magnet than the permanent magnet for many purposes, particularly as the magnetism is also much stronger. If a piece of hard iron or steel is used instead of the soft iron the magnetism does not all disappear when the current is switched off and the steel becomes a permanent magnet. This is the way in which permanent magnets are made. The electromagnet can be made in the shape of a bar magnet or as a horseshoe magnet or in any other desirable shape.

The electromagnet is an extremely valuable piece of apparatus, in fact, the science of electrical engineering could hardly exist without it. A very simple application of it is in the construction of an ordinary electric bell—a horseshoe shape of magnet is used as shown in Fig. 94. This electromagnet has a winding on it through which a current can be passed by applying an electric pressure of 2 or 3 volts between the two terminals. A piece of soft iron is attached to a spring fixed at the point A ; when a current is passed through the magnet coils this piece of iron is attracted and causes the striker to hit the gong ; as soon as this happens the electric circuit to the magnet is broken at the contact B and the current stops so that the striker falls back under the action of the spring ; this, however, completes the circuit again at the contact B and the whole process is repeated. This goes on continually many times a second so long as the electromagnet is connected to the source of current. Some types of electric motor horn work in a very similar way except that the soft iron hits

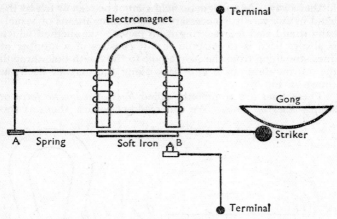

Electromagnet

Terminal

Gong

A Spring Soft Iron B Striker

Terminal

94. The essentials of an electric bell system

against a diaphragm in the horn instead of making a striker hit a gong.

When lifting steel rails, scrap iron or other similar material, a large electromagnet can be used instead of the complicated arrangement of ropes, hooks and slings which was usually employed, and much time can be saved. Magnets capable of lifting several tons can be built for this purpose—they will require a current through the magnet coils of 20 or 30 ampères at a pressure of about 200 volts. An interesting application of magnets of this type is the salvaging of material from under water without having to employ divers to go down and fix hooks.

PICTURING THE INVISIBLE FORCES WHICH SURROUND A MAGNET

WE know that if we take an ordinary permanent or electro-magnet, the space around that magnet is not quite the same as any other space, because, if we put a piece of iron in that space it becomes magnetised and attracted towards the magnet in a certain way. The effect on the iron will be greater the nearer it is to the magnet. The space around the magnet in which such effects can be observed is called the *magnetic field* of the magnet ; this magnetic field is strongest near the poles of the magnet and gradually gets weaker as we get further away. As a magnetic field cannot be seen or felt by the hand in any way it is necessary to have some means of visualising it and also representing it on paper; the method which is always used is to imagine that it consists of a number of lines stretching from the North pole to the South pole through the surrounding space and back along the magnet itself, as shown in Fig. 95.

These lines are commonly called *lines of magnetic force* or simply *lines of force*. We can readily visualise them as sta-

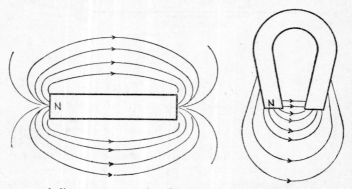

95. *A diagram representing the directions taken by the lines of force surrounding a bar-magnet (left) and a horseshoe magnet.*

tionary, spread in the space round a magnet, but how do they grow when the current is switched on? Do they start from the N. pole and travel through the air to the S. pole like rockets trailing life-lines or do they grow outwards from the inside of the magnet like a balloon when it is blown up? It is found most convenient to imagine that the latter takes place. As soon as the current of the electromagnet is switched on the proper number of lines of force immediately grow outwards and take up their appointed positions and when the current is switched off again they all collapse back into the magnet. In springing outwards and collapsing it is evident that the lines may be considered to cut through the wires of the coil carrying the current. This idea of the lines springing outwards from the centre of the magnet and cutting through the current-carrying conductors is very important.

Before leaving the question of the magnetic field it is

desirable to see how it is measured. The obvious way is to place a value on the lines of force and state how many there are, and this is what is actually done ; thus an ordinary bar magnet may have 20,000 lines coming from its N. pole and going back into the S. pole. This figure is called the total *magnetic flux* of the magnet. It does not, however, tell us anything about the closeness of the spacing of the lines—for measuring this we state the number of lines passing through an area equal to 1 square inch or 1 square centimetre. This figure is called the *flux density*. In the case of the bar magnet the flux density will be large near to the poles and smaller at greater distances from them. The magnetic field plays an important part in nearly all electrical machinery and apparatus and the flux densities used are generally somewhere between about 6,000 and 12,000 lines per square centimetre.

THE BIRTH OF ELECTRICAL ENGINEERING : FARADAY'S FAMOUS EXPERIMENT

THE discovery that a magnetic field is produced by an electric current immediately led scientists in all countries to wonder whether it would not be possible to reverse the process and produce an electric current from a magnetic field. Many experiments were made to try to produce electric currents in this way, but none were successful until Faraday's great experiments in 1831, 11 years after Oersted's discovery that a current produces a magnetic field.

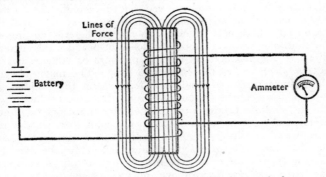

96. *Faraday's famous experiment in diagrammatic form. By changing suddenly the current in one circuit he produced a current in a second circuit which was wound, as shown in the diagram, over the same electromagnet.*

Faraday, working at the Royal Institution in London, used apparatus as shown diagrammatically in Fig. 96. Current was passed through the winding of the electromagnet from the battery and a fairly strong magnetic field was set up with the lines of force as shown ; on the electromagnet a secondary winding was also wound and Faraday hoped that when current was passed through the first, or primary, winding, a current would be induced in this secondary winding and cause the ammeter to deflect ; to Faraday's disappointment this did not happen. He did notice, however, that when switching the current on or off, the ammeter gave a momentary kick and then returned to zero showing that there was just a momentary current, so that although the experiment did not work out as he had hoped, it did give the key to the solution of the problem, namely that a current is produced in the secondary circuit when the magnetic field is set up or allowed to die away.

Now what exactly happens when the magnetic field is set up by switching on the primary current? We have already seen that the magnetic lines of force may be considered to cut through the conductors of the electromagnet. In Faraday's experiment they must also cut through the conductors of the secondary circuit, and this led Faraday to suggest that a current can be produced by means of a magnetic field if the lines of force of the field are made to cut through a wire or conductor. Faraday and many other workers did other experiments which definitely proved that this actually is the case.

The next thing to consider is how much current will be produced ; here it is necessary to realise that the cutting of the lines of force by a conductor does not produce the current directly, but produces an electric pressure or voltage and it is this which causes the current to flow. The magnitude of the voltage produced obviously depends on the number of lines of force which are cut and upon the rate at which they are cut, and careful experiments show that if 100,000,000 lines of force are cut by a conductor per second then an electric pressure of 1 volt will be produced. It does not matter how the lines are made to cut the conductor ; it may be done by making them grow out of the magnet by starting or stopping the current as described above, by moving the conductor in front of the pole of a stationary magnet or by moving a magnet so that its lines of force cut a stationary conductor ; the effect is precisely the same in each case.

The fact that an electric pressure can be generated in a conductor by making it cut the lines of force of a magnetic field led to the invention of the electric generator as a source of electric currents on a large scale, and also to all other types of electric machinery, so that the science of electrical engineering may truly be said to date from Faraday's great discovery in 1831.

THE ENGINEER TAKES CHARGE : ELECTRIC GENERATORS

Having now seen how an electric pressure can be produced, we must consider how a machine can be constructed which will have an arrangement of magnetic field and conductors which can generate large electric pressures suitable for providing current for heating and lighting buildings, driving trams and trains and doing the numerous other things for which electrical energy is used. Obviously we shall require very large magnetic fields and a large number of conductors, and the conductors must be moving very quickly relatively to the field in order to cut the lines at the maximum rate.

The construction of a typical generator is illustrated in Fig. 97. It can be seen that there are a number of magnetic poles, in this case four, arranged in a circle and giving alternately North and South poles. Rotating inside this is the armature, which is made of thin sheets of steel securely bolted together and fixed to the shaft. The space between the armature and the poles is called the air gap and is usually $\frac{1}{8}$ to $\frac{1}{2}$ inch wide, depending on the size of the machine. The lines of force of the magnet make their circuit from the N. pole, across the air gap, through the armature, back across the air gap to the S. pole and so along the yoke back to the N. pole. In slots cut axially along the surface of the armature are placed the insulated conductors, so that when the armature is rotated these conductors cut the lines of force of the magnets and therefore have a voltage generated in them. The voltage generated in each wire will be one or two volts only, or even less in a small machine, so that in order to get several hundred or thousand volts it is necessary to connect a large number of conductors together; the complete arrangement of conductors when connected together in this way is called the winding.

The direction of the voltage in a conductor, that is, the direction in which it would send a current, can easily be found

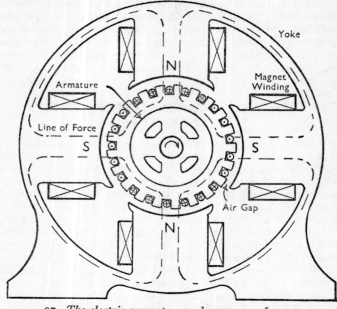

97. The electric generator, modern source of power

from a simple rule called the Right-Hand Rule. Make the *forefinger* of the right hand point in the direction of the lines of force of the magnet (remembering that the lines of force come out of a N. pole and go into a S. pole), and arrange the *thumb* at right angles to this and make it point in the direction in which the conductor is *moving*; arrange the *second finger* at right angles to the other two and it will then be pointing in the direction of the *voltage*. If this rule is applied to the conductors under one of the N. poles of Fig. 97 it will be found that the current will be flowing along the conductor into the paper; this is represented by placing a cross on the conductor (which is supposed to represent the back view of an arrow going into the paper). The same rule may be applied to the conductors under the S. poles and it will be found that the current would be coming out of the paper. This is represented by a dot, supposedly the front view of the arrow coming out of the paper.

When the conductors are connected together it is necessary that the current be flowing in the same direction along the whole of the circuit, so that the conductors under a N. pole must be connected to conductors under a S. pole by a connection along the back or front of the armature. The *winding diagram* shows the man who winds the machine exactly which conductors must be connected together after they have been placed in the slots. In practice there may be only one conductor in each slot or possibly as many as 20 or 30. The ends of the winding are brought out to the terminals of the machine from which the current may be obtained.

A difficulty is met with here because with the arrangement shown in Fig. 97 the armature and winding are rotating while the terminals must of course be stationary; where it is necessary to make current pass from a moving to a fixed portion of the machine slip rings are employed. These consist simply of a polished brass or steel ring mounted on and insulated from the shaft of the rotating part and a carbon block commonly known as a brush, fixed to the frame and connected to one of the terminals. Current is then led to the ring from the winding and is collected by the brush and passed on to the terminal. It returns to the winding, of course, through another similar ring and brush.

HOW MOTION IN A MAGNETIC FIELD PRODUCES ALTERNATING CURRENT

CONSIDER again a single conductor on the armature of a generator. As the armature rotates this cuts first the flux from a N. pole and then the flux from a S. pole, and so on, so that the voltage generated in it is first in one direction and then in the other; that is to say, an alternating voltage is generated and alternating currents are obtained from the machine. In going past one pair of poles one complete cycle of alternating current is generated, so that the frequency of the currents depends on the number of poles and the speed at which the armature is running. A little consideration will show that the following formula gives the frequency in cycles per second:

$$\text{Frequency} = \frac{\text{No. of Poles}}{2} \times \text{Revs. per sec.}$$

$$= \frac{\text{No. of Poles} \times \text{Revs. per min.}}{120}$$

As an alternating current generator, or alternator as it is often called, usually has to generate at the standard frequency of 50 cycles, the number of poles which it must have is quite definitely fixed by the speed of the machine which drives it, usually a steam turbine, water turbine or an oil engine. Steam turbines run best at very high speeds, so that two pole alternators running at 3,000 r.p.m. or four pole alternators running at 1,500 r.p.m. are generally used where this form of drive is employed. Large water turbines run at very low speeds, sometimes as low as 100 r.p.m., so that alternators driven by these will have to have 50 or 60 poles, and will therefore be of very large diameter. Except with very small machines it is found easier to build them with the magnet poles rotating and the armature stationary, and this is the construction invariably adopted for alternators. In order to make a generator give current from its armature winding, it is necessary to supply some current to the windings on the magnet poles in order to produce the magnetic field, this current being known as the field current or exciting current; it is generally obtained from a separate little generator mounted on the same shaft as the main generator. Large alternators are usually built to give about 6,000 or 11,000 volts and several hundred ampères, although machines to give 20,000 or 30,000 volts have been built and operate quite satisfactorily. Special precautions have to be taken, however, to secure satisfactory insulation when dealing with windings to give such high voltages.

A SIMPLE DEVICE GIVES A ONE-WAY CURRENT

IT has been seen that the type of generator already described produces an alternating current. If a direct current has to be generated it is necessary to include a commutator in the construction of the machine as well as the armature and field magnets. The commutator simply changes the direction of the alternate half waves of the alternating current which is actually generated, so that the current at the terminals is always in the same direction. The way in which the commutator does this can most easily be explained by considering a very simple generator having only two conductors as shown in Fig. 98, the two being of course connected together at the back end of the armature. The commutator in this case consists of a ring mounted on the shaft and split into two halves insulated from each other and each attached to one of the conductors. In Fig. 98 the current in conductor A is, by applying the Right-Hand Rule, seen to be coming out of the paper on to the segment of the commutator and through the brush to the terminal H and so to the lamps ; from the lamps it returns via the other terminal and brush as shown.

Now after the armature has rotated a little further the conductor A comes opposite the S. pole, and has a current generated in it in the opposite direction ; similarly with conductor B, which now has a current coming out of the

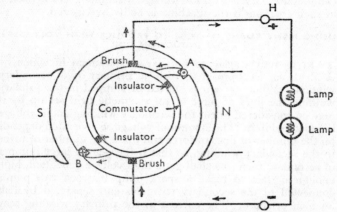

98. How the commutator provides a one-way current

paper. The split on the commutator has now, however, passed the brushes and the segment attached to conductor B is now under the brush attached to terminal H, so that current is still flowing out to the lamps from this terminal although the direction of the current in the conductors on the armature has reversed. Terminal H therefore always has current flowing away from it and is the positive terminal of the machine. An ordinary generator has, of course, many conductors on it and each one or each small group of these is attached to one commutator segment, so that the commutator of an actual machine may have a hundred or so segments instead of the two shown in the diagram. There may also be more than two brushes, one brush for every pole being the usual arrangement.

Another very important feature of a direct current generator arises from the fact that, as a direct current is being generated, a portion of it may be used to excite the field winding instead of having to use a separate source of supply for this purpose as with the alternator. A generator of this type is said to be self-excited.

Normally, direct current generators are not built to give more than about 600 volts, although it is possible by special designs to get as much as 3,000 volts. It is difficult to go beyond this because of the danger of bad sparking at the commutator. Even with low voltage machines there is danger of such sparking if the machine is badly overloaded.

USING MANY TURNS OF WIRE TO PRODUCE HIGH VOLTAGES : THE INDUCTION COIL

LET us return again to Faraday's experiment in which he had an electromagnet with a primary and secondary winding. When current is started or stopped in the primary winding the lines of force of the magnetic field set up by it may be considered to cut the secondary winding and a voltage is generated in it. The amount of voltage so generated depends on the number of lines of force and upon the number of turns in the secondary winding, so that if there are a large number of secondary turns we shall get a high voltage generated, high enough in fact to make a spark jump between two points connected to the secondary terminals and separated by half an inch or more. The current in the primary winding may be produced from a small battery or other source giving as low as 4 volts, so that we have here a means of obtaining a high electrical pressure from a small one in much the same way that a pumping station may be installed to raise water pressure when it is necessary to transmit the water to a high level.

The amount by which the voltage is raised depends, as previously mentioned, on the number of turns on the windings —if there are 1,000 times as many turns on the secondary as there are on the primary, then the secondary voltage will be 1,000 times that of the primary. In order that the secondary voltage shall be obtained more or less continuously, a contact maker is generally fitted which is continually making and breaking the circuit in exactly the same way as the contact-maker of an electric bell. Coils of this sort are called induction coils and are used for a variety of purposes ranging from the toy equipment used for giving people shocks to the large coils capable of producing sparks of a foot or more in length. The most common use is probably for providing the spark necessary for running a motor-car engine, which may require 1,000 or more volts.

CHANGING THE VOLTAGE TO FIT THE PURPOSE : THE TRANSFORMER

THE function of the contact-maker in the induction coil is to make the lines of force grow up and die down more or less continuously in order to give a more or less continuous voltage at the secondary terminals. Precisely the same effect can be obtained by supplying the primary winding with an alternating current instead of direct current interrupted in this way. The flux due to the current grows to a maximum in a positive direction when the current is positive and then dies down and grows in a negative direction when the current is negative, so that lines of force are continually cutting the conductors of the secondary winding and an alternating voltage is generated in it of the same frequency as that supplied to the primary.

As with the induction coil, the ratio of the secondary voltage to the primary voltage depends on the ratio of the number of the secondary turns to the number of primary turns, so that if there are 100 turns on the primary and 1,000 turns on the secondary and the primary is supplied with a 500 volt, 50 cycle current, then current at 5,000 volts and 50 cycles will be obtainable from the secondary. A coil used in this way is called a *transformer* ; if it is used to raise the voltage it is a step-up transformer, while if the number of turns on the secondary is less than that on the primary so that the secondary voltage is lower than the primary voltage, then it is called a step-down transformer.

The construction of a transformer such as is used for raising or lowering the pressure of large amounts of electrical energy is shown in Fig. 99. Except in very small sizes the core and windings are immersed in a tank containing oil, as this helps to insulate the windings and also enables the heat which is generated during operation to be got rid of more easily by radiation from the surface. The pipes on the outside of the tank are for increasing the surface area and so more effectively cooling the oil ; an alternative method used on very large units is to circulate the hot oil through a cooler and then return it to the tank by means of a pump.

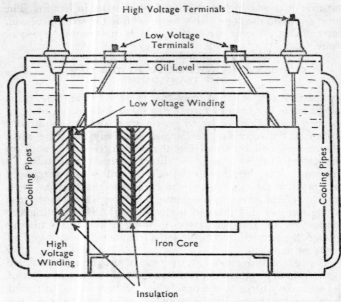

High Voltage Terminals

Low Voltage Terminals

Oil Level

Low Voltage Winding

Cooling Pipes

Cooling Pipes

High Voltage Winding

Iron Core

Insulation

99. *A modern transformer for changing the voltage of large amounts of electrical energy. Its coils, shown on one side only, are immersed in a tank of oil.*

For testing electrical apparatus to see if it will withstand very high voltages, transformers giving as much as 1,000,000 volts are used ; with such a voltage it is possible to obtain a spark 8 or 9 feet long, a not unworthy imitation of the lightning of the heavens.

FINDING A FORMULA FOR ELECTRICAL POWER AND ENERGY

BY means of an electric generator we can convert the mechanical power developed by the steam engine into electrical power ; the mechanical power is measured in horse power—how are we going to measure the electrical power? The unit which has been chosen is the *watt*, and it is the amount of power which a generator would give if it had a voltage of 1 volt and were giving a current of 1 ampère ; the amount of power in an electrical circuit can therefore be easily

calculated simply by multiplying the voltage by the current :
volts × amps = watts. The watt is a very small amount of
power, in fact it takes 746 watts to make an amount of power
equal to 1 horse power, so that another bigger unit is also
used called the kilowatt (kW.) which, as the name implies, is
equal to 1,000 watts, and is therefore a little bigger than a
horse power.

When buying electrical energy we must not only consider
the amount of power which we are consuming, but also the
length of time for which we consume it. The unit of electrical
energy is the kilowatt-hour, which is the amount of energy
consumed if we use 1 kilowatt for a period of one hour. Thus
an electric stove which consumes 2 kilowatts will, if used for
3 hours, take 2 × 3 = 6 kilowatt-hours of electrical energy.
The quantity of electrical energy, the kilowatt-hour (usually
written kWh.), is often simply called a " unit," and it is these
units which are recorded on the dial of the meter which is
installed where the supply comes into one's house. The cost
of buying a unit of electrical energy varies somewhat, but is
generally somewhere between ½d. per unit where fairly large
quantities of energy are used and 3d. per unit where only a
little is used.

THE POWER STATION : CENTRAL SOURCE OF ELECTRICAL ENERGY

IT is cheaper to produce electrical energy by means of a
few large generators rather than by a number of small
ones, so that a town or group of towns is generally supplied
by four or six such generators situated in a power station.
In this country the generators are usually driven by steam
turbines and the power station must therefore contain the
necessary boilers, condensing plant and other auxiliaries as
well as the electrical equipment. The demand for electrical
energy is so great that a large town requires a power station
capable of delivering 50,000 to 100,000 kilowatts of electrical
energy, equivalent to 40,000 to 80,000 horse power. Such a
power station will burn 1,000 or more tons of coal per day
and will require thousands of gallons of water for its condensers, so that it is necessary that it should be situated near
a river along which barges full of coal can be brought and
whose water can be used in the condensers. It should also
be situated somewhere near the centre of the town which it is
to serve in order that the electric current does not have to be

transmitted over long distances. The choice of a suitable site for these enormous power stations is therefore a complicated problem.

HOW ELECTRICAL POWER IS BROUGHT TO EVERYMAN'S DOOR

THE development of the enormous power stations from the simple experiment of Faraday has been described in the last section. Having thus obtained a suitable means of generating large amounts of electrical energy—the electric generator—and also a means of raising its voltage if necessary —the transformer—we can now go on to consider how all this energy can be transmitted to the thousands of homes and factories where it is to be used.

The generators for producing large quantities of electricity will almost certainly be alternating current machines and will be situated in a power station ; if steam turbines are used to drive the generators the power station will be situated not more than 10 or 20 miles from the district which it has to supply, but if it is a water power station it will have to be situated where there is a suitable fall of water, probably in a mountainous region, which may be a hundred miles or more away. In either case the electrical energy will have to be transmitted over some distance.

Now a given amount of electrical energy can be transmitted either at a high voltage with a small current or at a small voltage with a large current, just as a water turbine of a certain output can be driven by a large quantity of water at a low head or pressure or a small quantity of water at a high head. In transmitting electrical energy it is always best to use a high voltage and a small current because a large current would require very large and expensive conductors to carry it. The use of a small current is especially important where the energy has to be transmitted for very long distances, so that where the power station is fairly near the load (a work to be done by the electricity), the voltage used for transmission will usually be about 20,000 or 30,000 volts, while where it is a very long distance away the pressure will be 100,000, 200,000 or even 300,000 volts.

As generators cannot be built for more than about 11,000 volts in most cases, it will be necessary to install transformers in the power station to step up the voltage to the value necessary for transmission. The conductors for carrying the current may be suspended from towers like telephone wires or they may be laid under-ground. A steel tower or pylon for supporting the conductors is shown in Fig. 100 ; such towers are used for the more important lines where the voltage is greater than about 20,000 volts, while for less important lines at lower voltages, wooden poles are often used.

The wires themselves are always stranded, that is, made up of a number of small wires bunched together, so that they shall be flex-ible and easy to install on the towers. Stranded copper wire is used for small lines where the span between tow-ers is not very great, but where there are long spans on the more important lines steel-cored aluminium con-ductors are used to give greater strength. These conductors have some strands of steel to provide mechanical strength, surrounded by strands of alumin-ium, which is nearly

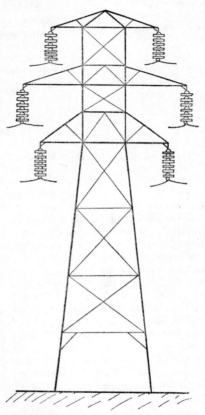

100. The modern steel pylon carrying porcelain suspension insulators, which supports the high voltage transmission lines of the grid system.

as good a conductor as copper and which carries all the current. No insulating material is wrapped round the con-ductors as the current cannot easily leak away through the air, but where they are supported at the towers, insulators must be used. These insulators are generally of porcelain and for low voltages up to about 30,000 volts are of the pin type as shown in Fig. 101, while for higher voltages they are of the suspension type shown in Fig. 100; with this type higher voltages can be withstood simply by adding more discs to the string.

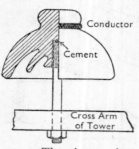

101. The pin-type insulator which is used with lower voltages.

TAKING THE CURRENT UNDERGROUND

OVERHEAD lines are somewhat unsightly and also they are liable to damage from lightning, and so the conductors are sometimes laid underground, although this method of laying is much more expensive. Also in towns there is the difficulty of finding sites for placing the towers and the danger of people on housetops touching the live conductors. Where the conductors are laid underground they must be surrounded by a thick layer of insulation to prevent the current leaking away into the earth ; protection must also be provided against moisture getting into the insulation and against damage due to movement of the soil, workmen's pick-axes, etc.

The conductor itself is always of stranded copper and this is surrounded by layers of paper tape thoroughly soaked and impregnated with oil and wrapped tightly on, to a thickness of $\frac{1}{2}$ to 1 inch depending on the voltage ; outside this is placed a lead sheath about $\frac{1}{8}$ inch thick to keep out the moisture, and then if necessary a steel tape or steel wire armouring is placed around the whole (to prevent mechanical damage) and finished off with a layer of tarred jute or hemp.

Very great care must be taken in manufacture to avoid any air spaces in the insulation, as these, in conjunction with the high voltage, damage the insulation and cause it to break down. To prevent air spaces, oil-filled cables are sometimes used in which holes are left running the whole length of the cable. These are filled with oil, which percolates into and fills up any small air spaces which may have been left in the insulation. After manufacture the cable is wound on the big wooden drums 8 or 10 feet in diameter which are often seen by the roadside ; a trench is dug 2 or 3 feet deep and the cable laid in it and the earth filled in again. The cable is then ready for carrying current.

CONTROLLING THE LARGE CURRENTS OF POWER TRANSMISSION

WITH transmission lines carrying large currents it is just as necessary to be able to switch the current on and off as it is with the electric light or electric radiators in our houses. Stopping such large currents, however, is a much more difficult matter. Just as a train cannot stop immediately the brakes are applied, so a current cannot stop immediately the contacts of the switch are broken, and after the contacts have separated a little way, the current tries to jump across the gap and makes a spark or an arc. This arc lasts for a fraction of a second only, but it may do a great deal of damage by burning the contacts of the switch, especially when fairly large currents at high voltages are stopped. In order to put out this arc very quickly the contacts of switches for dealing with more than 20 or 30 ampères are immersed in oil. Also, as with the small tumbler switch used for lighting circuits, a spring is used for making the contacts separate quickly. Medium sized oil switches can be operated by hand, but very large ones, which sometimes stand 10 or 12 feet high, must be operated by means of a powerful electromagnet or by compressed air.

TRACING THE CURRENT'S JOURNEY FROM POWER STATION TO CONSUMER

WE can now trace the journey of the current from the power station to the consumer. A diagram of a complete system is shown in Fig. 102. At the power station, where the current is generated at 6,000 to 11,000 volts, it is stepped up to a high voltage for transmitting to a main sub-station at about the centre of the area which it is to supply. Here another transformer is installed which steps down the voltage to about 10,000 or 20,000 volts and distributes it amongst several feeders. Each of these feeders goes to a secondary substation situated in some convenient part of the town—these secondary substations often consist only of a single transformer in a small metal or brick kiosk which can be seen at street corners and in other suitable places. This transformer steps the voltage down again to a value which is safe to take into houses and workshops—about 230 volts is used for lighting circuits and about 400 volts for driving motors. Current at this low voltage is supplied along distributor cables laid along each side of the street, with tappings taken off to go into each of the houses to a main switch and a meter for measuring the amount of energy used. From the meter the path of the current is further split up and goes by wires under the floor boards or in the ceilings to the various lighting points.

In a few cases the secondary substations contain special apparatus—rotary converters or mercury-arc rectifiers—for converting the alternating current into direct current, which is then fed along the distributor cables to the consumers.

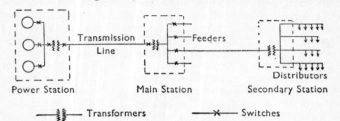

102. From power station to consumer : a diagram explaining the system by which electric current is distributed to house, shop, and factory.

An actual power system is usually rather more complicated than the one shown in the diagram because the main and secondary substations each have at least two possible routes of supply so that if the cables break down on one route current can still be transmitted over the other. Protective equipment is installed which automatically switches out of circuit any cable which breaks down or becomes damaged in any way so that as little disturbance as possible is caused to the consumers.

THE NETWORK SPREAD OVER BRITAIN : THE "GRID"

As the demand for electrical energy increased one or more power stations were erected in almost every town in this country. In small towns, stations generating only about 4,000 or 5,000 kW. were required, while in large towns such as Manchester and Birmingham large stations giving 50,000 or 100,000 kW. were necessary. There were therefore many hundreds of power stations built. Now it is well known that electrical energy can be generated very much more cheaply in large power stations than in small ones just as almost any product can be produced more cheaply in large quantities than in small quantities ; also every power station must have at least one and probably two spare generators together with the corresponding turbine and boiler equipment which can be used in case of a breakdown of one of the regular units, but which is normally lying idle.

It was therefore very soon realised that energy could be generated much more cheaply by connecting all the towns by transmission lines and generating all the energy in a few large up-to-date stations than by having a small and inefficient station in each town. By this arrangement the amount of spare plant could be reduced, as, in the event of a breakdown in one station, energy could be transmitted to it from one of the other stations.

Between the years of 1917 and 1925 steps were taken to link up some of the towns in this way and some of the oldest stations were closed down, but not very much was done. In 1925, however, a committee was set up with Lord Weir as chairman to consider the whole problem ; this committee suggested that certain of the largest and most efficient stations should be " selected " and used for supplying the whole country with electricity while all the other stations should be closed down, and also that these selected stations and all the towns should be interconnected by a network of high voltage transmission lines criss-crossing the country like a grid-iron. It was calculated that by this scheme it would be possible to supply electricity over the whole country very much more cheaply than formerly.

These findings of the committee were incorporated in an Act of Parliament in 1926, and a body called the Central Electricity Board was set up which had to construct all the transmission lines and to operate them and also to operate all the selected stations. All the transmission lines, the most important of which are shown in the map, Fig. 103, were completed in 1933 (although of course extensions are continually being made) and they are commonly known as the Grid. The voltage used is 132,000 volts for the main circuits and 33,000 volts for the smaller less important circuits. Although the lines cover the whole of England, Scotland and Wales the country is, for convenience, divided into the nine areas indicated on the map.

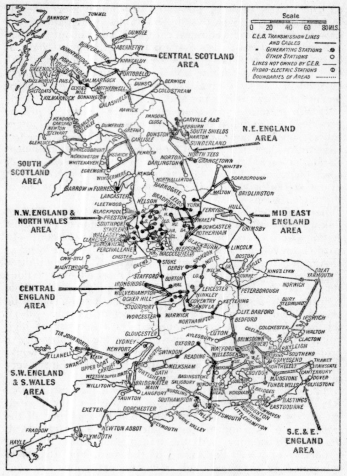

103. THE NATIONAL GRID SYSTEM

At about the centre of each area is situated a control room in which are stationed engineers who control the supply to the whole area in such a way that the energy is supplied in the cheapest and most satisfactory manner. These engineers can by simply pressing a button see the exact voltage and current at any of the important points on the system and also can find whether any particular switch is open or closed. They can also telephone by a system of private telephone lines to all the points, and by this means give orders for the opening or closing of switches, starting up or shutting down of generators, and so on. The engineers at the various power stations are not allowed to carry out any operations of this sort except by instructions from the control room of their area.

The Central Electricity Board does not own any of the power stations but simply operates them and purchases energy from them for transmission to the various towns which have now no generating stations of their own. The electricity companies of these towns buy their electrical energy from the Board at a certain price or tariff, and this price is always less than that at which they could have generated the energy in their own old power stations ; the company then has its own feeders and distributors for conveying the energy from the main substation where it is purchased from the Board, to the various consumers ; the price charged to the consumers by the company must therefore be sufficient to pay the initial cost of the energy and also to pay for the distribution system together with a suitable profit for the company.

SETTING THE ELECTRICITY TO WORK : THE ELECTRIC MOTOR

HAVING seen how electricity is generated and transmitted to the consumer, we must now see how he can make use of it—the chief uses are for heating and lighting, for communication by telegraph and telephone, and for operating electric motors for driving all kinds of machinery ranging from a small domestic vacuum cleaner to electric trains and the large machinery used in factories. We will consider the electric motor first, heating, lighting and communications being dealt with later.

Very soon after Oersted's discovery that an electric current produced a magnetic field, it was found that a conductor carrying a current and lying in a magnetic field had a force exerted on it. If therefore we take the electric generator shown in Fig. 97 and instead of driving the armature by a steam engine we pass a current through the conductors on it, these conductors, since they are lying in a magnetic field, will have a force exerted on them and the armature will rotate. We now have an electric motor and the armature can be attached to some other machine and used to drive it.

Just as we could find the direction of the voltage produced in a conductor by using the Right-Hand Rule, so we can find the direction of the force on a conductor in a magnetic field by means of the Left-Hand Rule. Arrange the *left* hand so that the forefinger is pointing in the direction of the lines of force, the second finger in the direction of the current in the conductor, and the thumb will then be pointing in the direction of the force on the conductor, i.e. in the direction in which the

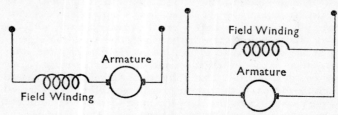

104. Two ways in which the magnet winding of an electric motor may be connected to the commutator : left, the series motor ; right, the shunt motor.

conductor will move ; as with the right-hand rule the fingers and thumb must all be held at right angles to each other. If therefore we supply current to an electric generator instead of supplying mechanical power, the generator will operate as a motor and give out mechanical power at the shaft.

In order to make a direct current generator operate as a motor it must be supplied with a direct current at the same voltage as that which it would normally generate. A direct current motor is therefore exactly the same in construction as a direct current generator, with a rotating armature and commutator and stationary field magnets. Just as with the generator, the field magnets may be excited with a part of the current supplied to the motor, either by passing the whole current through the winding as in the figure on the left of Fig. 104, or by passing only a small part of it through the field winding as in the figure on the right in Fig. 104; the former arrangement gives what is called the series motor and the field winding consists of a few turns of thick wire, while the latter gives a shunt motor of which the field winding consists of a large number of turns of very fine wire as it only has to carry a small current. A shunt motor runs at approximately the same speed whatever the load, while with a series motor the speed falls off when load is put on ; the series motor is therefore used for trains and trams, cranes and other purposes where a low speed at heavy loads is desirable.

ADAPTING THE MOTOR TO ALTERNATING CURRENT

VERY small d.c. (direct current) series motors such as are used for driving vacuum cleaners and refrigerators can be made to operate equally well on alternating currents, but a d.c. shunt motor will not work at all on an alternating current circuit. Large series motors can, by very special design, be made to work on alternating current, and are used on electric locomotives where the supply is alternating current. If an alternating current generator is supplied with alternating current instead of being driven by a steam engine, it will work as a motor in an exactly similar way to a d.c. motor.

A motor of this sort is called a synchronous motor, and in construction is exactly the same as an alternator ; the field magnets must be excited by a separate source of direct current, which makes such a motor rather complicated, and therefore only suitable for fairly large sizes. The speed at which a synchronous motor runs depends only on the number of poles and the frequency of the alternating current supply, so that its speed is normally absolutely constant no matter what the load is—if too much load is put on, the motor simply stops. In very small motors the difficulty of having a separate source of supply to excite the magnets can be overcome by using a permanent magnet, and motors of this sort are used for driving electric clocks. As the speed is absolutely constant, such clocks keep perfect time.

The a.c. (alternating current) series motor and the synchronous motor are used very widely, but by far the most common type for use on alternating currents is the induction motor. This motor has a fixed stator or yoke with a winding on it, and also a rotor with a winding on it. Both windings are arranged in slots just like the winding of the armature of a d.c. motor or generator. An alternating current is supplied to the stator winding, and although it is not arranged to have projecting magnet poles like the d.c. machine, it produces a magnetic field which crosses the air gap and cuts the conductors on the rotor.

When the current is switched on with the machine stationary, it is exactly like a transformer as the alternating currents in the stator produce an alternating magnetic field, and this cuts the conductors on the rotor and generates a voltage in them. The conductors of the rotor winding are simply joined to form a closed circuit without any connection to an external supply or circuit, and the voltage generated in them therefore produces a fairly large current. Although there is no supply to the rotor winding there is therefore a current produced in it by " induction " from the stator, and this current interacts with the magnetic field in the air gap to produce a force on the conductors and the motor starts to rotate and runs up to full speed. A motor of this sort thus has no commutator, and requires no separate source of supply for exciting field magnets, so that it is extremely simple and robust. Like the d.c. shunt motor, its speed is approximately constant at all loads.

HOW THE ELECTRIC MOTOR DRIVES RAILWAYS AND TRAMWAYS

ONE of the most important uses of the electric motor is for the driving of electric trams and trains. The difficulty here is to get the current to and from the motor, since it is on a moving vehicle ; this problem, however, is solved by having an additional rail laid by the running rails or underground or by having a trolley wire suspended above the rails. The rail is connected to one terminal of the supply, and a sliding contact attached to the vehicle rubs on it, collects current from it, and supplies this current to the motor. From the motors the current returns to the supply by the wheels of the vehicle and the running rails, as shown at the top of Fig. 105.

With the overhead trolley wire the current is collected by means of a little wheel at the end of a long trolley pole, or by a bow collector consisting of a strip of metal about 2 feet long which rubs on the wire. The bow collector is used for tramways where the speed is fairly high, and always for railways. Direct current at a pressure of about 600 volts is used for tramways, and the positive terminal of the supply is always connected to the trolley wire and the negative terminal to the rails. As the rails are in contact with the earth all the way along the route, there can be practically no electrical pressure between them and earth, so that there is no danger of shock if a person touches the rails, although of course it would be dangerous to touch the trolley wire, as there is a pressure of 600 volts between this and the earth.

Railways may operate by either alternating or direct current ; in this country direct current is used in all cases except for one short experimental line (Heysham-Lancaster line).

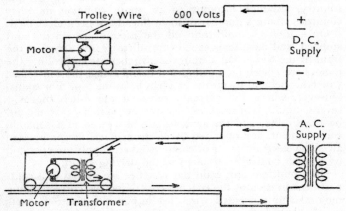

105. How current is supplied to electric trains and trams. Direct current at low voltage (above) is used for tramways, high voltage alternating current (with step-down transformer, shown in the lower diagram) for some railways.

The London Underground Railways and the electrified portion of the Southern Railway employ 600 volts with a third rail for leading the current to the trains ; for special technical reasons the Underground railways use a fourth rail to return the current to the negative terminal instead of using the running rails. Electrified sections of the L.M.S. and L.N.E.R. in the North of England (round Manchester and round Newcastle) use 1,500 volts, and a trolley wire for the supply.

In Switzerland and Germany alternating current is used, and the voltage of the trolley wire is 11,000 or 16,000 volts. Current at this pressure is collected by means of a bow collector as with the lower voltage lines, taken to a transformer mounted on the locomotive as shown in the lower diagram of

Fig. 105, and so away to the wheels, running rails and the other terminal of the supply. The transformer steps the voltage down to about 400 volts for supplying the motors, which are of the a.c. series type. The electric motors may all be mounted in one vehicle, which is then called the electric locomotive, and is used to pull the train in the same way as a steam locomotive, or they may be mounted under some or all of the coaches ; the latter arrangement, known as the multiple unit system, is nearly always employed in this country, although locomotives are more common in other countries where a number of main lines have been electrified.

On a multiple unit train all the motors are started and stopped, and have their speed controlled by one driver at the front of the train. On a tram the switches for controlling the motors are placed on a cylindrical barrel called the controller, which is operated by means of a handle at the top. For trains, however, where the currents required are much bigger— several hundreds of ampères—a controller of this sort would not be practicable, and the switches are all placed in a separate compartment, and operated by electromagnets or compressed air. The electromagnets or compressed air supply are operated by a small controller situated in the driving cabin.

On a multiple unit train the switches are placed in a compartment in each of the coaches containing the corresponding motors, and the small wires leading to the electromagnets which control them are taken to a small controller in the driving cabin at the front of the coach. If, however, there are several motor coaches in the train, these wires must all be taken right along the train to the front motor coach and attached to the controller there, which will then operate the switches on all the motors of the train. On any multiple unit train the jumpers for joining these wires up from coach to coach can easily be seen hanging between the coaches.

THE TROLLEY BUS AND A TRAVELLING POWER STATION

IN large towns where there are a very large number of passengers, the ordinary tram is the cheapest means of transport, but it is sometimes inconvenient, as rails have to be laid in the roadway and a breakdown of a tram causes a serious dislocation of traffic. To overcome these disadvantages another type of electric vehicle has been developed, called the trolley bus, which has two overhead trolley wires, one for supplying the current and the other for returning it, so that there is no longer any need for rails and the vehicle can be mounted on pneumatic tyres just like a petrol bus. Such a vehicle must, of course, keep more or less underneath the trolley wires, but as the trolley poles are made to swivel it can manœuvre in the traffic to some extent, which is often an advantage. Also it is not so noisy as the tram. The overhead equipment is rather expensive, but where the traffic is fairly heavy a trolley-bus system is generally found to be cheaper than the petrol bus.

Electric trains are easier to control and are much cleaner than steam trains, and they possess various other advantages as well, but unless there is fairly heavy traffic it does not pay to install the trolley wires or extra rails and other necessary auxiliary equipment for leading the current to the motors. This difficulty can, however, be overcome by generating the current on the train. A Diesel engine is employed for driving the generator, and this supplies direct current to the motors in the ordinary way.

It might well be asked : why not let the Diesel engine drive the train directly ? The answer to this is that a Diesel engine, just like the ordinary motor-car engine, only runs satisfactorily at somewhere near its full speed and only in one direction. On the motor car this difficulty is overcome by using a fairly complicated gear-box for obtaining slow speeds and for reversing, but such an arrangement would not be practicable with the much larger power required for driving a train. With electric motors, however, both speed control and reversing are quite simple, so that in the Diesel-electric train the electrical equipment simply takes the place of the gear box of the motor car. Trains of this sort are used on many lines, and with one or two coaches speeds of 100 miles per hour or more can be obtained.

HOW THE MODERN LINER IS DRIVEN BY ELECTRICITY

EVER since its invention, the electric lamp has been used for lighting on board ship, and electric motors have been used for driving deck hoists, winches and other gear, but now electricity is also used actually for driving the ship. Obviously the power station for generating the electricity must be situated on board, and the generators in it are driven by steam turbines in the case of battleships and large liners and by Diesel engines in the case of small tugs and ferry boats ; alternating currents are used by the larger ships and direct currents by the smaller ones.

Again it may be asked: why install this electrical equipment when ships have been driven quite satisfactorily for many years by steam turbines and Diesel engines directly? As with the Diesel-electric train, one of the answers is the ease of control, but in this case there are also other reasons; for instance, the engines and boilers must in any case be placed approximately amidships and if used to drive the propellers directly, this involves a long propeller shaft, whereas if electric motors are used these can be situated in the stern of the ship and the long shaft eliminated; besides saving space and expense this also reduces vibration. Further, in a directly driven ship there must be special turbines installed for running astern, as a turbine is not reversible, but with the electric drive no special reversing equipment is necessary other than a simple switch for the motors.

COMMUNICATION BY WIRES : THE ELECTRIC TELEGRAPH

by A. D'A. HODGSON, Associate Member of the Institute of Electrical Engineers, Associate Member of the Institute of Radio Engineers.

SOON after the properties of the electric current and electro-magnetism became fairly fully understood, attempts were made to obtain communication between two points some distance apart by means of electric currents flowing in waves.

In the very first attempt the indicator consisted of a vertical board on which the letters of the alphabet were marked in a diamond formation, and at the centre of this formation five magnetic needles were pivoted. Behind these needles were coils of wire, and by means of the magnetic force created when a current passed through these coils the needles were made to deflect so that two needles would point towards the required letter.

At the transmitting end there were a number of flexible metal strips which could be depressed to make contact with metallic points beneath them. The letters of the alphabet were so arranged in conjunction with these keys that the depression of two particular keys at once resulted in the magnetic needles at the receiver swinging on their pivots in the required direction.

A \/   B /\\\   C /\/\   D /\\   E \   F \\/\

G //\   H \\\\   I \\   J \///   K /\/

L \/\\   M //   N /\   O///   P \//\

Q //\/   R \/\   S \\\   T /   U \\/   V \\\/

W \//   X /\\/   Y /\//   Z //\\

A ·—   B —···   C —·—·   D —··   E ·   F ··—·

G ——·   H ····   I ··   J ·———   K —·—

L ·—··   M ——   N —·   O ———   P ·——·

Q ——·—   R ·—·   S ···   T —   U ··—   V ···—

W ·——   X —··—   Y —·——   Z ——··

1 ·————   6 —····

2 ··———   7 ——···

3 ···——   8 ———··

4 ····—   9 ————·

5 ·····   10 —————

*106. How the Morse Code has developed. Above, in sloping
lines for the needle telegraph ; centre, in dots and dashes for
the sounder ; below, how numbers were introduced.*

This was obviously a clumsy and laborious system, and in
1838 the invention of the Morse code by S. Morse paved the
way to a practicable system. This code is based on a system
of dots and dashes, and for the Morse needle telegraph, movement of the indicator to the left indicated a dot, and to the
right a dash. For this purpose, therefore, the code was written
as shown at the top in Fig. 106. Later on, when the Sounder
and finally other audible systems were used, the code was
rearranged and written as shown in the centre of Fig. 106, so
that a short signal indicated a dot and a signal of longer
duration a dash. Fig. 106 shows also how figures were introduced.

The indicator first used for communication by Morse code was somewhat similar to the original alphabetical system in as much as a pivoted and magnetised needle was still used, but in this case the needle was deflected to left or to right, by means of one or two small electromagnets, to the dots and dashes of the Morse code. At the transmitting end two metal keys were so arranged that they could be depressed to touch a metal contact and thus complete the circuit, and according to which key was depressed so the small electromagnets near the needle became energised, causing the needle to be deflected to left or to right.

HOW THE MORSE SIGNALS ARE TRANSLATED INTO SOUNDS

THIS system proved to be fairly satisfactory and was used largely for railway telegraphs, but it was always difficult for an operator to watch the needle and write down the message at the same time and thus the system was slow.

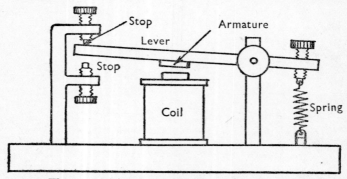

107. The essentials of the sounder used in electric telegraphy. One coil only of the horseshoe magnet is shown.

The Sounder was therefore produced by Morse and is now in extensive use. By means of this, audible signals of the modified Morse code were received, the double contact key was replaced by a single key and a considerable increase in working speed obtained.

The sounder illustrated in Fig. 107 consists of two coils placed one behind the other and provided with soft iron cores, the bottom of these cores being fixed on an iron strip or yoke, thus forming in effect a horseshoe magnet. A brass lever pivoted at one end carries a soft iron armature which is directly over the poles of the two coils ; the other end of the brass lever rests against a metallic stop and is held there by a spring having an adjustable tension. Beneath the brass lever is another stop. When a current flows round the coils the magnetic field created pulls the armature down and thus pulls the lever down until the bottom hits the lower stop with a sharp click, when the current ceases to flow and the lever springs back and hits the top stop with a click. The stops are so made that these two clicks have a slightly different sound, and the characters of Morse transmission may be easily read.

The sounder has been in use for some time, and is still used in many places. It is quite satisfactory for speeds up to 15–20 words per minute, but needs as a rule some 60 milli-ampères to operate it (a milliampère being a thousandth part of an ampère). Another form of sounder is the polarised type, in which the soft iron core of the coils is replaced by a magnet. By this arrangement the speed of working has been increased and the current required reduced to 3–5 milliampères.

TWO-WAY MESSAGES ON ONE LINE

So far we have only considered single-line telegraphy or one-way traffic, and we have assumed that for two-way telegraphy double circuits will be necessary. This is not so, however, and in the circuit of Fig. 108 it will be seen that one line and an earth return will enable two stations to obtain

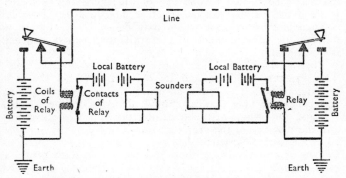

108. The system which transmits two-way messages on one line, showing the " relays " which strengthen the current reaching the sounders.

telegraphic communication. If these two stations are fairly far apart it will be realized that the voltage necessary to produce 3–5 milliampères in the sounder coil might have to become very large. Therefore, to enable a reasonable voltage to be employed, a sensitive " relay " is used : an instrument which, operating on very little current, closes contact in a local battery circuit and thus operates the sounder.

This relay by suitable modification may be used as a repeater. The number of words per minute which can be transmitted along a given line depends on its length, as we shall see. In order, therefore, to keep the highest speed possible, a " repeater system " is used and the line kept down to a reasonable length between repeaters. These repeaters are simply relays which bring into operation additional batteries and repeat the message or correspondence in one or both directions as may be required.

THE ELECTRIC BUZZER : TELEGRAPHISTS' MAID-OF-ALL-WORK

IN order to give an audible note for the reception of telegraphic signals instead of the click of the sounder, the buzzer was developed, and has since been used for a variety of purposes. A simple buzzer is illustrated in Fig. 109. Supported from one side of the small horseshoe electromagnet is a flexible iron armature which extends across the poles of the magnet. A silver or platinum contact is fixed in the centre of this armature, and the end fixed to the pole of the magnet is connected to one end of the energising coil. In front of the magnet and its armature, and insulated from it, is an adjustable contact which may be so arranged that it touches the silver contact on the armature when no current is flowing through the coil.

This arrangement is just another make-and-break device. The armature vibrates, and its rapid movements create a buzzing noise. The speed at which the armature vibrates, and hence the note that is emitted, depends on the weight, size and springiness of the armature, the pull of the magnets and the distance of the armature from the poles. By suitable adjustment of these particulars the armature may be made to vibrate several thousand times per second and to create a high-pitched note.

There are a number of different variations to this simple buzzer according to the purpose for which it is required. It is used, for example, for telegraphic signalling reception

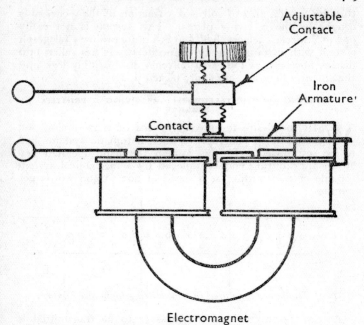

Adjustable Contact

Iron Armature

Contact

Electromagnet

109. The construction of the buzzer, useful in many telegraphic operations. The vibrations of the armature, due to the make-and-break action, produce a high-pitched note.

and transmission, line testing, calling apparatus for telegraph offices, calling apparatus for telephone offices and a variety of other purposes.

In one form of telegraphic signalling, what is known as a power buzzer is used, and no line or wire connection need exist between the sending and receiving station. This is a system which is particularly useful for portable telegraph apparatus such as is required by the Army.

In this case the coils of the buzzer have a second winding connected to two terminals, and connections to these terminals are made to two plates buried some distance apart. The receiver consists of two similar plates with connections going to an amplifying system and telephones. The currents between the two plates of the transmitter spread themselves through a wide area of soil and a fraction of their energy is caught by the receiving plates. This system is not really one of " wireless telegraphy " but is a quite ordinary telegraph system with extremely leaky connections. It has fallen into disuse, however, as the earth currents disobligingly leak into the enemy's lines and are easily picked up.

SPEEDING UP THE TELEGRAPH : RECEIVING A PRINTED MESSAGE

WITH the desire for greater speeds of transmission and reception on telegraph circuits, automatic systems had to be introduced. In this system the hand-operated key at the transmitting end is replaced by a mechanical system capable of transmitting at a speed of 200 to 300 words per minute.

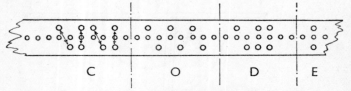

110. The paper tape used in transmitting high-speed Morse

At the transmitter end the message to be transmitted is typed out on a machine very much like a typewriter, but it is actually punching holes in a paper tape, so that the message is translated into Morse code on the paper in the form of perforations. Fig. 110 shows a strip of this paper tape. The centre row of perforations provides a means of driving the paper through the transmitter by a toothed wheel. Diagonally spaced perforations from top to bottom represent the dashes of the Morse code, and vertically spaced perforations the dots. Thus the first letter has one diagonal, one vertical, one diagonal, one vertical, and is therefore the letter C.

As this tape is driven through the transmitter two small pins which are oscillating in synchronism with the speed at which the tape is moving are free to pass in and out of each hole as it reaches a suitable position. Thus as the first perforation at the top reaches this position the pin passes through it and causes a " marking " current to be sent via a movable contact down the telegraph line. As this pin is withdrawn from the top hole, the presence of the unper-

forated portion below prevents the current to the line being
reversed until the bottom hole has moved sufficiently forward
for the bottom pin to enter; as soon as this happens the direction of the current transmitted is reversed and a dash has
been transmitted.   This is followed immediately by the
top perforation for the dot approaching the operating position.
In this case the paper immediately below the top perforation
is also perforated, and thus the length of flow of the current
is much shorter and a dot is transmitted.

At the receiver end another paper tape is being moved
beneath a stylus at a uniform rate.   Until the perforations
begin to operate the transmitter the stylus is held away from
the paper by the current flowing through the operating
coils, which form a polarised magnetic circuit moving the
stylus by means of a steel armature and levers.   When the
current is reversed at the transmitter the stylus touches the
paper and draws a long or short line according to the transmission.

In another form of receiver, known as the undulator,
the stylus in the form of a light siphon draws a continuous
line down the centre of the tape and the current reversals
produce humps above or below this line by deflecting the
stylus from side to side ; for example, dashes below and dots
above.

This form of Morse inker is used mainly for cables where
a somewhat more delicate instrument is necessary.   Although
it demanded less attention from the operator than previous
systems, the automatic transmitting system, however, still
produced its results in code which had to be translated, and
the next step was to type the message to be transmitted on
a typewriter, and to receive the reply also in a typewritten
form.

TYPEWRITING OVER A THOUSAND MILES : THE TELEPRINTER

To this end the printing telegraph leading to the modern
teleprinter service was produced.   Strangely enough, a
number of mechanisms for the printing telegraph were
produced before telegraphy itself was in a very advanced
state of development.

The first printing telegraph to be at all widely used
was developed during 1855–1863 by Hughes ; this did not
use the Morse code, but a code of its own. A variety of
systems was produced between 1855 and 1905, but of these

the most successful was that by a Frenchman, Maurice
Baudot, which is extensively used on British and continental
lines. With the complete Baudot system which uses a five
unit code and not the Morse code, it is possible to transmit
eight messages at once at speeds up to 30 words per minute
over one line.

The simplest form of printing telegraph is one in which
the transmission of a current down the line operates an
electromagnet which brings the tape against the rim of a
rotating wheel which carries on its rim in raised type the
letters of the alphabet. In order to make sure that the current
is sent down the line at the correct moment to print the

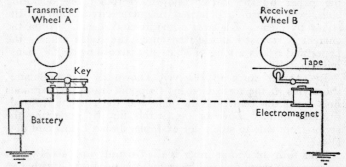

*111. Transmitting and receiving systems in a simple teleprinter,
showing in diagrammatic form the synchronised wheels A and B,
the electromagnet and the tape on which the messages appear.*

letter required, a second type wheel must be available at
the transmitting end and must rotate in synchronism with
the one at the receiving end, so that it acts as an indicator
to the operator. Thus in Fig. 111 wheel A is the indicating
wheel at the transmitting end, and wheel B the printing
wheel at the receiver, and both are rotating in synchronism
during the transmission of messages.

With the development of the thermionic valve and its
application to telegraph signalling, and with the development of signalling by alternating currents and combined
alternating and direct current, the complication of the printing
telegraph has been reduced and has resulted in the modern
teleprinter which is being used on an increasing number of
telegraph circuits.

ELECTRICITY CONTROLLED BY SOUND: THE TELEPHONE

SOUND is propagated by means of wave motion through the air or any other material substance. The source of the sound, be it a musical instrument or an explosion, creates vibrations in the air surrounding it, and produces a series of waves which we call sound waves. When these waves are intercepted by any object they set up similar vibrations in it, and thus sound waves arriving at the diaphragm or drum of the human ear cause it to vibrate and stimulate the nerves which create the sense of hearing in the brain.

In 1860 the telegraphs were working well and England was connected to the Continent by submarine cables, and so attention was turned in the direction of telephony. The very first attempt was made by a German, Philipp Reis. His system consisted of a stretched diaphragm which vibrated when it intercepted sound waves, and by means of a pair of contacts opened and closed an electrical circuit in proportion to the vibrations. Although he succeeded in transmitting simple sounds, it is doubtful whether he had any measure of success with intelligible speech.

In 1872 the telephone industry was really born, for Graham Bell, a professor at Boston University, U.S.A., turned his attention to the transmission of sound by electricity, and in 1876 produced the first really satisfactory system. It might be of interest to recall the actual circumstances which led to Graham Bell's development of the telephone system, as the history is an indication of the value of careful observation in the course of experimental work.

Bell was initially experimenting with a special form of telegraph, which employed a number of buzzers, tuned to different notes and connected by wires to a similar number of electro-magnets having tuned reeds or springs in front of them. It was very necessary that these springs should resound to the same frequency as the buzzers, and in course of tuning these springs the contact on one of the buzzers stuck. Bell's assistant, in attempting to free the contact, plucked the spring of the buzzer with his finger. Bell who was listening to the receiving reed heard its vibrations cease, and then heard a reproduction of the pluck which his assistant had given to the buzzer spring. He instantly realised the importance of this, as it indicated to him that any complicated vibrations of the buzzer spring could be reproduced by a similar spring in front of another electromagnet.

GRAHAM BELL'S FIRST SIMPLE TELEPHONE

AFTER experimenting with a variety of diaphragms and vibrating systems, a simple telephone was produced which is shown diagrammatically in Fig. 112. The case has a bar magnet in it, and on the end in front of the opening of the case a small coil of insulated wire is fixed. In front of the opening and near the coil is an iron diaphragm. When sound

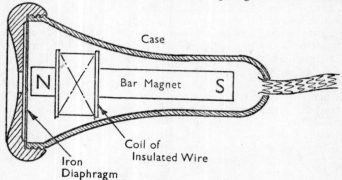

112. The first type of telephone, produced by Graham Bell

waves are intercepted by the diaphragm it is set into vibration, and so varies the lines of magnetic force in front of the bar magnet. This variation causes currents of electricity to be induced in the coil.

If this coil is connected by a pair of wires to another coil in a similar instrument, the varying current will travel down to the other coil and will produce variations in the lines of force from its own magnet. These variations will cause the iron diaphragm to reproduce the original sounds fairly faithfully.

This type of telephone system worked fairly well over short distances, but the currents produced in the coils were too small to lead to results over any considerable distance, and so attention was turned to the microphone transmitter, which in effect produces varying current through a changing resistance rather than changing magnetic force.

THE SECOND GREAT STEP IN SOUND TRANSMISSION :
THE MICROPHONE

IF an electric current is passed through a box of powdered carbon, variations of the pressure on the carbon dust or granules will cause changes of resistance to occur which will vary the current flowing through it. The reasons for this are obvious when it is realised that with very light pressure the carbon particles may be only just touching, and thus present a very high resistance, and as soon as they become more tightly compressed the resistance is lowered.

If this variation of pressure could be made to occur by sound waves, then it could be utilised for telephonic transmission. The first microphone to utilise this principle of varying resistance was produced by Thomas Edison. In this microphone Edison used a fine carbon dust contained in a small capsule with a platinum diaphragm. On top of this diaphragm was an ivory button which made contact with the main diaphragm in front of the mouthpiece.

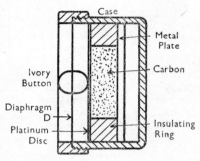

113. Thomas Edison's microphone

Fig. 113 shows the construction of the microphone. Sound waves striking the diaphragm D set it vibrating, thus making the ivory button vibrate and hence varying the pressure between the platinum disc and the carbon granules. The platinum disc is connected to one terminal of the circuit, and the plate at the back of the carbon granules to the other ; the current passing across the carbon dust is therefore varied in proportion to the changing pressure on the carbon.

THE EVOLUTION OF THE MODERN MICROPHONE

FOLLOWING Edison's microphone a number of other investigators started work on this subject, the next most successful microphone being the Deckert type shown in Fig. 114. The case contains a carbon block having serrations which are very close to the carbon diaphragm, and are filled with carbon granules. A pad of felt on the outside edge of the diaphragm serves to keep the granules in. Vibration of the diaphragm changes the resistance between these granules.

The telephone circuit employing a carbon microphone is shown in Fig. 114, in which the microphone, battery, and

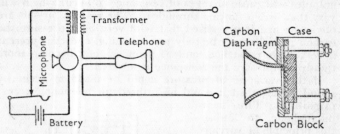

114. (Right) The Deckert microphone. (Left) A telephone circuit using a carbon microphone.

telephone are connected together. It will be seen that the changing current produced by the microphone will affect the receiver diaphragm, and so the speech variation will be reproduced. This system is the direct prototype of the modern telephone, and from Edison's early microphone and Bell's telephone all the variety of microphones for broadcasting and other work has been developed.

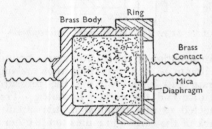

115. A button-type microphone with mica diaphragm.

In the transverse current microphone, a block of marble has a series of four or more compartments cut in it, the dividing walls being carbon rods. This block of marble is fixed in a case of moulded bakelite, and in front of the compartments is a rubber or silk diaphragm stretched tightly. Each compartment is filled with carbon granules, in some cases different sizes of granules being used.

The current flows across the face of the microphone from one end of the compartment to the other, hence the name transverse current, and the vibration of the rubber diaphragm varies the pressure on the carbon granules, and so produces a varying resistance.

In another form of microphone known as the button type, or solid back, a mica diaphragm with a brass contact faced with polished carbon in the centre is used. This is shown in Fig. 115. The brass body is filled with carbon granules and the mica diaphragm with the brass contact is held over the body by the ring. Current flows from the brass body through the carbon to the contact, which may be fixed to a larger diaphragm or any other object from which it is desired to transmit sound, as for example the body of a violin.

HOW THE POST OFFICE TELEPHONE WORKS

THE microphones and receivers used on the Post Office instruments are very little different from the original productions, in fact on the Post Office table instrument the receiver is practically identical with the arrangement used by Bell, except that the coils are placed on " pole pieces " instead of directly on the magnet, and the magnet is horseshoe-shaped, thus utilising both poles instead of one.

In the receivers used in the hand telephone equipment or microtelephone, the long bar magnet is replaced by a small semicircular magnet having two upturned poles on which bobbins of fine wire are placed, the whole assembly being as shown on the left of Fig. 116, where the magnet and coil are fixed in a metal or moulded bakelite case, which carries the iron diaphragm just clear of the poles of the magnet. A moulded earpiece holds the diaphragm in position.

Although the principle of the P.O. microphone remains the same, the construction used results in the active part of the microphone being built up into a self-contained capsule or inset (Fig. 116, right) where the carbon block is contained in a metal case which holds the diaphragm, consisting of a spun and corrugated aluminium disc carrying a thin carbon disc against the face of the block and carbon granules. The perforated front allows waves to reach the diaphragm, but protects it from damage. This construction allows a damaged unit to be quickly replaced.

From the simple circuit used by Bell, the telephone circuit has become an amazingly complicated system. The first attempt to use the telephone in such a manner that one subscriber could speak to any other resulted in an " exchange " or control room where all calls were received by an operator, written down and then passed on to the subscriber for whom they were intended—a very crude affair, but one which sufficed while the knotty problem of producing a switching system which would enable any subscriber's apparatus to be connected to any other was investigated.

Bell came to England in 1877 and demonstrated his equipment to a number of people and even to Queen Victoria, and achieved considerable success. In spite of this the Post Office authorities stated that they were not aware of the telephone

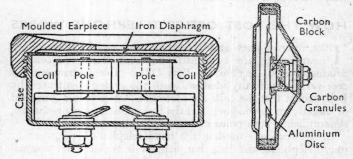

116. (Left) The hand telephone receiver with iron diaphragm. (Right) The efficient self-contained P.O. microphone with its spun and corrugated aluminium disc.

invention and in any case could not see what scope it would have, as its application would be very limited. They therefore did not take much interest in it, and as a result a private Company known as the Telephone Company was formed. With the expansion of Bell's telephone, a number of other telephone companies came into being, each one with a different system, and although conditions were somewhat chaotic, the competition between the various companies and the necessity for the development of new circuits and apparatus to avoid infringing patents held by rivals, led to a very rapid advance in the design of the telephone.

THE FIRST TELEPHONE EXCHANGE

THE system first put into use by the Telephone Company was sufficient to cater for about 100 subscribers. Each subscriber was provided with an instrument consisting of two Bell telephones, one for transmitting and the other for receiving, a battery, a bell and a push button. This was connected by a single overhead wire to the exchange, the circuit of which is shown in Fig. 117.

When a subscriber wishes to make a call, he presses the push button on his instrument, thus sending a current along the line and operating his indicator. This indicator is wired in series between the subscriber's line and earth via the jack

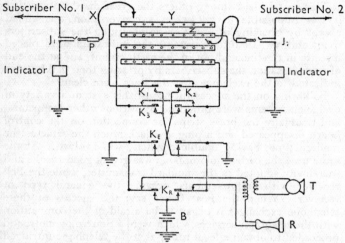

117. The exchange system used by the first Telephone Company.

connection J_1 in Fig. 117, and bears a number corresponding to the subscriber's number.

The jack J_1 consists of two metal strips making contact in such a manner that they may be separated by the plug P which has an insulating body with a metal contact on one side only. Inserting this plug opens the earth connection and connects the subscriber's line to the flexible lead X, at the far end of which is a solid round plug which may be plugged into any of the free holes in the horizontal brass strip Y, a number of these brass strips being arranged in pairs such as YZ, etc., according to the number of subscribers for which the exchange caters. For each pair of brass plug strips, there is a pair of operating keys K_1 and K_2, K_3 and K_4, etc.

Having received a call from subscriber Number 1 and plugged his line on to Y, the operator presses K_1 and the earthing key K_E which connects his receiver and transmitter, R and T, to the calling subscriber. On ascertaining the number required, the operator inserts the plug for Number 2 in J_2, and the other end of the lead into the strip Z ; then depressing K_2 and K_E, he rings the bell of subscriber Number 2 via the battery B. When a reply has been received, he releases all keys and the two subscribers are connected through.

This system had among others the great disadvantage that it was impossible to tell when a conversation was ended except by breaking in and thus interrupting the subscribers momentarily. In future systems the indicators were placed directly in the line and not in the earth circuit, and at the end of a conversation the subscribers by pressing their call buttons indicated to the exchange that the lines were clear.

Following on the successful use of this system a variety of exchange systems were produced by various other companies; and gradually the brass strips for connection on the control board disappeared and a plug and jack much the same as the modern type, having double contacts, was evolved. At the same time the carbon microphone was giving good results and was finally adopted as the standard transmitter, while the Bell receiver with improvements became the general type of receiver. When the Post Office saw the success of these telephone exchanges it began to be afraid of the competition with the telegraph services, which were a State monopoly, and proceeded to obtain a legal ruling that the telephone infringed their monopoly and was in fact a form of telegraph. They then began to produce a telephone system of their own.

The competition between the various telephone companies including the Post Office at this time was really fierce, each company trying by any means possible to obtain the maximum number of subscribers. On one occasion one company had made preparations to erect a new pole near their exchange on a site which another company were trying to acquire ; their workmen had dug the required hole and made all preparations, and were much surprised to find on the following morning that the rival concern had erected their own pole over night in the hole which had been kindly dug for them. This type of competition, however, soon came to an end and an amicable working arrangement was arrived at, which finally culminated in the Post Office taking over the whole telephone system.

THE POST OFFICE ERECTS ITS FIRST EXCHANGE

WHEN the Post Office erected its first exchange it used the Bell telephone for reception, and a form of microphone made by Gower. A subscriber's equipment then consisted of a microphone, receiver, battery, bell, and push button. At the exchange all that was required was a similar telephone equipment and a series of indicators of a similar type to that already described. Each indicator was connected to the subscriber's instrument, and had a jack mounted immediately below it.

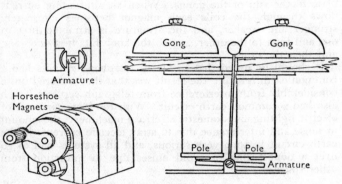

118. (Left) The hand-operated magneto (a small electric generator) and (right) the bell used on private lines and internal factory systems for calling purposes.

When a subscriber pressed his call button the indicator dropped, and the operator plugged his own telephone into the jack, then after calling the required subscriber by ringing his bell with the aid of a battery at the exchange, the two jacks were linked across by a double line. This system therefore did away with the brass contact strips and keys described in the earlier system.

A system which was employed at a number of exchanges and is still in use for some private lines and internal factory telephones, employed a hand-driven magneto for ringing and calling purposes, the battery being used only to provide power for the microphone.

This magneto is merely an alternating current generator, having two horse-shoe magnets with soft iron pole pieces as shown on the left of Fig. 118, and an armature rotating between them and driven by means of a train of gears from the handle. The two ends of the windings on the armature are connected to two brass rings fixed on the shaft, the output terminals being connected to two copper brushes which make contact on the rings.

The bells for use with these magnetos are known as polarised bells, as they employ two permanent magnets with bobbins of wire on them (Fig. 118 right), where the armature is pivoted and is free to swing in front of the poles of the magnets ; a long arm carries the ringing knob through a hole in the top plate to the rim of the gongs. When an alternating current flows through the coils each magnet becomes alternately stronger and weaker, and the armature is attracted first to one and then to the other, and so the knob hits first one gong and then the other.

It should be noted that so far all telephone circuits had a common earth return ; the result was that they suffered quite considerably from interference from telegraph services which also had a common earth circuit. With the increasing use of electric lighting and domestic electrical machinery, the amount of noise and interference due to stray electric currents in the earth circuit became very serious, and all systems had to go over a double line to avoid noises due to induction from other sources.

THE MODERN TELEPHONE CIRCUIT

SUBSCRIBERS now no longer have a battery with their instruments. All the power required for the telephone service is obtained from a central battery at the exchange, and is said to be a Central Battery system, or C.B. system. The subscriber's apparatus now consists only of a terminal box with an induction coil and bell, and an upright stand with microphone contact hook and receiver. The circuit is shown in Fig. 119.

If the microphone were applied directly to the telephone line the variation of resistance due to speech would be so small in comparison with the total resistance of the circuit that the variations of current would be very small and speech would be weak. By putting the microphone in series with the primary of the coil and connecting the secondary to the line, the varying resistance of the microphone is increased in value according to the ratio of secondary turns to primary turns.

Another way of saying the same thing with more technical accuracy is as follows : Any pair of wires carrying an alternating or varying current is said to have a characteristic impedance which depends on the diameter of the wires and their distance apart. For maximum transmission of power along these two wires the impedance of the transmitter must be equal to the impedance of the line, and hence as the microphone has quite a low impedance the transformer is necessary to " transform " it to the required value.

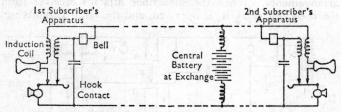

119. A diagram of a simple modern telephone circuit, showing how the current used by both subscribers is received from a battery at the exchange.

HOW THE MODERN EXCHANGE WORKS

IN place of the shutter type of indicator which was used in the majority of early exchanges, lamp indicators are now employed. As soon as the subscriber lifts his receiver a lamp on the exchange board glows, and the operator plugs into his line the jack which is fitted just below the indicator.

These indicators and jacks are all fitted on to a vertical panel, and on a horizontal shelf in front is a series of flexible cords with plugs at each end. These cords are kept in an orderly group by means of a weight and pulley system below the shelf. Now as each subscriber may require to be connected to any one of a vast number of other subscribers, it would be quite impossible to have only one jack for each subscriber, and to have row upon row of different subscribers following on ; for if, for example, there were 1,000 subscribers, and their jacks were arranged in one row, a very long lead would be necessary to connect No. 1 to No. 999.

To avoid this length of lead, the subscribers are broken up into groups and interleaved ; for example, 1–20 may be one group, and then 1–10 would be interleaved between 20 and 30, and so on. Such an arrangement is called a multiple switch board, and groups may be repeated many times according to the size. Having plugged into the subscriber's line and ascertained the number required, the operator links the two jacks across after ringing the number required and getting a reply. The lights then go out but reappear when conversation is finished, and the subscribers' receivers are returned to their hooks. The operator then clears the line by removing the jacks.

The circuit of Fig. 120 shows the calling and metering arrangements. When the subscriber lifts his receiver from the hook, the relay R_1 is operated, and the lamp L lights up.

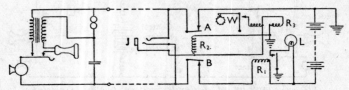

120. How a call is put through and automatically metered.

The operator plugs into jack J, the relay R_2 is operated, and contacts A and B break the battery circuit. On connecting the subscriber through to the number required, R_2 remains in circuit ; in addition R_3 is operated by the plug circuit, and moves the ratchet W round one notch, thus counting the call and automatically charging it to the subscriber's number. When the subscribers hang up their receivers the whole circuit is restored ready for another call.

THE MODERN WONDER OF THE TELEPHONE : AUTOMATIC EXCHANGES

THE operation of the switching and calling circuits of an exchange is brought about entirely automatically by the most ingenious use of relays and rotary switches, and the present position of the automatic telephone is due to the care and ingenuity which has been applied to the design of these component parts over a number of years.

It is now possible for a subscriber to call any other subscriber without any human assistance ; the result is an increase in the speed of operation and improved privacy. The speaking circuits of the automatic system are very little different from the manual system, also the subscriber's apparatus remains the same except for the addition of the dial, which is used for calling the number required. Nearly all exchanges in the London area are now automatic, and the few remaining manual exchanges are being gradually changed. Trunk lines and trunk exchanges are still manual.

It would be quite impossible to attempt a full description of the vast and complicated structure which goes to make a modern automatic telephone exchange. For such a description reference can be made to the numerous theoretical and practical books which have been written on the subject, and to the *Post Office Engineering Journal*. We can only

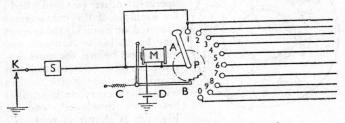

121. Explaining the working of a simple automatic system.

attempt a description of the principles of the circuits and the main component parts.

The whole object of the automatic system is to avoid the need for an operator to answer calls and find the number required. By referring to Fig. 121, we can see the principle of the operation of a simple automatic system. A subscriber S is connected by a single line to a rotary switch A, which has a ratchet and pawl operated by the magnet M, the battery D supplying the necessary current.

When the subscriber lifts his receiver from its hook the magnet circuit is completed through the contact K, and current flows round the magnet attracting the arm of the pawl B and thus stretching the spring C and moving the pawl round to the next notch on the ratchet. Now if the circuit is broken at K the pawl will drop back under the action of the spring and will move the switch round to the first contact. When the circuit is again made and broken at K the switch will move round through another contact, and so on.

Thus if subscriber No. 1 wishes to call No. 5, he lifts his receiver, operates the contact K five times, and the switch moves round to contact 5 and connects his instruments through to No. 5 subscriber. In practice of course double lines are employed, and the lines are arranged in multiple groups as for the manual exchanges, and as each row of switches is connected through the exchange by a number of separate lines, additional switches have to be used for the purpose of finding the correct line.

It will be obvious that for satisfactory operation the speed at which the contact K is operated must be controlled; for example, if the contacts are operated very quickly the magnet may be unable to complete one movement before the next impulse arrives. To control this speed the dialling mechanism with which everyone is familiar has been developed, and in Fig. 122 is shown in schematic form.

122. The dialling mechanism on the automatic telephone.

The dial consists of a body with a rotatable cover J. On the body the numbers 1–10 are painted, and also the letters of the alphabet. The cover has a number of holes near its outer edge, each hole disclosing a number and a group of letters, and is of sufficient size for a finger to be inserted for operation. The cover rotates on a shaft on which the gear wheel A is fixed, and also the toothed wheel G, these two being underneath the body. The toothed wheel is not fixed rigidly to the shaft, but is operated through a spring-controlled friction drive, and thus when the dial is pulled to the right the toothed wheel does not move.

The speed of rotation is controlled by a centrifugal brake, the gear A engages with the worm B, which with the brake mechanism is carried on the bearings F. The brake consists of flexible spring E, with weights fixed in the middle. These weights have a leather or felt surface which can press on the drum D. All this arrangement ensures that the actual work of sending out the impulses is carried out by a piece of carefully governed machinery. If the timing of the impulses were left to the subscriber the machine at the exchange would have to interpret the effects of too many " telephone temperaments!"

WHAT HAPPENS WHEN A NUMBER IS DIALLED

To operate the dial a finger is inserted in the number required, and the cover pulled round until the stop S prevents any further movement. This action winds up a spring not shown in the sketch, and on releasing the dial the spring returns it to its starting position. In doing this, the worm B revolves, and the centrifugal action of the weights makes the springs E expand until the leather surfaces of the weights are in contact with D. Any attempt by the dial to go faster merely increases the pressure between the weights and D, which prevents a rise in speed, and thus the spring returns the dial at a constant and predetermined speed. The toothed wheel G therefore makes and breaks the contact between H and I a number of times according to the number dialled, and at a definite rate, and these impulses operate the switches at the exchange.

Dials with numbers only are usually used only for private automatic exchanges known as P.A.B.X.s. As separate exchanges are linked together by the automatic system in addition to the subscribers to each exchange, the letters of the alphabet are placed on the dial and the first three letters of the name of each exchange are dialled before the number.

The effect of this is to send a certain group of impulses to the exchange which operates a series of line finders, and connects the subscribers through to the required exchange via his own exchange. The arrival of the impulses corresponding to the number operates a further assembly of rotary switches until the line is connected through to the subscriber required. As soon as this occurs the line is connected to an alternator via an interrupter, and the familiar periodic ringing of the automatic system is heard. If the subscriber called is in use and the circuit operations cannot be completed, then the calling subscriber's line is connected to a high-note buzzer which puts a periodic high-pitched buzz through to his receiver.

The fundamental details of the automatic telephone have been completed, but development still proceeds, and it will not be long perhaps before trunk lines and even continental and radio telephone calls can be made entirely by automatic switching systems.

THE TRUNK LINES AND CABLES WHICH ENCIRCLE THE EARTH

As we have already stated, the original telegraph and the early telephone circuits were all carried out on overhead lines with earth returns. When the telegraph circuits were working satisfactorily, attention was naturally turned towards linking up the Continent with London by a telegraph system. This meant running a line across the Channel, and obviously it could not be done overhead, it had to go under the sea.

The story of cable laying at sea is an epic story of a struggle against the forces of nature, and success by perseverance against the most disastrous failures. In particular the laying of the Atlantic cable is a remarkable story of determination. The history of the laying of the first cable has been told many a time; it will not, therefore, be repeated here; suffice it to say that the first cable was laid across the Channel and consisted of a single copper wire with a gutta-percha covering half an inch thick.

Following on this, numerous other cables were laid, and it was found that as the length of cable increased so the speed at which telegraphic signalling could be carried out became less, and the shape of the signals received on recording receivers became very bad. It was soon found that the reason for this was that a long cable had an appreciable electrostatic capacity, or in other words, it took some time for the voltage on the cable to build up and a corresponding time to die away. By careful construction of the cable this capacity was kept to a reasonable value and with the aid of the syphon recorders trans-Atlantic telegraphy gave good service.

When the telephone system had been giving good service on local circuits, it was natural that attempts should be made to obtain telephonic communication between different towns and also with the Continent. At this time knowledge on the subject of voice frequency transmission over long lines was very limited, and in any case to achieve telephonic communication over very long lines appeared to require very considerable power at the exchange or subscribers' station. Although as a matter of interest a distance of some 100 miles had been covered with a Bell telephone and Edison microphone, attempts to obtain telephonic communication over a cable were completely unsuccessful.

At this time Oliver Heaviside had been giving some attention to the theory of cables and long lines and produced a mathematical explanation of the failure of telephony over cables and indicated the necessity for inserting inductance coils at definite intervals along the cable, or as we now term it, loading the cable. It was not until this was done by Pupin, who produced the first loading or Pupin coils, that telephony over cables became successful.

The human voice in normal speech covers a range of sound frequencies between 100 to 3,000 cycles per second, and these sound frequencies falling on the diaphragm of a microphone vary its resistance and produce electric currents of the same frequencies. The telephone cable was therefore required to present the lowest possible opposition or impedance to the passage of these frequencies, whilst at the same time whatever the value of this impedance it was essential that it should be the same for all frequencies.

By addition of the Pupin loading coils at definite distances along the cable, the cable was in effect transformed from a single large capacity to a complicated circuit of capacity and inductance so proportioned, that the range of telephonic frequencies mentioned suffered the least possible opposition to their passage; in other words, the cable became a filter circuit.

THE COMPLICATED MODERN TELEPHONE CABLE

THE modern multi-circuit submarine cable has been built up as the result of years of patient research into the conditions under which the cables work, and as a result cables can now be produced which will stand the pressure of the great depths of water under which they run, and the action of tides, rocks, etc. The first successful Atlantic cable was 2,500 miles long and required 20,500 miles of copper wire for the conductors, and 367,500 miles of iron wire for the armouring, so the magnitude of the task of making this first cable can be appreciated when it is realised that little or nothing was known of the art.

In general, modern telephone cables are made as shown in the cross-sectional diagram, Fig. 123. The wires are insulated by special paper, around which is a binding of impregnated tape followed by a layer of bituminised jute; round the jute is an armouring of steel wire woven round the cable, and then a final covering of tarred hemp cord.

HOW THE REPEATER AMPLIFIES THE TRUNK CALL

LOADING coils were also applied to overhead telephone lines resulting in a great improvement in long distance telephony, but it was still somewhat unreliable, so that some means or other were vitally necessary to relay or amplify the

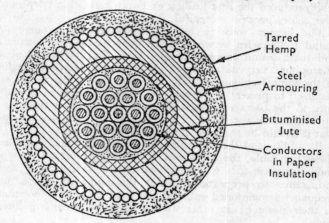

123. A section of a modern telephone cable.

telephonic currents when they began to weaken. A variety of schemes was tried but without success until at last the "Aladdin's Lamp" of all modern communication, the "Thermionic Valve" was produced. A full description of this device is given in the radio section of this book, where there is also an explanation of circuit diagrams, so we will merely concern ourselves with its application to telephone communication in its all important capacity as a "repeater" or amplifier.

We shall see that the three electrode valve, or triode as it is called, can be made to act as an amplifier of alternating voltages by connecting the valve into a suitable circuit and applying the voltage to be amplified to the grid circuit of the valve.

In order to make this quite clear let us refer to Fig. 124, in which a triode V has the secondary of a transformer T_1 connected between the grid and the negative terminal of the battery GB : the primary of the transformer being connected to the telephone line $L_1 L_2$, the speech voltages of which it is desired to amplify. The anode of the valve is connected to the primary of another transformer T_2 the secondary of which connects the amplified output to the telephone line $L_3 L_4$. The battery GB supplies a fixed negative potential to the grid of the triode, FB supplies the current to heat the filament of

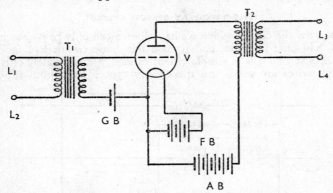

124. How the triode is used as an amplifier.

the triode and AB supplies the power for the anode circuit at a voltage considerably greater than the others. For example GB may be of the order of 10 volts, FB 6 volts, but AB may be as much as 200 volts.

When the subscriber connected to $L_1 L_2$ starts to talk, the current variations due to his voice produce variations of voltage across the primary of T_1, and the varying magnetic field induces a voltage of similar characteristics in the secondary. This secondary voltage may be greater or less than the primary according to the ratio of secondary turns to primary turns, but in general the secondary voltage is greater, and the ratio of the transformer is made as large as possible without introducing any distortion into the speech.

These voltage variations are applied to the grid of the triode and voltage variations on the grid will affect the current flowing to the anode. This current will increase and

decrease as the grid voltage varies about the bias voltage of
the battery GB, and these current variations can be made
to be very much larger than the original current variations
in the telephone line. On flowing through the primary of T_2
they develop across it a voltage exactly similar to the original
telephone line voltage, but of very much greater amplitude,
and thus the original telephone signals have been strengthened and are passed on to the line $L_3 L_4$, where they continue
their travels until they become so weak that further amplification is necessary.

THE TWO-WAY SPEECH CIRCUIT

Now the circuit which we have shown can only pass speech
in one direction, and if each telephone circuit had four
wires it would be a simple circuit to use. Unfortunately only
two wires are used, and these carry speech from both sub-

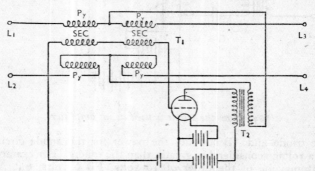

125. Arranging the triode to amplify speech both ways.

scribers, and, therefore, some system whereby the triode
can be applied to two lines and enable amplification to be
obtained in both directions is necessary. This two-way
speech amplification is obtained by the following circuit,
Fig. 125.

The transformer T_1 now has its primary windings P_y
connected direct between L_1 and L_3 and L_2 and L_4. This
transformer has its windings arranged differentially, that is
to say, one primary winding is wound or connected in the
opposite direction to the other, and this can clearly be seen
from the figure, where the windings in the L_2–L_4 connection

are connected in the opposite direction to L_1–L_3 section. By this means the secondary SEC which is coupled magnetically to all the primary windings will have voltages induced in it from both lines, and these voltages will be applied to the grid.

The anode circuit is connected to a transformer T_2 the secondary of which is connected to the centre point of the primary windings. Now if the lines L_1 L_2 L_3 L_4 are carefully balanced so that each line is electrically the same, then equal currents will flow to L_1 and L_2 and L_3 and L_4 through the primary coils and no voltage will be induced into the secondary

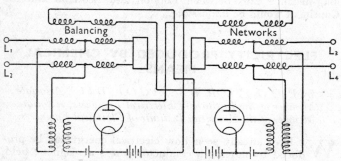

126. A balanced repeater circuit which will prevent howling. Without such circuits placed at suitable intervals, long distance trunk calls would be impossible.

of T_1. In this way the device will be quite stable and will not tend to howl back by feeding some of the output energy back into its own grid circuit; the triode will, therefore, amplify speech both ways, and in many cases overall amplification of 500 times the normal level is obtainable.

If two such repeaters are used on a long line, there will be a good chance of their howling by virtue of the fact that half of the power flows down each line and hence the two repeater stations will have an opportunity for interaction.

To overcome this and one or two other difficulties, special circuits have been evolved which employ line balancing equipments to prevent any form of reflection on the lines. This circuit is shown in Fig. 126 and it will be seen that two valves or triodes are employed, and the lines split up, so that part of the current from the repeater will be absorbed by the balancing networks, and only the current flowing in the required direction will be passed to the line. Any number of repeaters may therefore be used without any fear of interaction and howling. In this circuit it will be noted that the anode transformer coils are differential wound and coupled to L_3 and L_4, and the grid transformer is connected to the centre point of the primary windings.

The success of the modern trunk circuit and the ease with which long distance calls can be made over thousands of miles are entirely due to the repeater stations which will be found at definite points along the line. Without the repeater, long-distance calls between London and Scotland and the Continent would be impossible.

ELECTRICITY PRODUCED BY CHEMICAL MEANS

by E. O. TAYLOR, B.Sc., A.C.G.I., D.I.C., Associate Member of the Institute of Electrical Engineers, Associate Member of the American Institute of Electrical Engineers.

WE have already seen how electrical energy can be produced by moving a conductor across a magnetic field, and how this has been developed to the electric generator of to-day. Most people are familiar with another source of such energy, from chemical action in a cell, or battery. Actually batteries were used for producing electrical energy long before Faraday's discovery that currents could be produced by means of magnetic fields, and they were the only source of current available to experimenters before Faraday's time. Although a battery is not a convenient means of producing large amounts of electric energy, it is very much used for producing currents necessary to supply flashlamps, wireless sets, the lighting for motor-cars and many other similar purposes.

The voltage available from a single cell such as the Leclanché used for door-bells, or the dry-cell used in pocket lamps is only 1·5 volts. This is often not enough for the purpose in hand, for instance the high voltage or high tension supply to a wireless set must often be about 100 volts. Voltages above 1·5 volts can, however, easily be obtained by having a number of cells and connecting them in *series* as shown at the top left-hand side of Fig. 127. The positive terminal of one cell is connected to the negative terminal of the next and so on so that the voltages add up. The high voltage battery of a wireless set may consist of 70 cells connected in this way giving a total of $70 \times 1.5 = 105$ volts. An electric bell usually requires two cells connected in series giving about 3 volts. Since there is only one path through the cells for the current, the amount of current which can be obtained from a battery of cells in series is only the same as that which could be obtained from one of them.

Another possible way of arranging a number of cells is to connect them in *parallel* (see Fig. 127, below at left) by con-

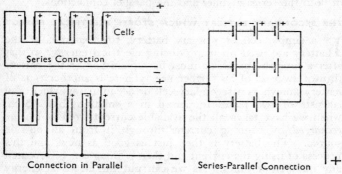

127. The three ways of arranging a battery of cells.

necting all the negative terminals together and all the positive terminals together. In this case the current from each cell flows into the main circuit giving a large total current in just the same way as the water from the tributaries of a river goes to swell the flow of the main stream. The pressure, however, is only that of a single cell, i.e. 1.5 volts.

If we want a high voltage and a small current, therefore, we must connect a number of cells in series, but if we want a large current and only a small voltage they must be connected in parallel. Currents and voltages between these two extremes can, however, be obtained by yet another method of connection called the series-parallel connection. This is also illustrated on the right in Fig. 127, which also shows how a battery is usually represented in a diagram. In this case the cells are connected into several groups, each group having all its cells connected in series ; the groups are then connected in parallel. In the arrangement of 9 cells shown in Fig. 127 on the right, each group contains three cells and therefore gives a pressure of $3 \times 1 \cdot 5 = 4 \cdot 5$ volts, while the total current obtainable will be three times that of one cell, as there are three sets in parallel feeding into the main circuit. It is important, however, to remember that in making a series-parallel connection the number of cells in each group must be the same, so that the total voltage of each group is the same.

It is not usually necessary to connect primary batteries in anything but the series connection, but secondary batteries which are described in the next paragraphs are often arranged in both the series-parallel and the parallel connections.

THE SECONDARY BATTERY WHICH STORES ELECTRICAL ENERGY

IN a simple cell or primary battery, the materials of the battery are used up in producing electrical energy, so that after a time the materials must be replenished or the battery thrown away as of no further use. There is another type of battery known as a secondary cell or accumulator which also consists of two plates immersed in a solution, but which, when we have taken all the available current from it, can be *recharged* by running current through it from an outside source. The battery is then just as good as new, and this process of using the current and then refilling can be repeated any number of times. As we can put the electrical energy into the battery at any convenient time and then draw it out when required, it is really a method of storing electrical energy in the same way as water can be stored in a reservoir or gas in a gasholder, and such a battery is also called a storage battery. The chief trouble with it is that it can only be used with direct currents, and not with alternating currents. In spite of this, however, it is very much used and in some ways is better than the primary battery because it can give larger currents.

The type of secondary battery most commonly used is the lead-acid type, so called because it consists of two lead plates immersed in dilute sulphuric acid. The two lead plates are made in the form of grids and the spaces so formed are filled with a paste of oxide of lead in one of the plates and of finely powdered or spongy lead in the other. These are then arranged in a glass container as shown in Fig. 128. A cell of this sort has chemical action going on in it which produces an electrical pressure of two volts between the plates, the plate with the oxide of lead in it being at the higher pressure and being therefore the positive plate. If an electric circuit is connected between the two plates, current will flow from the positive plate to the negative as shown.

When current is taken from the cell in this way the chemical action which goes on causes both the lead oxide on the positive plate and the spongy lead on the negative plate to turn into sulphate of lead and the sulphuric acid in the solution is gradually used up. Taking current from the cell is called

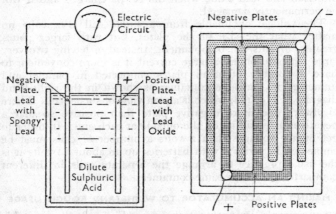

128. The lead-acid secondary battery : (left) illustrating the action which takes place ; (right) the plates arranged in the container (seen from above) to give maximum area.

discharging the cell and as all the available electrical energy is used up, the voltage gradually falls to about 1·9 volts ; when this point is reached the cell should be recharged, i.e. more current should be put in.

Now when the cell is being discharged the current is coming out at the positive terminal and going through the circuit, and back into the cell at the negative terminal—in order to charge the cell it is therefore necessary to make it go through the cell in the opposite direction, i.e. in at the positive terminal. When this is done the chemical action which went on before is reversed and the lead sulphate is converted back to lead oxide on the positive plate and spongy lead on the negative plate. When the cell is fully charged the voltage should be about

2·1 volts. In an actual cell the positive plate can easily be distinguished from the negative plate because the former is dark brown in colour and the latter is grey.

If the cell is discharged too far, that is, if current is taken from it after the voltage has fallen to 1·9 volts, the lead sulphate which is formed becomes a hard white substance which either sticks to the plates or falls off on the bottom of the container, and can often be seen in a very old cell. If a cell is allowed to get into this state the lead sulphate cannot be reconverted back into lead and lead oxide when the cell is charged and it will be permanently damaged.

The voltage obtainable from a single cell is 2 volts no matter what the size of the plates, but with larger plates greater currents can be obtained. Instead of having two very large plates to obtain a large current it is more convenient to have a number of small plates connected in parallel and immersed in the same container as shown in the right-hand diagram of Fig. 128, which is a plan view of such a cell. There is always one more negative plate than positive so that a negative plate will be on the outside at each end. In order to get higher voltages than 2 volts a number of cells must be connected in series; with batteries up to about 12 volts it is the usual practice to arrange the separate cells in different compartments of the same container.

MAKING AN ACCUMULATOR TO WITHSTAND ROUGH USAGE

THE simple arrangement shown in Fig. 128 is not suitable for practical use, and certain modifications in the construction must be made in order to make batteries withstand ordinary rough usage. In order to save space the plates must be placed fairly close together—for motor-car batteries where space is particularly valuable only about $\frac{1}{8}$ of an inch is allowed between plates, while in other cases where space is not important about an inch is allowed. With close spacings there is a danger of pieces of the paste getting dislodged and touching both plates, a condition which would cause a short-circuit in the battery, and would very soon permanently damage it. Also, due to continued charging and discharging, the plates may warp or buckle slightly and touch each other.

These possibilities are guarded against by having a spacer of thin wood between the plates as shown in Fig. 129, which is a cross section of a battery suitable for a motor-car. In time some of the paste falls to the bottom of the cell and in order to prevent the plates from touching this and becoming short-circuited they are kept well clear of the bottom by being supported on ridges. A glass container is generally used as this is not attacked by the acid but where this is too fragile a hard rubber or moulded ebonite container is employed ; if the cell is to be portable it must of course be sealed off at the top, although a small hole must be left to allow of the escape

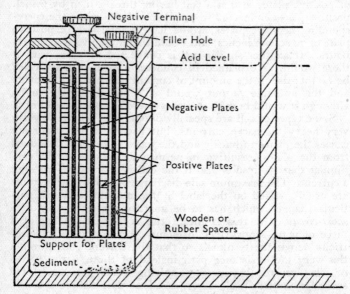

129. A section of a motor-car battery, arranged to be economical in space and to withstand rough usage.

of the gas which is generated when the cell is being charged. The acid must always completely cover the plates otherwise the parts uncovered will be spoilt ; if the level sinks below its proper height it can be made up with distilled (boiled) water, but not ordinary tap water as this contains impurities which may cause damage.

The output which can be obtained from a battery may be measured in watt-hours, but as the voltage is fixed definitely by the number of cells in series it is more usual to measure the output in ampère-hours—a cell having an output of 10 ampère-hours will be capable of giving a current of about 10 ampères for 1 hour, 5 ampères for 2 hours, 20 ampères of $\frac{1}{2}$ hour, and so on, although actually a slightly greater number of ampère-hours can be obtained if the battery is discharged at a low current.

The number of ampère-hours output which can be expected from a cell is about 8 ampère-hours for every 12 square inches of positive plate, so that a cell having three 4 inch by 6 inch positive plates connected in parallel, with of course the corresponding negative plates, would have a total size of positive plate of 72 square inches, and would therefore give 48 ampère-hours. If another similar cell is connected in series with it there would, as explained in connection with primary cells, be no increase in the amount of current which could be taken and the available output would still be 48 ampère-hours, although it would now be at a pressure of 4 volts instead of 2.

Some types of cell are specially designed to be able to carry very heavy discharge currents, but usually a heavy current causes the plates to buckle and the paste to become dislodged from the plates, resulting in permanent damage to the cell. Similar damage results also if the cell is charged at too high a current. The maximum safe discharge and charging currents are usually stated on the label by the manufacturer. A particular danger which has to be guarded against is that of a *short-circuit* ; by this is meant the accidental placing of a piece of wire, screwdriver, or some other conductor of electricity across the terminals so that the current goes through this very low resistance path instead of through the valves or whatever the battery is supplying. The resistance of a secondary battery itself is very small, so that if there is a very low resistance in the rest of the circuit also, there is bound to be, according to Ohm's law, a very large current and this will damage the battery. A primary battery also should not be short-circuited, but in this case the current will not be so great because a primary battery has itself a fairly large resistance, and this limits the short-circuit current to some extent.

HOW A STORAGE BATTERY IS RECHARGED

WE have already explained that when all the available current of a battery has been used up, i.e. when the battery has been discharged, it can be recharged simply by putting more current in. This is done by connecting a current supply to the battery in such a way that it sends current in to the positive terminal instead of allowing current to come out of it ; the connections of a simple circuit for battery charging are shown in Fig. 130. The positive terminal of the battery is connected to the positive terminal of the supply, and the negative terminal of the battery to the negative of the supply, with a suitable ammeter in series for measuring the current, and a resistance for controlling the magnitude of the current. The supply used must, of course, be direct current, as an alternating current would simply put current into the battery during one half-cycle and take it out during the next.

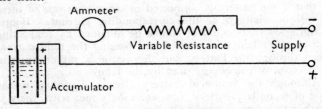

130. The circuit used for charging an accumulator.

Now the battery is exerting an electric pressure or voltage trying to send current out of its positive terminal while the supply voltage is trying to send current in the opposite direction, and if these two voltages are equal there will obviously be no current. If the battery voltage is higher then it will win, and current will come out of the battery, while if the supply voltage is higher current will go into the battery. The voltage of the supply must always therefore be larger than that of the battery which it is to charge. Thus to charge a 12 volt battery a voltage of 16 to 20 volts will be necessary. If 20 volts is used there will be 12 of these used up in balancing out the 12 volts of the battery, leaving the remaining 8 volts to push the current round the circuit. The amount of current which this 8 volts will produce depends on the resistance of the circuit, or, since the resistance of the battery itself is negligible, on the resistance which is connected in series. The size of this resistance can therefore be calculated by means of Ohm's law. In the above case, suppose it is desired to charge at 16 ampères, then the resistance must be

$$R = \frac{V}{I} = \frac{8}{16} = 0 \cdot 5 \text{ ohms.}$$

In order to be able to adjust the current the resistance should be variable. Any voltage can, of course, be used as a supply so long as it is greater than the battery voltage, provided a suitable resistance is available to limit the current to the correct value.

A simple way of charging small 2 or 4 volt batteries requiring charging currents of less than about an ampère is by means of the domestic 200 volt supply, if it happens to be direct current, and some ordinary lamps as resistance. A 200 volt 40 watt lamp takes a current of 0·2 ampère, a 200 volt, 60 watt, lamp takes 0·3 ampère, and a 100 watt lamp takes 0·5 ampère, so that if the battery is connected in series with one of these it will be charged at the corresponding current. Bigger charging currents could of course be obtained by connecting two or more lamps in parallel and passing the total current taken through the battery, but this becomes rather wasteful on account of the energy used by the lamps.

Although the lead-acid battery already described is the type of secondary battery most commonly met with, there is another type known as the alkaline or nickel-iron type, which has plates of steel made in the form of grids and containing nickel oxide in the positive plate and iron oxide in the negative plate, these being immersed in a solution of potassium hydroxide. As this does not attack iron or steel, a metal container can be used. The voltage of a single cell of a battery of this type is only about 1·2 volts, but it can stand more rough usage than the lead-acid type. It is, however, rather more expensive.

THE MOTOR-CAR BATTERY'S SPECIAL USES

THE modern motor car depends on electricity for its lighting, starting of the engine, operation of the windscreen wiper, direction indicators, electric horn, and for the ignition, that is, the production of the spark in the cylinders. The current for all these purposes is supplied from a generator driven by the motor itself, and a battery for use when the motor car is not running, with the possible exception of the ignition which is sometimes supplied from a special magneto generator.

When the car is running the generator supplies the electric current for lighting and other purposes, and also charges the battery so that the latter is always ready to supply current for lighting when the car is stationary and for starting the engine. The current required for lighting will only be 2 or 3 ampères, and that for electric horns, direction indicators and other fittings possibly 6 or 8 ampères, but for starting the engine 100 or 200 ampères may be required, although, of course, it will only be for a few seconds and that only infrequently.

Motor-car batteries are usually made to give 6 or 12 volts and it is evident that they must be of extremely robust construction in order to give the very heavy starting current, particularly as they have also to withstand considerable vibration, and the possibility of careless treatment by people who know little about them. The lead-acid battery is nearly always used because it is not easily possible to get the very heavy starting current from an alkaline battery of the same size, although it would be suitable from other points of view. A cross-section of a lead-acid motor-car battery is shown in Fig. 129. The life of such a battery is about two years with ordinary usage and provided reasonable care is taken not to over-discharge it or allow the acid level to become too low.

If a battery is to be disused for any length of time, such as when a car is laid up for the winter, the terminals should be greased with vaseline to prevent corrosion and the battery fully charged ; it will maintain this charge for several months, although it is advisable, if possible, to give it intermediate charges at intervals of one or two months. The acid should on no account be emptied out, or the plates will deteriorate, although this can be done without damage for a period of a few days, if it is necessary to transport the battery.

DRIVING A MOTOR-CAR DIRECT FROM A STORAGE BATTERY

IF a sufficiently large battery is installed on a car it can be used for actually driving the car instead of for the minor purposes described in the previous paragraphs. In this way the rather complicated petrol engine is done away with and at the same time there is no need to lead the current to the car by an overhead wire as with the electric tram or trolley bus. The battery for an ordinary-sized car or tradesman's delivery van would require an output of about 150 ampère-hours and would weigh half a ton or more. The weight renders the battery-driven vehicle rather unsuitable for use as a private car but such vehicles are eminently suited for small delivery vans and are largely used by a number of big stores for this purpose. Facilities have to be provided either for charging during the night, when the vehicles are not in use or by making the battery easily removable so that when discharged it can quickly be replaced by another fully charged unit.

Very many other uses are found for batteries, ranging from the small units for lighting miners' electric hand-lamps to the much larger installation in all up-to-date theatres, hospitals, and other important public buildings for giving an emergency supply in the case of a failure of the supply from the power station. In this latter application a switch is arranged which automatically changes all the circuits over on to the battery if the main supply fails, and this is done with hardly a flicker of the lights.

HOW AN ELECTRIC CURRENT CAN GIVE HEAT AND LIGHT

IT is well known that light cannot be produced artificially without heat and that the production of heat is very often accompanied by the production of light, so that the subjects of heating and lighting dovetail into each other. The electric current is an excellent means of producing both heat and light and it can be used for this purpose in either of two ways : the current may be passed through a fine wire having a high resistance or it may be passed through air or a gas in the form of a continuous spark or arc.

Taking the first of these methods let us consider why a wire gets hot when a current is passed through it. It has already been explained that an electric current is really a movement of electrons along the conductor. Now if we keep hitting an anvil with a hammer it will become hot, and precisely the same thing happens when the electrons travel along the conductor and collide with the atoms making up the conductor. The conductor therefore gets hot and the more of the electrons there are and the faster they are moving, i.e. the bigger the current is, the hotter will the conductor get. This explains why a wire gets hot ; but why do some wires get hotter than others ? Thus, in the ordinary electric radiator the wires leading the current to it are quite cool, while the wire on the radiator itself is red hot.

A copper conductor has its atoms spaced fairly widely apart so that electrons can travel along it easily without making very many collisions ; a wire of nickel-chromium alloy, however, has its atoms very closely packed together so that when electrons travel along it they are continually making collisions, and such a wire gets very much hotter than a copper wire of the same size when the same current is passed along it. Now consider two wires of the same material but having different diameters. Let us pass the same current through both of them. The number of electrons moving along the wire will be the same in each case, but in the thinner wire they will be much more crowded together as they have a smaller space to move in and the number of collisions will therefore be greater than in the thicker wire. The smaller wire will thus get hotter than the larger one although the same current is flowing in both.

A wire in which the electrons cannot travel along easily is said to have a high resistance and requires a fairly large electrical pressure or voltage to send a current along it. The resistance of a piece of nickel-chromium wire is about 60 times as great as that of copper wire having the same length and diameter ; wires of most other metals have resistances somewhere in between these two.

Therefore if we want to produce heat by means of an electric current we must pass it through a piece of fine wire made of a material of high resistance. The amount of heat produced depends on the square of the current, that is to say, if we double the current passing through a wire, the heat produced will be increased to four times its previous value ; if we have three times the current we shall get nine times the amount of heat, and so on. If the amount of current passing through a wire is gradually increased, the wire will first become red hot, then white hot and finally it will melt ; when the wire is white hot it is giving out light as well as heat and it can then be used as a source of light. The ordinary metal filament electric lamp consists simply of a wire made white hot in this way.

USING ELECTRICAL ENERGY TO HEAT A ROOM : ELECTRIC RADIATORS

THE ordinary electric radiator for domestic use consists of a long piece of high resistance wire, usually nickel-chromium alloy, wound into a spiral and mounted on a piece of porcelain or firebrick about a foot long and 3 inches wide. A unit of this sort is called the heating element and requires a current of about 5 ampères at a pressure of about 200 volts to make it red hot. One, two, or three of these heating elements are connected in parallel and mounted in

an ornamental frame to make the ordinary electric " fire."
For office buildings a method called *panel heating* is often
employed in which the heating wires are embedded, with
suitable insulation of course, in the plaster of the walls and
ceiling so that the whole of the sides and top of the room
become heating elements ; the temperature of the wires in
this case, instead of being about 1,000° C. as in the radiator
type of heater, is only about 60° or 70° C., but as there is a
very much greater length of wire a sufficient amount of heat
can be produced.

COOKING THE DINNER BY ELECTRICAL ENERGY

MANY housewives now use electricity for cooking. The
oven used for roasting has the heating elements situated
at the sides and top ; these elements may be similar to those
used for electric radiators or they may be of the embedded
type in which the wire is embedded in moulded insulating
material giving an effect somewhat similar to panel heating for
buildings.

For boiling kettles and saucepans, heating elements are
placed on the top of the cooker and, to prevent damage from
liquids boiling over, and danger of electric shocks, these
are usually of the embedded type. A cast-iron plate with
grooves on the underside is used and the heating wires are
embedded in insulating material in these grooves ; such
plates take several minutes to get heated up after the current
has been switched on, but otherwise they are quite satisfactory.

To try to get a shorter heating-up time some makers have
built an open type of element consisting of a relatively short
piece of wire about $\frac{1}{8}$ or $\frac{1}{4}$ inch thick ; a very large current
is required to make such a piece of wire red-hot, but as it is
short and thick the pressure necessary to send such a current
through it is only a few volts and there is therefore no danger
of shock ; its great thickness also makes it very robust. An
ordinary embedded type of boiling plate takes a current of
about 10 ampères at 230 volts when fully switched on, but
one of the open type of plates described above requires about
200 ampères, but only at a pressure of 10 volts or so, and
the total amount of power required by the two is about the
same. The low voltage necessary for operating the latter
type of plate is obtained from a small transformer mounted
in the cooker and connected on the primary side to the

230 volt supply. It gives about 10 volts on the secondary side.

MAN TRIES TO REPRODUCE DAYLIGHT : THE ELECTRIC FILAMENT LAMP

IN an electric lamp we want to produce light without at the same time producing any heat. Unfortunately no method of doing this has yet been discovered. Further, we want the light to correspond approximately to daylight, that is, to the light produced by the sun ; again this is not possible and most of our lamps produce too many red waves and not enough of the green and blue, so that nearly all artificial lights have a reddish tinge. In the electric lamp, however, the hotter we can make our wire the more nearly is white light approached, and if we could have the wire at a temperature of about 6,000° C. quite a good approximation to daylight would be obtained.

In order that the wire shall have a sufficiently high resistance so that it will get red or white hot when a small current is passed through it, it must be made very fine, not more than a few thousandths of an inch in diameter. A lamp employing a fine wire of this sort is called a filament lamp, and the production of the filament is a source of considerable difficulty in the manufacture of such lamps, as at the high temperatures employed it tends to burn away.

The first electric filament lamps were made by Swan in this country, and Edison in America about 1879. They used a filament of carbon drawn out to a very fine wire and enclosed in a bulb from which all the air had been removed. Carbon could be heated to a higher temperature than any of the metals then known and the exclusion of the air prevented its burning away, but even so the temperature was limited and the carbon lamp gave a very reddish light. The next step was the use (about 1904) of certain rare metals having a high melting point, also enclosed in a vacuum.

In 1913 the idea of filling the bulb with some inert gas such as argon, which would definitely tend to prevent burning of the wire was developed, and the gas-filled lamp was made. Tungsten is generally used for the filament and this can be run at a temperature of about 3,500° C., so that it gives a light much nearer to daylight than the previous lamps, although it still contains too many red waves and not enough of the green and blue. Furthermore, the proportion of light waves to heat waves is greater in this type of lamp, so that more light is obtained for a given amount of power than in the earlier types.

The amount of light given out by a lamp is measured in *lumens*, and a small gas-filled lamp gives about 16 lumens of light for every watt of electrical power which it consumes ; an ordinary 40 watt lamp such as is often used for domestic lighting thus gives out about $40 \times 16 = 640$ lumens of light. If some future invention enables the filament of a lamp to be run at a temperature of about 6,000° C., a lamp giving a light similar to that of daylight would be possible and also such a lamp would give much more light for a given amount of power.

LIGHT FROM THE SPLUTTERING ELECTRIC ARC

IF, instead of passing current along a wire we pass it through the air between two electrodes spaced about half an inch apart we get another source of light and heat called the electric arc. When a voltage is first applied to the electrodes no current flows and nothing happens because the air has a very high resistance, being in fact an insulator. If, however, by some means it is possible to start a flow of electrons travelling across the gap, these electrons will get up such a tremendous speed under the influence of the voltage that when they collide with ordinary atoms of air they will dislodge more electrons. These will also get up a high speed and produce still more, and so on, so that there are soon so many free electrons in the space that the air has become a conductor and can carry a large current.

This process is called ionising the air and the collisions and general disturbance produced cause the air to become white hot. It is then called an arc ; the temperature of such an arc is between 3,000 and 4,000° C., and in addition to the heat waves produced, there are also light waves which give a fairly white light. As explained above, the arc will not start itself and in order to start it the two electrodes must be made to touch and then immediately separated, when a small spark will be formed which will immediately develop into an arc. An arc of this sort can be used as a source of light, and in fact was so used before the invention of the filament lamp, and continued in use for lighting of streets, exhibition halls and other similar buildings until quite recently. Nowadays it is only used for theatre spot-lights, cinema arcs, searchlights or other purposes where a very intense source of light is required.

The chief reason which led it to be superseded by the filament lamp was that the electrodes, which are carbon rods of half to one inch in diameter, were gradually burnt away, necessitating some automatic device continually to adjust the gap to the correct length, and necessitating also replacement at fairly frequent intervals. Furthermore, it is not possible to build them in sizes small enough for ordinary domestic use. A somewhat similar principle is employed, however, in the most modern form of lamp, the gas discharge lamp.

HOW THE COLOURED "SKY-SIGNS" GET THEIR LIGHT

THE gas discharge lamp employs as its source of light a current passing between two electrodes in a similar way to the arc lamp. In this case, however, the electrodes are placed in a glass tube from which all air has been pumped and replaced by a very small quantity of some other gas. The pressure in the tube is so low that we no longer get a fierce arc but only a gentle glow, commonly called an electric discharge, and this gives a very pleasant sort of light. By having different sorts of gas in the tube, light of different colours can be obtained. For instance, with neon gas the bright red light is obtained which is so often used for advertising, with sodium vapour a greenish-yellow light is obtained, with mercury vapour a bluish-white light is obtained which makes red objects look blue. Magnesium gives a green light. Other colours can be obtained by mixing certain gases or by using tubes of coloured glass—a mercury vapour lamp, for instance, in a special glass gives a green light. Again, where gases are not suitable for mixing, two lamps of different colours may be mounted side by side. Unfortunately, no gas or mixture of gases has yet been found which will give a light similar to that of daylight.

STARTING AND USING THE NEON LIGHT

THE earliest of the modern types of discharge lamp was the now familiar neon tube used for display purposes and giving a bright red light. With this type of lamp, just as with the arc lamp, some means must be provided for starting the discharge. In the neon lamp this is done by using a very high voltage, which is applied between the electrodes and which causes the insulating properties of the gas to break down and therefore starts an arc. Once it has been started a much smaller voltage is sufficient to keep it going.

The normal voltage of the supply available is about 230 volts, so that a transformer must be used to step the voltage up to the required value. This transformer is specially constructed so that as soon as the current begins to flow the voltage appearing at the secondary terminals falls off to a value just sufficient to keep the tube alight. The voltage necessary to start the discharge is about 300 volts per foot length of tube, so that a lamp several feet long will require a transformer giving several thousand volts. This transformer can usually be seen mounted close to any neon tube installation. Apart from its use for advertisement displays, the neon lamp is also very suitable for shipping lights and airway beacons, as the nature of the light gives it a much greater penetrating power than other types of light in foggy weather.

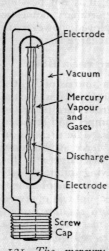

Electrode

Vacuum

Mercury
Vapour
and
Gases

Discharge

Electrode

Screw
Cap

131. The mercury vapour lamp, which gives a brilliant bluish-white light.

Apart from its colour, the neon lamp is unsuitable for many purposes on account of the high voltage required. This difficulty does not exist with the mercury vapour lamp which can be operated from an ordinary 230 volt circuit. A rather special construction is necessary for this type of lamp as shown in Fig. 131. The two electrodes are placed in a tube containing the mercury vapour together with certain other rare gases. This tube is then contained in another outer tube and the space between the two is evacuated. The reason for this second tube is that the temperature of the gases has a very important influence on the operation of the lamp and by having the inner tube surrounded by a vacuum in this way the heat which is produced by the discharge can be prevented from escaping and the gases kept at the correct temperature. The light produced by one of these lamps consists of different colours, but the blue light predominates and a bluish-white light is produced.

It has already been explained that the filament lamp gives about 16 or 20 lumens of light for each watt of electrical power supplied. The gas discharge lamp can, however, give about twice as much as this, and is therefore much more economical than the ordinary filament lamp. At present, however, it is made only in sizes which are too big for ordinary domestic use, although they are quite suitable for street lighting. The difficulty about the colour of the light also, at present, precludes their use for many purposes.

MAKING THE BEST USE OF THE LIGHT FROM THE LAMP

THE waves of light which are emitted by any form of lamp travel outwards from the lamp in all directions. When, however, they meet some solid object, several things may happen ; if the object is transparent like glass the light will simply pass straight through. If it is opaque like an ordinary wall they will either be reflected from the surface or will be absorbed by it and altogether lost. The angle at which light is reflected from a flat surface is always the same as that at which it falls on the surface, so that by fixing a reflecting surface at a suitable angle to a beam of light it can be thrown in any direction. This property of reflection is made use of by fitting lamps with reflectors which collect the light which is going in directions where it is not required and turn it so that it falls on the surface which is being illuminated.

For instance, to light a desk or table a reflector as shown in Fig. 132 would be used ; all the light going in an upward direction away from the table is caught and reflected back on to it ; the whole light of the lamp is thus usefully employed, whereas without the reflector a lot of it would simply be going upwards and illuminating the ceiling. Another interesting application is the searchlight. Here a reflector is used to collect all the light and direct it along a parallel-sided beam as shown in Fig. 132. As all the light of the lamp is now going in practically the same direction a very intense beam can be produced.

With a good reflecting surface such as enamelled steel or mirrored glass practically all the light falling on to it is reflected, but other surfaces such as the walls of a room, or curtains, absorb a good deal of the light and waste it, while a dull black surface will reflect no light at all.

PREVENTING GLARE BY DIFFUSING THE LIGHT

IF we look at a bright source of light the eyes experience a dazzling sensation and cannot pick out any other surrounding objects at all clearly. This is particularly noticeable when meeting motor-car headlights at night. This phenomenon is called glare and is a very important factor to be considered when fixing up a lighting installation. Some metal filament lamps have the filament enclosed in clear glass bulbs so that the light is very glaring and such bulbs should never be used within the direct range of vision.

To avoid this effect to some extent an opal or frosted bulb can be used for the lamp or it may be placed behind an opal screen or shade which diffuses the light as shown in Fig. 132. The rays of light are scattered in many directions so that although almost the same total amount of light is emitted, it is spread over a larger area and does not therefore appear to be so intense. Even a lamp with an opal or pearl bulb is rather glaring if it is larger than 60 watts, and it should then be shielded from direct vision by the eye.

For interior lighting, glare can be almost entirely avoided by placing the lamps in inverted reflectors as shown in Fig. 132, so that all the light is reflected upwards on to the ceiling and then reflected again from there down into the room. Such an arrangement is known as indirect lighting and gives a very even distribution of light over the whole room, although, of course, as there are two reflections, more of the light is wasted than with ordinary direct lighting. If a bowl of opal glass is used, then some of the light is transmitted directly downwards, with suitable diffusion, into the room while the rest is reflected from the ceiling. This arrangement is commonly used and is called semi-indirect lighting.

THE NEW ART OF FLOODLIGHTING

IT is now quite common practice to illuminate or floodlight important or beautiful buildings at night. Powerful 1,000 or 1,500 watt lamps are mounted in reflectors, in this case usually called projectors, which direct all their light on to the surface of the building. The appearance of a building floodlit in this way is not quite the same as when illuminated by daylight as in the former case the light falls on it from only one or possibly two directions while in daylight it falls from all directions, so that shadows cast by projecting parts appear quite different in the two cases. If the floodlighting projectors are placed directly in front of the building no shadows are visible to a person standing in front and it looks exactly like a building painted on a piece of scenery. If, however, the projectors are placed at the sides, a more natural

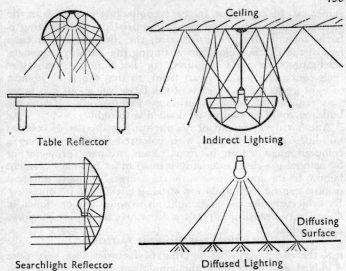

Table Reflector

Indirect Lighting

Searchlight Reflector

Diffused Lighting

132. The radiating lines show the direction of typical light rays from the lamp, and illustrate (left) how reflectors can be used to concentrate the light in a required direction, (right) how the light may be diffused to prevent glare.

effect is obtained and the beauty of the building may even be enhanced.

In order to get the best effects, the fact that a building is to be floodlit should be taken into account by the architect when designing it, and the various projecting parts arranged so that their shadows fall correctly and also so that suitable places can be made for housing the projectors. Many flood-lighting schemes have been ruined because some of the actual light sources were visible or because the projectors themselves completely spoiled the architectural beauty of the building in daytime.

Floodlighting is also employed for illuminating advertisement hoardings at night. The value of an advertisement depends on the number of people who see it, so that by lighting it up during the winter evenings its value can be almost doubled and well repays the cost of the equipment necessary and the electricity used. Tennis courts, football pitches and other sports arenas can also be floodlit so that games can be carried on in the evenings just as well as in the daytime. The amount of power required for floodlighting is fairly considerable. For instance, the illumination of each face of the Big Ben clock tower during the Faraday centenary celebrations in 1931 required 35 floodlighting projectors each containing a 1,000 watt lamp, so that the total amount of light projected on to each of the faces was about 600 times that required to light an ordinary living-room. Truly the building could be said to be flooded with light.

Another development of floodlighting is the use of colour ; buildings can be flooded with coloured light by placing a coloured glass screen in front of an ordinary projector or by using a gas-discharge lamp instead of an ordinary filament lamp. In the former case a moving screen of many different colours can be used and very striking effects can be obtained. By projecting the coloured light on to fountains or clouds of steam, very beautiful effects for decorative or display purposes are possible.

LIGHTING THE MODERN FACTORY

IN the olden days the lighting of factories was very poor indeed and after dark the employees had to strain their eyes very severely in order to do their work. Even after the introduction of electric light the managers often considered it unnecessary expenditure to provide even reasonably good lighting. Now, however, this attitude is gradually being changed, as it has been found by experience that not only does good lighting reduce the number of accidents and promote good feeling amongst the employees, but that they can do their work so much more easily that the increased output obtained more than pays for the cost of the improved installation.

Another means whereby the use of electricity has enabled better lighting to be installed in factories is by the use of electric motors built into each individual machine to drive it instead of the old system of belts and pulleys suspended from the ceiling; by elimination of these the ceiling space is left free for lighting equipment which can illuminate the working area without casting any shadows. In addition to the general lighting thus provided, each machine has an adjustable lamp which the worker can arrange to suit his own convenience. In certain up-to-date, well illuminated factories it has been found that about a fifth of the total electrical energy consumed goes in providing adequate lighting.

TACKLING THE PROBLEM OF LIGHTING THE ROADS

ONE of the most difficult problems in lighting is that of illuminating our streets to make them safe for motor and other traffic after dark. The present system whereby each motorist or cyclist has to illuminate his own little bit of road as he goes along is decidedly unsatisfactory, especially for main roads. The problem has been attacked in towns and fairly powerful street lamps are mounted on standards about 25 feet high at intervals of 50 to 100 yards on all the main thoroughfares. Special reflectors must be used which will throw all the light from the lamp on to the roadway, and none on to the adjacent buildings or upwards into the sky. At the same time glare must be avoided as far as possible by having the lamps sufficiently high to be out of the direct line of vision of the driver of any vehicle when he approaches within 100 yards or so of the lamp. Glare due to reflection from shiny road surfaces must also be avoided, but this is a problem for the civil rather than the electrical engineer.

It is thus clear that the design of a suitable reflector is rather difficult, and added to this is the further problem that the whole lighting fitting must be dust-proof and water-tight. Although electricity is rapidly superseding other methods of illumination for street lighting purposes, the systems at present employed are far from perfect, and new types and arrangements of lamps and reflectors are continually being developed. The latest installations use mercury-vapour or sodium-vapour gas discharge tubes. These lamps give more light for a given amount of power than the filament types of lamp, and the peculiar monochromatic nature of the light enables moving objects on the roadway to be seen more clearly. The colour of the light produced is, of course, a disadvantage, but for lighting of main roads this is of little importance. How soon motorists will be able to travel on our roads at night just as easily as in daytime no one can yet tell, but the invention of the gas discharge lamp marks a very important step towards the attainment of this ideal.

LIGHT WITHOUT HEAT : CAN MAN IMITATE THE GLOW-WORM?

IT is quite easy to produce light electrically, and also by other means, but no one has yet found a method of producing light without at the same time producing a very large amount of heat. Quite apart from the waste of energy incurred in producing this unwanted heat, it is a nuisance because it means that lamps and reflectors, particularly large units, have to be designed to withstand the high temperatures produced and sometimes special means have to be provided for cooling them. Although the gas discharge lamp is an improvement on the filament lamp in this respect, man has not yet approached to within measurable distance of solving the problem of how to produce light alone. As in so many other things, however, nature has provided a solution. The firefly or glow-worm produces its familiar glow by means of some obscure chemical reaction without at the same time producing any appreciable amount of heat. Man, however, has not so far been able to reproduce this extremely interesting phenomenon.

The filament lamp was invented in 1879, and after about 20 years had come into fairly general use ; a further 20 years served to bring it to the stage approaching perfection which it now enjoys. The gas discharge lamp has in a few years advanced from the experimental stage to a stage of general use. Will the next few years see a further advance bringing it to a perfection equal to that of the filament lamp? No one can say, but the signs and portents seem to indicate that they will, and that our future homes will be illuminated by artistically designed strips and columns of light instead of by the few isolated points now employed.

HOW INDUSTRY USES ELECTRICAL HEATING

JUST as electricity can be used for heating buildings so also can it be used for heating the various types of furnace used in the different manufacturing processes. For many purposes electric ovens, like that of an ordinary electric cooker but on a larger scale, can be used. The temperature attainable is limited to about 1000° C. as above this the resistance wire would melt. Large ovens of this sort are used by bakers for baking bread, biscuits and confectionery, by the makers of metal products for annealing and similar purposes, for hardening and drying enamelled goods and for many other purposes requiring heat.

Ovens heated by electricity are better in many ways than those heated by coal or gas, because there are no waste gases or fumes to spoil the products and no dirt of any sort ; also the temperature can be very easily controlled, and by setting the electric regulator in a certain position the operator knows that the temperature will always be exactly the same, and a particular process can be repeated at will at any time. The cost of the electricity required for heating is often more than that of the corresponding amount of coal or gas, but the savings due to the greater cleanliness and ease of control frequently outweigh this.

To make special steels such as manganese steel which is very hard, nickel steel which is very ductile, tungsten steel which is used for permanent magnets and various other alloy steels, the right amount of the appropriate metal must be added to molten steel. The temperature required to melt steel is about 1,600° C., so that a furnace giving 2,000 to 3,000° C. is desirable. Several types of furnace have been used for doing this during the last 100 years or more, and since electricity can do so many things and can often do them better and more economically than the older methods, engineers turned their attention to producing steels by electricity.

The resistance type of furnace is obviously unsuitable on account of the low temperature which it attains, and two other types—the induction furnace and the arc furnace—were developed. Although these cannot usually compete with the very big furnaces used for producing steel in large quantities, they are widely used in sizes capable of holding up to about 10 to 15 tons, and for producing high grade and special alloy steels where cleanliness and ease of control are essential features.

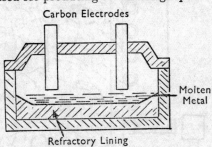

133. The electric arc furnace in section.

It has already been explained that an electric arc produces a very high temperature, and this can also be made use of for steel melting. A diagram of such a furnace is shown in Fig. 133. The arc is struck between two carbon electrodes, which in a large furnace may be 6 inches or a foot in diameter, placed just above the charge to be melted. A very large and fierce arc is maintained carrying possibly several thousand ampères and having a temperature between 3,000 and 4,000° C. The voltage required to produce this arc is only about 50 or 60 volts, so that a special transformer must be used to step the voltage down to this value. Some types of furnace have the arc struck between one electrode and the charge itself, the current then flowing away by a terminal attached to the bottom of the furnace.

THE INGENIOUS FURNACE WHICH MELTS BY INDUCTION

IN the induction furnace, the current is actually passed through the material to be melted. The apparent difficulty with this method is to lead the current into the charge, which

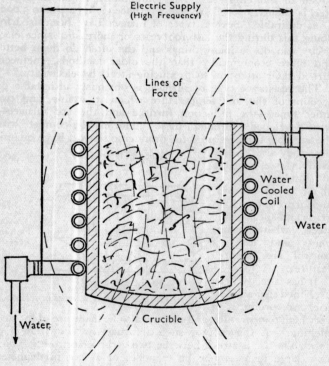

Electric Supply
(High Frequency)

Lines of
Force

Water
Cooled
Coil

Water

Water

Crucible

134. The induction furnace, in which currents set up in the metal itself raise it to melting point.

consists of chunks of iron contained in a crucible of refractory material to withstand the high temperatures ; this difficulty is solved, however, very easily by surrounding the crucible with a coil as shown in Fig. 134, and passing an alternating current through it. The current in the coil sets up an alternating magnetic field with lines of force as shown in the diagram, and as these lines grow up and die down they may be considered to cut through the pieces of iron in the furnace in the same way as lines cut through the secondary winding of a transformer. Currents are therefore generated in the pieces of iron, and as there is no connection to any external circuit these currents simply circulate round and round the iron and heat it up until finally it melts. As the currents are " induced " in the charge in this way by means of the magnetic field, a furnace of this type is called an induction furnace.

In order to get a big inducing effect the frequency of the alternating currents used is generally between 1,000 and 2,000 cycles for large furnaces capable of holding several tons, and up to about 10,000 cycles or even more for very small furnaces as used in laboratories for melting only a few pounds of metal. In large furnaces the outside coil itself gets very hot due to the high frequency currents passing through it and it has to be specially cooled ; this is often done by making the conductor in the form of a copper pipe circulating cold water through it. With furnaces of this sort very pure steel can be made, but as they have to have a special generator to give the high frequency supply they are rather expensive. Not only steel can be melted in such furnaces but also brass and any other metal which is a good conductor of electricity.

JOINING METALS BY ELECTRIC WELDING

UNTIL recently, when it was necessary to join metals, such as for making the large girders for bridge building, the steel plates for the hulls of ships, and many other smaller purposes either bolts or rivets were used. The development of electricity has, however, led to another method, namely electric welding. The two pieces of metal to be joined are placed together in their correct positions and an electric current is then used to melt the metal at the joint, so that they fuse or weld together. Other methods, such as oxyacetylene flame, are available for melting the metals in this way for welding, but the electrical method is the most widely employed. The heat can be produced in two ways. The first is resistance welding, in which the current is actually passed through the joint, as shown on the left in Fig. 135, and so much heat is produced by the current in getting across the joint that the metal on each side is melted and a weld is formed. The other method, arc welding, employs an electric arc between the metal to be welded and an electrode, as shown on the right in Fig. 135.

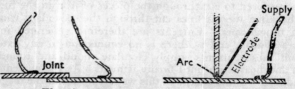

135. Electric welding, in which the heat is produced either (left) by the resistance of the metal itself or (right) by striking an arc at the joint.

With both methods a skilled welder can make a joint between two metals which is just as strong as the metal itself ; in fact if two pieces of metal are joined in this way and then tested it is often found that the metal will break and not the joint. Besides its use for the making of ships, steel frames for buildings, bridges, etc., welding can also be employed for numerous smaller objects. The frames of electric motors and generators are now nearly always made from sheets of steel cut to shape and then welded together ; instead of the castings formerly employed. Many manufacturers have, in fact, closed down a large part of their foundry and replaced it by a welding shop.

COMMUNICATING WITHOUT WIRES : THE MODERN WONDER OF WIRELESS

by A. D'A. HODGSON, Associate Member of the Institute of Electrical Engineers, Associate Member of the Institute of Radio Engineers.

THE possibility of producing waves like light in the ether by electric currents was first predicted mathematically by Clerk Maxwell, and later Hertz obtained experimental proof of Maxwell's mathematical predictions. This was followed by experimental work by Marconi, which led to the development of practical methods of using wave motion in the ether for communication.

Radio waves are areas of electrical energy undulating at high frequencies in a medium conventionally known as the ether. They are of exactly the same nature as light waves and heat waves, but their wave-length (the distance between two crests) is about 100,000,000 times as great. This energy is radiated from a conductor or aerial system which in a simple case consists of a wire elevated above the ground and insulated at the far end, the near end being connected to the source of energy and the ground. The area of energy alternately charges and discharges the aerial.

Now the fact that there is an electric charge along the wire means that the surrounding ether is in a state of strain. When the aerial discharges the strain collapses, and the repeated process of charge and discharge sets the whole ether vibrating, the areas of electric strain move outwards and are radiated in all directions. For reception a similar arrangement is used, but in this case the wire intercepts some of the radiation, and the resulting current flowing in it produces a signal at the receiver.

In practice aerials may take many forms, varying from the simple wire described to complicated structures of vertical and horizontal wires for transmission and reception in one direction only. In the case of the simple transmitting aerial its length determines the length of the waves which can be radiated. As it would be impracticable to have the considerable lengths of wire required for a long wave-length, an aerial may be " loaded," i.e. artificially lengthened by connecting a coil of wire in series with the wire and the source of the energy. Such a coil of wire has an interesting effect on currents ; it opposes any change in their value. By making the aerial current more sluggish the aerial is made to radiate a longer wave. An aerial so adjusted to radiate a definite wave-length is said to be tuned.

For reception a tuned aerial is not necessary, the aerial may be used purely as a conductor of electrical energy, and a circuit tuned to the wave-length required and arranged to pick up some of the energy in the aerial will enable the correct wave-length to be obtained. Under these conditions the aerial is said to be coupled to the receiver aperiodically (that is to say, without any definite " period " of its own electrical vibration).

For reception of radio signals, as a general rule the aerial system required is very simple, consisting usually of a single wire with a vertical and horizontal portion. Special aerials have, however, been designed for short-wave reception, for receiving maximum signals from one direction only, and for " direction-finding " systems.

DESIGNING THE AERIAL WHICH TRANSMITS THE WAVES

For transmission, a number of considerations have to be taken into account. The length, height, and capacity of the aerial are all important. For good radiation and minimum loss of power the aerial must be high, and well insulated to stand voltages very often up to several hundred thousand, and its proportions must be such that the maximum possible power goes to stir up the surrounding ether, the minimum goes to waste, merely heating the aerial wires. The result of this is that the whole aerial system must be carefully designed, and the masts placed in a suitable position and of sufficient strength to carry the strain of the aerial, which may often consist of several thick wires arranged parallel and several feet apart on " spreaders."

For short-wave transmission and reception special aerial systems are often used, particularly at the beam telegraph transmitting and receiving stations. These aerials are arranged to be more sensitive in one direction than another, and consist of an array of wires of definite length depending on the wave-length being used, arranged horizontally or vertically with reflecting aerials behind them. Such aerial assemblies may be seen at numerous places, such as Bodmin in Cornwall, Dorchester, Ongar, Somerton in Somerset, and can be easily recognised by the fact that they resemble a curtain of wires hung between rows of T-shaped lattice steel masts. They are, in fact, often known as " beam curtains " or " beam arrays."

WAVE-LENGTHS AND KILOCYCLES, THE UNITS OF BROADCASTING

We have already stated that radio waves are areas of electrical energy undulating in the ether. The length of these waves is specified as the distance from crest to crest, and is measured in metres. Now wireless waves are of the same nature as light, and travel with the same speed, 300,000,000 metres (or about 186,000 miles) per second.

Picture a section of these waves which has all been radiated in the course of one second. It will be 300,000,000 metres long. If we know the wave-length, we know the number of waves in this section. It is obviously 300,000,000 divided by the wave-length in metres. A 300 metre wave for example would repeat itself 1,000,000 times in the section. But since this number of waves is sent out every second, we can describe the wave by giving its " frequency " in kilocycles (thousands of cycles) per second. Thus our 300 metre wave is also a 1,000 kilocycle wave.

When a radio wave intersects an aerial it sets up currents in the aerial of similar character, that is to say, of similar frequency, and of proportional amplitude or strength, and this current flowing in the aerial is exactly like any alternating current, except that it has a very high frequency.

THE ELECTRICAL BALANCE WHEEL : "TUNING" A CIRCUIT

Two metal plates separated by an insulator will take up a charge of electricity when they are connected one to each terminal of a battery ; but when this charge has been taken up no more current will flow. This is much the same as the flow of gas into a tank from a pump ; when the pressure in the tank becomes equal to the pressure at the pump no more gas flows. The arrangement of plates and insulator is known as a *condenser*.

Now suppose this charged condenser is connected to a coil of wire. Such a coil opposes and delays any change in the current going through it, so the condenser cannot discharge at once : the coil insists that a short time-interval must elapse. But once the discharge current has built itself up fully, the coil opposes any slackening in it. The current is thus forced to continue until the condenser is charged the opposite way. The process is like the action of a balance wheel and spring : the strength of the spring is required to start the balance wheel moving, but once it moves it " overshoots the mark," and winds up the spring the reverse way.

Now if the balance wheel is given a series of taps at just the right moment, it will build up a wide sweep. In just the same way, if the electric circuit is given an impulse at the right moment, it will build up a strong oscillation. Large discharge currents will pass through the coil and a large voltage will build up across the condenser. This voltage may therefore be applied to a receiver, and maximum signals will be obtained on that particular frequency which gives the impulses at the requisite intervals. A frequency slightly

" off tune " will produce a smaller response, one far off tune very little response, and so on.

The parallel circuit just described is one of the foundations of radio transmission and reception, and from it a variety of complicated circuits can be constructed according to the results required.

CONVEYING THE ENERGY THROUGH "COUPLED CIRCUITS"

THE next important circuit to be considered is the " coupled circuit." By this is meant the arrangement of two tuned circuits of the type we have just described, so that the currents flowing in one circuit will induce similar currents in the other.

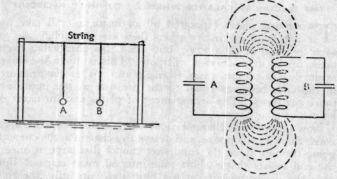

136. How the action in an electrically coupled circuit (right) may be compared to the effect upon one another of two swinging pendulums (left).

Suppose we have a string fixed between two posts as shown on the left in Fig. 136 and from this string we suspend two pendulums A and B of exactly similar length and weight. If pendulum A is set into motion and swings backwards and forwards it will soon be noticed that pendulum B begins to move and will gradually increase its swing until it is swinging at exactly the same frequency as A. This is brought about by the fact that the pendulums are in " time " and are coupled together by the string to which they are fixed, so that the motion of A is transmitted to B and sets it swinging too.

This action is exactly similar to the case of electrically coupled circuits, and on the right of Fig. 136 we have two parallel circuits A and B arranged so that part of the magnetic field of A intersects the coil of B. If B is tuned to the same frequency or wave-length as A it will build up a large circulating current in an exactly similar manner to the movement of the two pendulums, and the value of the current will depend on the closeness of the two circuits, or as it is termed the tightness or degree of coupling.

Although we have described a particular form of coupled circuit there are many ways in which the current flowing in one circuit may be made to produce a similar current in another circuit tuned to the same frequency, and in Fig.

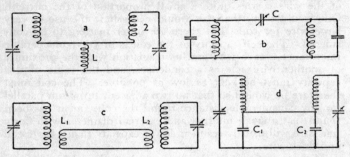

137. Four forms of "coupling" used in wireless circuits

137(a), (b), (c), (d) we show four forms of coupled circuits which are among those more frequently used.

In (a) the coil L is common to both circuits 1 and 2, and so couples the two circuits together by virtue of the fact that the current in both circuits flows through L. In (b) the condenser C serves to connect the two circuits, while in (c) the link circuit $L_1 L_2$ acts as the coupling medium. In (d) the coupling arrangements are similar to those in (c), but condensers C_1 and C_2 are used instead of the coils L_1 and L_2.

Continuations of these circuits are often built up into a series of coupled circuits or filter circuits as they are called, so arranged as to present a high impedance to some frequencies and a low impedance to others.

A COIL FOR EVERY RANGE OF FREQUENCIES

So far we have described a coil as being a more or less haphazard arrangement of wire wound on some form of bobbin. This, however, is not the case, for a great deal depends on the type of wire, that is, upon its size, its insulation, the number of its strands, and on the method of winding, size and shape of the coil and the type of varnish used to finish the windings.

All these details affect the resistance of the coil, and we have seen that the resistance is the only item limiting the current in some circuits. In the case of radio transmitters resistance is even more important, as it may represent quite a large loss of power.

At radio frequencies the current flowing in a wire tends to flow on the outside of the wire ; the core or inner section of the wire carries quite a small proportion of the current. One would think that this would necessitate the use of very large wire for coils, but there are other matters to be considered. The self-capacity of the coil is of very considerable importance : each wire and its insulation with the proximity of another wire acts as a condenser, and the value of this capacity must be kept as low as possible. The coil must therefore be wound so that no two adjacent turns run parallel for any considerable distance round the coil, and it has been found that a small internal and external diameter with fairly fine wire will usually result in lower capacity than a large coil and thick wire.

The use of fine wire does not produce the high resistance that might be expected, for intensive mathematical exploration into the subject of the resistance of coils has led to the discovery that for a particular range of frequencies there is a best shape, size and type of winding of coil, and size of wire and thickness of insulation.

Owing to the peculiarity of the maximum current flow being on the outside or skin of the wire, a special form of wire designed to have a very low resistance has been produced. It is known as Litzendraht, and consists of three fine strands of wire carefully insulated with enamel and then twisted together. The three are then insulated with silk, and three such groups again twisted together, and so on according to the size of wire required, always increasing in groups of three twisted together. By this method each strand of wire comes to the outside of the final cable in turn.

This type of wire is particularly useful for receiver coils between 200 and 1,000 metres, and further research has shown that for different wave-lengths, shape of coil, size, etc., there is a particular type of Litz wire (that is, a particular arrangement of strands and size) which gives the best results.

For long-wave transmitters this wire is very valuable, and is often built up into incredibly large cables ; for example, the aerial coils at the Rugby long-wave transmitting station of the Post Office (which is working on 18,000 metres) are 16 feet in diameter, and are wound with a cable consisting of 6,561 strands of No. 36 gauge copper wire, the aerial current being 750 ampères. The immensity of the task of making this coil will perhaps be appreciated when it is realised that every single strand must be carefully connected up to the rest of the apparatus.

For short waves below 100 metres where the frequencies are becoming very high, solid wire is best, for the value of inductance required is quite small, and a simple coil of bare wire is quite good. If really low resistances are required, a tube of copper having fairly thin walls may be used, and at wave-lengths from 10 metres down this is essential.

THE CONDENSERS : INTEGRAL PART OF THE WIRELESS CIRCUIT

A CONDENSER, we have stated, consists of two metal plates separated by an insulator ; broadly this is correct, but there are many variations to the manner in which the broad statement is put into practice. Condensers may be divided into two main groups—variable condensers in which the capacity may be varied according to some law, and fixed condensers where the capacity is unalterable. Fixed condensers may be divided into three classes, those having mica insulation between plates, those having impregnated paper, and those having a chemical or electrolyte. These condensers serve mainly for connecting various parts of circuits together, and for positions where it is desired to pass an alternating current and not a direct current.

Variable condensers, however, are directly connected with the high frequency parts of the circuits, where they perform the all-important task of tuning. The general construction of variable condensers is to have fixed metal plates of semi-circular shape spaced side by side and rotating between them thin movable semicircular plates, so that there is always an air space between the vanes. The fixed vanes are mounted on an insulating base which carries two bearings for the spindle of the moving vanes. By altering the shape of the vanes the law of the variation of capacity with angular rotation may

be made to suit any particular requirements. At the moment
square law variation is the most useful.

The mechanical rigidity, type of material used for the
base, and spacing of vanes all play an important part in the
value of the condenser, and it is quite as possible to obtain
a high-resistance condenser as a high-resistance coil.   In
circuits where the lowest possible resistance and losses are
required, it is often necessary to make the condenser vanes
of brass, silver-plated, and the insulation between the supports of the fixed and moving vanes, of quartz tube or rod.
Such special condensers usually are found only in measuring
apparatus.

Where several circuits have to be tuned together, and
they employ identical inductances, etc., it is usual to arrange
a number of condensers on one shaft and so adjust them that
their capacity variations are all alike. Such a condenser is
termed a 2, 3 or 4 ganged condenser as the case may be,
and by connecting it to the required number of identical
coils a number of circuits may be tuned to resonance at the
same time.

THE THERMIONIC VALVE : MODERN LAMP OF ALADDIN

by C. E. G. BAILEY, B.A.(Oxon.), A.M.I.E.E., A.M.I.R.E.

WE have seen how the ether waves which carry wireless
signals are inextricably bound up with a kind of very
rapid alternating current. This kind of current (for short
it is called a " radio-frequency " or R.F. current) surges up
and down an aerial system and calls into being a train of
ether waves. Ether waves in turn produce an identical copy,
in miniature, of the original R.F. current in the receiving
aerial.

R.F. currents of the right frequency can be selected, reson-
ated, encouraged to build up comparatively large surges of
R.F. voltage. But so far we have kept a discreet silence as
to the way in which these currents are produced, controlled
and handled. There is one engineering contrivance which,
in various shapes and guises, performs all these functions :
without which the present system of wireless communication,
of broadcasting, or transatlantic telephony would never
exist. This marvel is called the thermionic valve. (We will
refer to these contrivances simply as " valves.")

If a metal is heated to a red or yellow heat, the little electrons or current-carrying particles dance about violently, and would, if allowed, leave the surface of the metal. Two things only could prevent them : one is the repressive influence of particles which make up the air, which, though invisible to us, present a very real obstruction to the tiny electrons. House the heated metal in an evacuated (airless) globe, and the obstruction is gone.

The other thing that repels electrons is a *negatively* charged body. (They are themselves negatively charged, and " like charges repel one another.") So after the first lot of electrons have left the heated metal (called the " cathode ") they hang about in a cloud, a *negatively* charged cloud, and prevent any more electrons from leaving the metal. Therefore to clear away our second obstruction, enclose in the globe a positively charged body (the " anode ") and the electrons will leave the cathode freely, rush across the intervening space, and congregate on the anode. But put a *negative* charge on the anode, and the flow of electrons will straightway be inhibited. The flow is a " one-way " traffic stream.

Here we have obviously a very powerful tool for dealing with R.F. currents. For the tiny light electrons can start, stop, reverse, with enormous speed ; R.F. currents are not too quick for them, and an R.F. voltage, too fast in its alternations to operate any known relay, telephone or inker, can be applied between anode and cathode, and its positive anode impulses passed, its negative impulses stopped by the electron flow till it is converted (" rectified " is the technical term) into a pulsating but definitely one-way stream, which may operate, if it is strong enough, various sorts of telegraphic and telephonic apparatus. A useful tool, but with a little additional complication it can be made much more useful.

HOW THE VALVE CONTROLS THE ELECTRON TRAFFIC

THE little rectifying device just described is called a " diode " (" di " for " two ") since it has two electrodes inside it. The first great advance, made by de Forest (and it cost nearly a million dollars to make the Supreme Courts of the United States sure that it *was* de Forest), was to add a third electrode, called the " grid," and charge this slightly negative. This electrode is placed between cathode and anode, and it consists of a number of fine wires with a fair amount of clearance between them.

Fig. 138 shows a section through a "triode" ("tri" for "three") in which the anode is wrapped round the cathode. It also shows, in the dotted lines, a number of typical electron streams. Many electrons shoot from the cathode, come near one of the grid wires, and are repelled by its negative charge. Others slip between two grid wires, come under the influence of the positive anode charge, and win through to the anode.

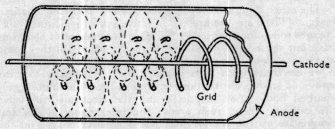

138. One type of three-electrode wireless valve, or triode, showing the path of typical electron streams, some of which (small dotted circles) are repelled by the grid.

Now the more negative the grid, the fewer electrons will slip through, and the less negative it is, the more electrons will reach the anode. In other words, the grid acts as a sort of traffic-policeman ; by putting on a negative charge it can check ultimately the whole flow of electrons past it. And like a traffic-policeman, it does not do the actual *work* of stopping and starting. A tiny amount of energy on the grid will control many times more energy in the circuit of the anode. The energy amplification of a typical modern valve may be 40,000 times. The cathode, which is coated with a special emissive substance, is a tube heated by fine wires inside it, except in the case of battery-operated valves when, to economise heating energy, the cathode itself is a fine wire heated by the current going through it.

CIRCUIT DIAGRAMS: THE PICTURE-LANGUAGE OF WIRELESS

BY this time we have delved deeply enough into wireless theory to invoke the use of a picture-language devised by wireless engineers for themselves. It is the only way of advance—words are too clumsy. Let us try a few. "Between aerial and earth is connected a condenser and coil in a parallel circuit : the junction of aerial, coil and condenser is connected to the grid of a triode : the junction of earth, the other end of the coil, and the other end of the condenser is connected through grid-bias to the cathode of the triode whose anode is joined through a parallel coil-condenser circuit to an anode battery whose negative terminal is again joined to the cathode." There you have it in clumsy words—here is the picture ; and how much more simple ! (Fig. 139.)

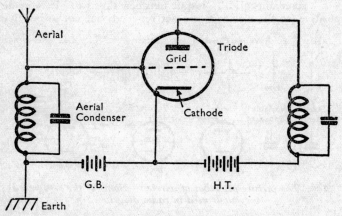

139. A simple circuit diagram (a selective R.F. Amplifier).

The component parts of this are as follows : G.B. is the " grid-bias " battery which gives the grid its small negative charge. H.T. is the anode battery which may be of a hundred volts or more and is called " high-tension " in consequence. If we wish to vary the tuning frequency of the aerial circuit we would do so by making the aerial condenser variable : drawn as in Fig. 140, where the arrow shows that one set of vanes is made to swing.

Now the aerial circuit is " selective " to R.F. currents of a certain frequency ; but like all engineering devices it is not perfect : a certain number of unwanted frequencies very close to the wanted one filter through. So the anode circuit not only receives *amplified* signals, it also *selects* them still further, by introducing, if it is " in tune " with the aerial circuit, some more filtering of its own. Thus the arrangement represents a *selective R.F. Amplifier* applied to an aerial.

The tiny currents from the wave sent by the distant trans-mitter have grown and have been weeded out.

Now a few complications arise. The triode is not so perfect a controller as it looks from this explanation. Unfortunately the anode circuit influences the grid circuit as well as the grid the anode, which is most undesirable. It does so in this way : anode and grid act as the plates of a condenser, and when the anode is charged, the grid follows suit. So a further grid —a " screening grid "—is put between the two. It is made positive (so the electrons are not repelled) but not so positive

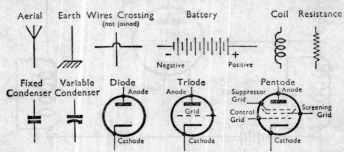

140. The picture-alphabet of wireless. Some of the recognised symbols used in radio diagrams.

as the anode (so electrons rush between the mesh to the anode).

After this screening grid is put in, the valve is still not quite an engineering job : it has an annoying electrical kink, which is smoothed out with one more grid—fine-wired, wire-meshed, connected to cathode, the " suppressor grid." We have now a cathode, control grid, screening grid, sup-pressor grid, anode, five electrical bodies dealing with the electron-stream : the valve is a " pentode." The sign-language is shown in Fig. 140, and we can now weave it into our circuit, which becomes as the first half of Fig. 141.

Now the appearance in black and white of this circuit giving energy-amplification of a few thousand times is in-centive enough to add another valve and amplify and select our R.F. currents still more. The complete Fig. 141 shows the result. The economical engineer resents the piling up of batteries in this circuit. He therefore replaces the coils in the anode circuits by two coupled coils, and by taking each coil to its own battery, he can use the same H.T. and the same G.B. battery, while the R.F. currents simply transfer themselves from one coil to another. He also puts a trans-

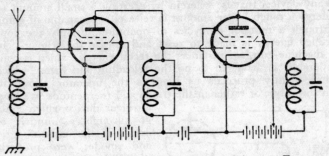

141. Steps in the building of a wireless receiving set. From Fig. 139 the triode has become a pentode, the circuit has been doubled, and variable condensers have been inserted.

former in the aerial circuit ; this makes it tune better. Finally a diode goes at the end of the chain, and we are presented with rectified, amplified, selected signals at the point X in Fig. 142. What devices are connected to the point X (which

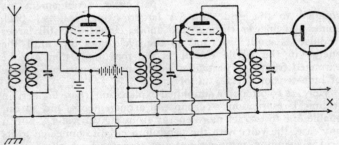

142. A step further, economising in batteries, adding a transformer in the aerial circuit and a diode at the end. In this circuit signals are rectified, amplified and selected during transmission to X.

has a condenser across it to make sure that the R.F. currents can travel round) are still to be described ; they depend on the nature of the transmission one wishes to receive, and we must therefore look into the transmitter circuits next.

THE PENDULUM DRIVES ITSELF: THE VALVE AS OSCILLATOR

IT is an engineering truism that any " trigger " device—any device, that is, wherein by exerting a small amount of energy a much larger amount is released—is capable of going through a number of cycles of operation, if only the controlled energy is made to reset and release the trigger. In a machine-gun, for instance, the recoil energy, which is considerable, is arranged to do the reloading and firing, which consequently proceeds as long as the operator allows it. In the valve, or rather in the triode and the pentode, we have a trigger device which could go through a number of cycles if the circuits, grid and anode, were properly arranged. One such arrangement is shown in Fig. 143.

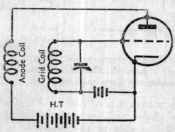

143. The triode arranged to produce oscillations.

Imagine that a little insignificant electrical impulse is given to the circuit in the grid. This releases a larger impulse in the coil in the anode circuit, which in this particular arrangement is coupled to the grid coil. A larger swing results : back comes the answer through the anode circuit. A still larger impulse is built up, and so the cycle goes on, until the energy in the whole circuit is the maximum that can be extracted from that particular valve, and that particular value of high-tension (H.T.) supply.

Here, as so often in a simplified explanation, there are certain technical reservations—certain coil arrangements, and so on, enable one to extract more energy from a given valve ; but in any case, the valve with the pendulum circuit connected to its grid is swinging away without any direction from the outside world. And the frequency of this oscillation is the frequency of the pendulum circuit. We have only to connect an aerial and earth system to the circuit, and wireless waves will be generated. And in order to transmit Morse messages, a key can be inserted in a number of different ways in the circuit. For example, the aerial circuits may be broken, and joined only when the key is pressed, or the valve may be starved of some essential supply. However the keying is done, the result is the same : a train of *continuous waves* is emitted when the key is pressed. This type of transmitter is called " C.W.".

RADIO TELEPHONY : TALKING ROUND THE WORLD

THE next step is to replace the on-off action of the key by a complex modulation to carry speech and music. We have already seen that electrical waves can be shaped by sound ; but the frequency of waves used in wireless transmission is much higher than that of any sound ; consequently a large number of R.F. vibrations can take place within the compass of a single one of the most complex sound vibrations. Therefore the type of wave used to carry radio telephony is a continuous wave, whose peaks, however, take a greater or less height with the varying value of the sound wave which they represent. This effect is easily visualised by looking at curves *a* and *c* of Fig. 144.

Curve *a* represents a typical sound wave in which the pressure runs up first steadily and then sharply to a small peak, then descends steeply to a trough, from which it rises again to normal. Curve *c* shows how the R.F. currents, though themselves swinging with great rapidity from peak

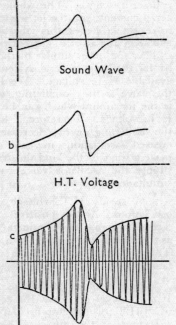

144. Shaping the high-frequency radio waves to carry speech and music.

to trough, trace out *with the general outline of their peaks* the sound wave which they represent. (For convenience in drawing we have represented 15 R.F. waves as taking place within the frequency of one sound wave. Actually the number would be in the thousands.)

We next have to see how these varied or " modulated " R.F. currents are produced. In the early days of the development of radio, when triodes were not invented and " C.W." was generated by a sort of rapidly flickering arc lamp, many ingenious devices were invented, some of which W. Heath Robinson would be proud to own. One consisted of a jet of copper sulphate solution impinging at a very small angle on a metal diaphragm. As the diaphragm vibrated, the jet varied, of course, in length. The whole device was made to carry the aerial current, and the jet wasted a varying amount of current in resistance losses, this vibration following the sound waves, and so giving an R.F. current pattern of the type in Fig. 81(c).

This and other similar methods are now quite obsolete and by far the most general system of modulation is to vary the available H.T. voltage. We have already seen [1] that when the valve is fully oscillating, the energy in its anode circuit is the maximum which can be extracted from that particular H.T. voltage. Therefore if the H.T. voltage be restricted, the oscillating energy decreases ; if the H.T. voltage is increased, oscillations increase also. In order, therefore, to make a wave of the kind illustrated in Fig. 144(c), we have to supply the oscillator valve with two sorts of H.T. supply simultaneously :

1. A steady H.T. voltage, enough to give fairly strong oscillations. Always positive.

2. A variable H.T. voltage whose wave form is the same as that of the sound wave, with swings to positive and negative. This voltage is supplied by a second valve called the " modulator."

Voltage 1 added to voltage 2 gives the result of Fig. 144. It must never go below the zero-line, or the valve, deprived of all H.T., would stop oscillating and hence fail to reproduce a section of the wave. The " control engineers " at the B.B.C. are always engaged in making sure that their " voltage number 2 " is not so large as to do this.

Often the best oscillator valves and circuits are not the best ones for feeding current into the aerial. So the same principle of " R.F. amplification " that we have studied in a receiver is employed. The difference is that the power is large, the amplification obtained smaller (about ten times per stage is fairly common). Then in most transmitters a stage

[1] See p. 474.

of amplification with a " sub-modulator " valve is included
between the microphone and the modulator, to amplify the
weak currents from the former. (There may even be a number
of " sub-sub-modulator " stages.)

Finally the oscillator itself is replaced by one of a chain of
R.F. amplifiers, the first of which has its frequency checked
by a mechanical vibrator, such as a tuning fork giving many
" harmonics," one at the right frequency, or a tiny piece of
quartz which is made to vibrate by electrical means and which
keeps its vibrations to a remarkably close constancy. The

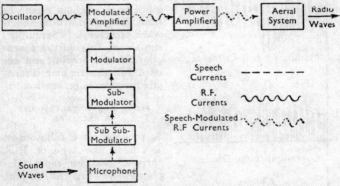

*145. From sound to radio waves—the progress of the
electric currents through a modern broadcast station
described in diagrammatic form.*

whole equipment, which is typical of a modern broadcast
station, is shown in diagrammatic form in Fig. 145, from which
it is possible to follow the whole progress of the currents
between sound waves to the microphone and radio waves from
the aerial.

Commercial telephone stations have to preserve some
secrecy in their transmission : this is done by " scrambling "
the speech currents. Imagine a piano with the strings and
frame taken right out and divided into two pieces, the lower-
and upper-register strings. Now suppose that the *upper*
register section is screwed back so that each of its notes is
operated by a key from the *lower* register and, to mix things
up still further, the *lower* strings are put opposite the *upper*
keys, but back to front, so that the higher the key, the lower

the note it strikes. Rhythm apart, a familiar tune played on this piano would be fairly unrecognisable !

The Post Office engineers have devised circuits which divide up the basic tones of the human voice in just this manner, and turn each tone into another one before applying the result to the final power amplifier. The result is called " scrambled " speech, and a very elaborate "de-scrambler" is necessary to restore sense to these apparently lunatic gibberings (which can be heard any day with a short-wave receiver). Scrambled signals of this sort are sent all over the world, and are used for the regular Trans-atlantic telephone service.

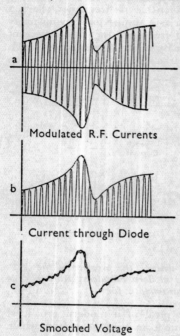

Modulated R.F. Currents

Current through Diode

Smoothed Voltage

146. From radio wave to sound wave. " Smoothing out the bumps " to prepare the currents for the loud-speaker.

HOW RADIO TELEPHONY IS RECEIVED

Now we have followed in detail the type of R.F. current used for radio telephony, we can fill in the remaining part of our receiver. We left off in Fig. 142 with a device X : we could not specify this unknown factor because we did not know what it was required to do. We have seen that our diode rectifier converts the R.F. wave into a pulsating one-way wave. The stronger the R.F. wave, the stronger the pulsa-tions of the D.C. wave. In Fig. 146(*a*) is redrawn the R.F. wave : (*b*) is the corresponding diode current. Now we take two steps simultaneously.

1. Make X an electrical resistance. Then the greater the current through it, the greater the voltage across it.[1]

2. Place a condenser across X. A condenser is the electrical

[1] See *Ohm's Law*, p. 372.

equivalent of a spring : it cuts down fast pulsations as a car spring cuts down the effects of sharp bumps in the road.

The resulting *voltage* across the resistance is shown in Fig. 146(c). This is larger when the R.F. peaks are larger : also the condenser has smoothed out the greater part of the sharp pulsations of (b) while preserving the general outline. (Car-springs " smooth out " bumps but do not " smooth out " hills and valleys.) Now (c), but for a certain tremulousness of outline, is a copy of the original speech-wave. We have very nearly retraced the steps taken in the transmitter circuit. These were : sound-wave—speech-currents—modulated R.F. —ether waves. We have now performed the transformation : ether waves—modulated R.F.—speech currents.

The conversion of speech-currents to sound waves can be made by the telephone receiver. But loud speakers are the more popular device for broadcast reception, and we have a stage or two more to travel. To begin with, for practical purposes, the diode currents are too weak to operate a loud-speaker. A job of amplification remains to be done which calls for a pentode of special type to deal with a lot of power. This time we want no tuning operations—these are over and done with. The pentode may operate directly into the loud-speaker, or a stage of amplification may be included with some device which does not distort the shape of the speech-current wave (a pentode or a triode, with a suitable electrical resistance to hand on grid *voltage* to the next amplifier proportional to its own anode current). The present tendency is to omit this latter stage of amplification, and put one " power pentode " between the diode and the loud-speaker.

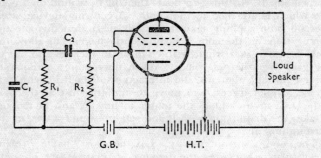

147. The receiving circuit completed. A new section from " X " of Fig. 142 onwards.

Here, then, in Fig. 147, is our receiver circuit from X onwards. R_1 is the resistance in the diode circuit. C_1 is the smoothing condenser. It seems a pity that R_2 and C_2 have crept in to complicate the issue, but here is the reason : the diode has the property of producing a negative voltage when it is rectifying, which is not in the least wanted on the pentode grid : it has the wrong value, and is apt to vary, so this steady negative voltage is stopped by C_2 (which has, you will remember, an insulator between its plates) and the speech-current fluctuations are passed on as charges and discharges. Then R_2 leads the right grid-bias from the G.B. battery to the grid.

THE LOUD-SPEAKER : A VERSATILE MIMIC

WE are left with the last link in the chain between ether and air—the loud-speaker. Although this is not essentially different in principle from the telephone—in both devices a diaphragm is driven by magnetic forces—yet modern forms of loud-speakers have such a unique mechanical construction that they need special description.

The moving-coil type of speaker, now by far the most popular, is shown in part-sections in Fig. 148. A moulded paper diaphragm (the cone shape is chosen so that the paper does not crinkle) has at its periphery a few corrugations A, to give flexibility : the part outside the corrugations is bolted to a steel frame with legs fixing it to a mild-steel plate. A magnet which may be permanent or electromagnetic, with a central rod for a pole-piece, causes a strong magnetic field in a ring-shaped gap B. In this gap floats the coil C, wound on a bobbin which is attached to the cone. A centring device stops the coil from rubbing against the pole-piece, but this and the corrugations in the cone are sufficiently flexible to allow the cone to move as a whole a fraction of an inch in and out of the gap, over the pole-piece. When fluctuating currents are passed through the coil, the interaction of its field with that of the magnet forces it to move to and fro (just as the field on a D.C. motor causes the motor to turn [1]), and in moving it takes the diaphragm with it and sets up sound waves in the surrounding air.

The cone is surrounded by a box, horn or " baffle " (plane sheet) which separates the regions of air-pressure on both

[1] See p. 398.

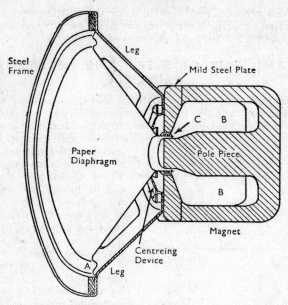

Steel Frame

Leg

Mild Steel Plate

C B

Paper Diaphragm

Pole Piece

B

Magnet

Centreing Device

A

Leg

148. A moving-coil loud-speaker in section.

sides of the cone, and prevents the air rushing in from a region, say, of pressure on one side, to one of suction on the other, thereby wasting its energy in useless eddying. The coil usually operates with comparatively small voltages and large currents, and a transformer is fitted to it to reduce these voltages from the comparatively large values produced by the radio-receiver.

Other forms of loud-speaker are being developed, one of which uses the force of attraction between the plates of a condenser to drive one of them which acts as a diaphragm. Another uses a queer twisting force developed by certain crystals when electrified, magnifies this movement with a lever system, and drives a cone diaphragm from the result. These types have their special fields of application, but the moving-coil speaker is probably the most versatile. A well-designed moving-coil speaker can follow fairly accurately vibrations between 40 and 10,000 cycles per second. It can give a very fair imitation of the human voice in all its inflections,

E.

16

and can reproduce with realism all the instruments of the orchestra. Surely no mean achievements for a contrivance of paper and a few turns of copper wire !

IN AND OUT OF STEP : THE HETERODYNE PRINCIPLE

IF instead of speech-modulations, the start-and-stop wave-pattern of a C.W. morse transmission was received on telephone or loud-speaker, they would be heard as a series of clicks and thumps, without musical character, and not very easy to interpret. These clicks and thumps can be turned into musical notes, however, by means of an oscillator valve in the receiving apparatus, operating on what is called the heterodyne principle.

Suppose two columns of troops to be marching side by side, one taking 50 left-and-right paces in every minute, the other 52. How often will they be in step ? The answer is twice in a minute, as a little thought will show : the difference between 50 and 52. Now two R.F. currents may be alternately in and out of step, if their frequencies are different. Fig. 149(*a*) and (*b*) shows a pair of R.F. current-waves, of slightly different frequency, *a* and *b*. They start in step at the point A. After a little time they are out of step again at B, and in step at C. The wave which results when they both traverse the same circuit is curve *c*. The peaks of this curve are very strong at A and C, where the waves supplement each other, and very

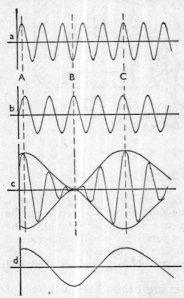

149. The heterodyne principle. How two trains of R.F. waves passing " in and out of step " result in a wave vibrating at sound frequency.

small in the neighbourhood of B where the waves tend to cancel one another out. And, just as in the problem of the columns of troops, the waves of "In-and-out-of-step-ness" have a frequency which is *the difference between that of waves a and b.*

Now wave *c* is of a familiar type—it is just like a modulated wave which corresponds to a sound-wave of the form Fig. 144(*a*). And this is exactly how our diode, amplifier, and loud-speaker will interpret it : they will conjure up a sound-wave of this form (it corresponds to a pure flute-like tone) and will emit this wave when the dots and dashes of Morse C.W. arrive. The principle of "in-and-out-of-step-ness" is called, in less ugly fashion, the heterodyne principle.

To fix this principle in our minds, let us take a specific set of figures. Suppose an R.F. current to be circulating in the receiver with a frequency of 1,000,000 cycles, or 1,000 kilocycles. Let our local oscillator induce in the receiver a frequency of 1,001 kilocycles. No loud-speaker could re-produce either of these frequencies, nor could the ear hear them. But the difference between the two is 1 kilocycle, and this is the frequency of the "heterodyne" note emitted by the speaker. (It is close to the C above the treble clef.) Note that the same result would be obtained if the local oscil-lator's frequency were 999 kilocycles.

THE GAMUT OF THE ETHER

IT is fortunate that methods, and accurate methods too, exist for "tuning in" definite frequencies : for all the present-day development of selective devices, much con-gestion exists among the various transmitting stations using the ether, as can be verified by tuning round the broadcast waves at night on a sensitive receiver, when a number of whistles and throbbing noises reveal the presence of a number of broadcasting transmitters with their frequencies insuffi-ciently removed. Let us examine the whole gamut of the ether, and see what frequencies are available for radio com-munication purposes. From Fig. 150 we see that the radio waves fill the spectrum from 10 kc. to rather less than 10^6 kc. The small "indices" at the side of the figures 10 indicate the number of o's following the 1. Thus 10^5 is 100,000.

The frequencies below 10 kc. are useless : they could only be used for very slow Morse and enormous aerials are needed to radiate waves at this frequency. And nothing startling is to be expected from the unexplored rays between 10^6 and 10^9 kc., which at present are difficult to produce. The frequencies

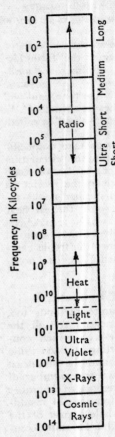

between 10 kc. and 10^6 kc. have been filled up and overfilled and partitioned and repartitioned between nations, services, and stations. The longer of these waves travel farther by day and are generally more reliable, while the shorter waves, although they have great carrying power, get to their destination by a series of reflections from a number of atmospheric layers. These reflect radio as the surface of a pond reflects light—images are continually broken up and reformed by surface disturbances—and so messages sent round the world by these reflected waves fade and reappear in a very arbitrary manner.

The ultra-short waves are only beginning to be exploited—there are all sorts of technical difficulties, slowly being surmounted—and their properties are very interesting. They can be directed like a searchlight beam, and their reliable range is " as far as the eye can see," that is, from any point to any other so long as the rim of the horizon is not in the way. Waves of nearly 10^6 kc., that is, ten million kilocycles, frequency are in use for regular telephone communication across the Irish Channel.

A reason why the higher frequencies hold the greatest future is the enormous number of transmitting frequencies which can be allotted among them without overlapping. Now although the telephony transmission may be said to be on a certain frequency, it really disports itself in a little band

150. From radio to cosmic rays : the whole spectrum of ether waves.

of frequencies. The physical effect of " modulating " a wave with speech or music is to cause it to emit a fringe of frequencies ; and these extend on either side of the original frequency for a width depending on the highest *sound*-frequency being transmitted. For example, tolerable commercial telephony can be carried out with sound-frequencies up to one and a half kilocycles. So the fringes (they are called " sidebands ") extend $1\frac{1}{2}$ kc. each way and the transmission takes up 3 kc. of the ether-gamut. Really high-quality musical transmissions need sound-frequencies up to 10 kc. and so take up 20 precious kilocycles on the ether.

The situation is not quite as bad as this : ways are known of cutting off one set of side-bands in commercial telephony (and cramming, therefore, twice as many stations in). Also quite a lot of overlapping is tolerable before stations begin to interfere badly. However, we can see the usefulness of the shorter waves at once. Between 300 and 303 metres there is 10 kc. difference,[1] which is room enough for a broadcast transmitter of fair quality (the 1934 Lucerne Convention allotted 9 kc.). But between 30·0 and 30·3 metres is 100 kc., room for 10 stations. And between 3·00 and 3·03 metres, 100 stations can be crammed.

SEPARATING THE HIGHER FREQUENCIES : THE SUPERHETERODYNE

ONE particular difficulty arises, out of several, as one works with higher frequencies. The discrimination shown by a tuned circuit, or a series of tuned circuits, is not absolute : there is no question of accepting one frequency and turning all the others down. No, the sharpness of this selective discrimination is a relative affair : it is easier to separate two stations at 100 and 110 kc. than at 1,000 and 1,010 kc. In one case, the separation is 10%, in the other only 1%. But an ingenious adaptation of the heterodyne principle provides an escape from this difficulty.

We have seen that a diode detector can generate from two R.F. currents a third current whose frequency is the difference between those of the first two. Now there is no reason why this difference-current should not be made a much higher frequency than any sound-frequency, that is, be made " supersonic," and then be selectively amplified as much as is required. This process is carried out in " superhet " receivers (slang for super*sonic*-het*erodyne*). Let us tackle the problem of our 1% separation by this method :

[1] See p. 462.

	Wanted	*Unwanted*
Incoming frequencies	1,000 kc.	1,010 kc.
Local oscillator frequency	1,100 kc.
Difference frequencies	100 kc.	90 kc.

Thus the problem has become one of 10% separation, which is much easier.

In practical superhet receivers the diode is made into a pentode, to do some amplifying as well as rectifying. The local oscillator, which is a triode, is often combined with it in the same bulb, sometimes as a triode-pentode, with both electrode assemblies side by side, or as an " octode." An octode has eight electrodes : cathode, grid of oscillator, anode of local oscillator, screen round oscillator section, pentode grid, pentode screening grid, pentode suppressor grid, and pentode anode, which altogether make up quite a complicated piece of valve engineering.

SEEING ACROSS SPACE : THE CHILDHOOD OF TELEVISION

TELEVISION is at once one of the most fascinating and one of the most discouraging problems presented to the electrical engineer. The desiderata are clear and obvious : a picture of a fairly high standard of definition must be re-produced with good illumination on a screen about two to four feet wide, in an attractive light, without flicker—and yet the finest brains of dozens of engineering concerns have spent years in realising even an approximation to this standard.

One of the prime difficulties is the extraordinary complexity of the " description " of the image which has to be sent over wires or ether from place to place. In a high-definition picture about 30,000 different little points of the picture must be kept track of, and any of these points may change its light-value in a twentieth of a second. That means that 600,000 individual pieces of intelligence must be sent across the ether in one second. Let us examine the way in which the problem has been tackled.

To begin with, the scene to be televised is " scanned," that is to say, every section of it is successively illuminated by a tiny spot of light, and the particular amount of light or darkness is noted in that section. For convenience the picture is scanned in a series of vertical strips, 180 in number. A flying spot of brilliant light is swept by an arrangement of mirrors and lenses from top to bottom of the scene. The instant the spot arrives at the bottom, another one starting slightly to the right of the first sweeps down, then another, till 180 spots of light have chased one another over the whole scene, and the first spot begins again. (An example of this scanning process covering a small dark circle, is given in Fig. 151.) This process is repeated twenty times a second, and to the human eye the whole scene seems to be bathed in a just slightly flickering light. A number of " photo-cells " hung

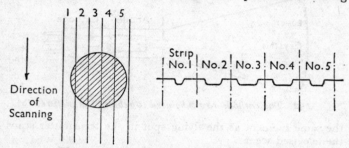

151. How a picture is translated into a photo-cell current. Left : the picture is scanned by a spot of light. Right : the variations produced in the resulting photo-cell current.

round the scene have picked up the light reflected from it. These photo-cells are large globes with a metal surface, the inside of which begins to emit electrons when light strikes it, and emits them in proportion to the intensity of the light. These electrons carry a current round an external circuit, and translate the light-values faithfully into electric currents.

These currents next have to be amplified by an amplifier which will faithfully repeat slow variations of 20 per second and fast variations of 600,000 per second. The amplified currents then modulate R.F. currents in a transmitter. Note that the side-bands are now 600 kilocycles wide each, so that the transmission occupies 1,200 kilocycles. Obviously there is only room for this in the short-wave band.

Reception is performed in a generally normal manner although tremendous care has to be taken in the receiver to amplify without distortion the complex wave-shape received. The currents are then turned back into light by a " cathode-ray tube." Cathode rays are nothing else than a stream of electrons emitted, just as in a valve, from a heated cathode (Fig. 152), and attracted towards an anode. The electrons fly through a hole in the anode, and hit a target in the shape of a fine layer of crystals on the far end of the bulb. These crystals are of a composition which emits a glow under this battering process. Two pairs of plates of which one pair is shown, are arranged to attract or repel the electron stream in order to make it " scan " the screen formed by the crystal layer in a series of vertical lines just in the same way and at

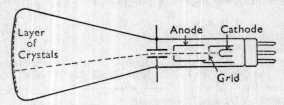

152. The cathode-ray tube used to rebuild the picture.

the same moment as the flying spot in the transmitter scans the televised scene.

This control of the electron stream is managed by special valve circuits connected to the plates and synchronised with the transmitter. The charge on a grid near the cathode controls the number of electrons emitted and hence the brilliance of the spot ; and in this way the picture is built up on the screen. Whenever the scanning spot touches a bright area in the televised scene, the photo-cells pass current, the transmitter sends out a burst of radio waves, the receiver picks these up, and the grid in the cathode-ray tube releases a stream of electrons. And since the position of the spot on the screen corresponds to the position of the scanning spot, the picture is a faithful copy of the original.

SEEKING A CAREER IN ENGINEERING

by E. W. ASHCROFT, B.A., formerly Editor of
" World Power "

IN one sense, engineering may be considered as one of the oldest activities of the human race, but it is only very recently in the history of the world that, owing to the greater complexity and delicacy of processes and machines, there has arisen a need for men with advanced scientific and technical training to direct engineering work. In other words, it is only recently that engineering has become a profession.

Broadly speaking, the jobs which are offered by engineering as a career can be divided into three categories : the first, those of a strictly professional kind which primarily require mental ability ; the second, those which require mental training and knowledge but also manual skill (for example the garage proprietor works with his own hands and yet must possess a knowledge of theory as does the operator of a wireless station) ; the third, those which require manual skill and works experience only. To-day the most usual acceptance of the word engineer implies someone who belongs to the first category.

For everyone who enters the engineering profession by the royal road of a university degree or technical college diploma followed by a student apprenticeship course, there are hundreds who enter as trade apprentices in the works at the age of fourteen or fifteen. Now mechanical and electrical engineering, compared with the Law or with Medicine, is a democratic profession, and facilities are offered for every boy who enters a workshop and has to earn his living from the start, to rise to the status of a professional engineer and to the highest posts in the profession, apart from the highly paid skilled jobs which are open to a trained mechanic or electrician who has given some of his time to theoretical study. We will follow briefly through the career of a boy who leaves his primary school at the age of fourteen with his way to make and who chooses mechanical engineering as his career.

THE WORKS APPRENTICE

BETWEEN leaving school and entering the works, the boy who has attended a junior technical school, if only for a year, has an advantage over one who enters the works at once. In any case, the most important consideration is the degree of educational facilities offered at the works, for let us state again, the goal which the apprentice must set before himself is the acquirement of theoretical knowledge. Practical experience he will obtain in his daily life.

To-day many engineering companies have schools at the works where the trade apprentice acquires valuable knowledge. Many companies also allow their promising apprentices to spend one day per week at an engineering college or institution. At the age of sixteen, the works apprentice will have started his evening classes. A typical course of evening classes lasts at least five years with two and a half evenings per week.

If the greater degree of scientific knowledge necessary to the engineer of to-day is a handicap to the apprentice who wishes to rise from the ranks, the application of this scientific knowledge to the engineering workshop is not without its advantages to him. Twenty years ago, when a mechanic had not only to use a much larger number of handtools but also, in many cases, to make them himself, it took a very long time to become a skilled mechanic. To-day the machine tool is the real craftsman.

The real asset in the majority of skilled engineering trades to-day is ability to aquire knowledge, and the experience of many jobs, with their varied difficulties. Thus our apprentice at the works will try and pass through as many different departments as he possibly can. These will include the turning, the fitting, the moulding, the pattern-making shops. He will try and get work in the outside erection department for the practical experience he will gain here will be of particular value if he is one day to be in charge of this machinery. Similarly, work on the breakdown gang is particularly important for the time to get a real insight into a machine is when it has broken down.

HOW THE TECHNICAL SCHOOL CAN HELP

THE last twenty years have witnessed a rapid growth in the number of technical institutions and colleges which enable our engineering apprentice to get his theoretical education at low cost. Every engineering centre has its institutions ; one of the most important, and one of the pioneer institutions, is the Manchester College of Technology. To give an idea of the number of institutions available, let us take the case of London. There are to-day under the direction of the London County Council eight whole-time junior technical day schools, three whole-time senior days schools, twelve centres for elder and thirty-seven for junior evening students devoted entirely or mainly to the training of engineers. This number does not include special industrial schools such as the six London centres where training for gas technicians is given.

A word should be said, in passing, with regard to these special industrial schools, the best known of which are the textile colleges in Lancashire. They exist for the specialised training of industrial hands to occupy executive positions in the particular industry—not for general engineering training. Their importance has grown in recent years with the increasing degree of scientific application in industry.

A survey of the syllabus of one of the best-known technical colleges in London shows the number of courses open to the engineering apprentice willing to study in the evening. First of all there are the National and Higher National Certificate courses which exempt the student who has taken them from parts of the examinations required for entrance to the professional institutions. These certificates are issued also for automobile engineering and practical mechanical engineering. There is then a course of evening study for a university degree in engineering. Other courses planned for entrance to the professional rank of various branches of engineering are in aeronautical engineering, radio engineering, illumination engineering, and automobile engineering. A course is also given for students preparing for the qualifying examinations of the Institution of Municipal and County Engineers.

For the apprentice who aims at obtaining a skilled position in a trade the following courses are open : motor vehicle mechanics, motor vehicle electrician, automobile construction, machinist, turners' and fitters' work, brass finishing, die-sinking and press-tool making, pattern making, foundry practice, smithing, welding, electrical installations, electrical machine manufacture course, and instrument making.

THE WAY THROUGH THE UNIVERSITY

LET us now follow through the education of an electrical engineer who is able to start his career with a university training, and who does not need to earn money, other than the nominal wages paid to students in some engineering workshops, until his training is completed. It is important to notice that there is no very marked difference in the theoretical training of a mechanical and electrical student until the third year. The general education of the prospective electrical engineer will not differ from that of any other boy at a public or secondary school up to the age of 16 or 17, the time when matriculation or the school leaving certificate is taken. Whilst neglect of humanistic studies is often regretted in after life, and whilst undue specialisation during the pre-matriculation period is to be regretted, the prospective engineer will obviously get as good a grounding in mathematics and science as possible.

The first year's work at the university or at one of the recognised technical colleges such, for instance, as Faraday House, will consist in essence of a continuation of that part of the secondary school curriculum which is obviously required for engineers—mathematics, physics, chemistry and modern languages. During the second year the education in technical theory begins, although modern languages are not left out. Thus both electrical engineering students and mechanical engineering students will study the theory of heat engines, electrical measurement, alternating and direct current theory and such subjects. A study of wireless theory is often recommended both because the experiments are of wide general importance, and because such knowledge may be of practical use later on. The student would be well advised to study costing and works administration, and a broad knowledge of elementary economic theory is also useful.

During the third year's work on the degree in electrical engineering, the student will continue to study physics and mathematics and will begin more advanced technical studies. It is during this year, perhaps, that a student of exceptional brilliance, may find that his interests lie very much more in the physical and mathematical aspects of his course and may decide that he will go in for physical research rather than engineering. The student will tackle aspects of electrical engineering such as the theory of dielectrics, single-phase and poly-phase currents, and the design of electrical machinery in general : he will however continue mechanical engineering subjects such as internal-combustion engines, boilers and turbines.

At the end of the third year, the examinations are usually taken. Many universities have also an honours course for engineering students. Here, the first year's work is omitted, the student having obtained a Higher Certificate when at school. By the end of the third year the honours student will have covered the ground previously described, and will also have specialised in some single branch of his subject.

HOW THE GRADUATE GETS HIS PRACTICAL TRAINING

THE practical training follows, as a rule, the theoretical training and consists of an apprenticeship with a firm of manufacturers. Before the war, it was customary for the manufacturer to charge a premium to a college apprentice. To-day that is no longer the rule, and a small weekly wage may be paid. Like the trade apprentice, the student will have experience in all sections of the works, and work in the erection department is particularly valuable. In the case of electrical engineering, experience in the testing room is also of particular importance. In the contract department, experience of commercial work will be of particular value to a man who intends to go in for the sales side of manufacturing, which is the highest paid branch of engineering activity.

To-day what is known as the " sandwich course " is widely adopted, and results in a shortening of the total time spent on education. Under this system, the student spends half his time at college and half at a manufacturing works, thus completing his practical training while at the university. The great disadvantage of this system is that the student is likely to receive a less thorough practical training and does not stand so good a chance of being taken on at the manufacturing works as a man who has completed a full-time course. This is not due in any way to prejudice against the system; but a manufacturer naturally cannot so easily appreciate the value of a man who is with him at intermittent periods as of one who is in his works for two full years.

COLLEGE OR WORKS TRAINING FIRST?

ON this subject and on that of whether it is better to have a college training or a works training first, there exists much difference of opinion. We cannot do better perhaps than quote Professor Miles Walker, Professor of Electrical Engineering at the College of Technology, Manchester, who considers that in the case of mechanical engineering there is much to be said both for a works education first and for the sandwich system. In the case of electrical engineering, he considers that the balance of advantage is strongly in favour of a college education first.

Picture the position of two apprentices working in an electrical factory. One has had a college training and understands the theory of the apparatus with which he comes in contact. In the case of the other apprentice, much time is wasted on half-understood mechanical operations. Nor has the student who has been through a works a corresponding advantage over the student who has begun with theory, because a properly designed college course will be sufficiently practical to keep the theoretical student in touch with reality. " Another advantage " states Professor Miles Walker, " of the college first course is that it enables a bright student to distinguish himself during his apprenticeship and thus gain promotion on a certain line of work, whereas the same student, even if he could impress his employers without having had a theoretical training, will have his time of work interrupted when he goes to college and the thread being broken may never be taken up again."

TRAINING FOR THE CIVIL ENGINEER

A word should be said on the training of the civil engineer. No marked differentiation between a civil or mechanical or electrical degree course is made until the third year, although during the second year, the civil engineering student will probably have spent a part of his summer vacation in surveying work, whereas the mechanical engineer may have put in a little time at a works. In the third year, the civil engineering student will study the theory of structures and structural design, hydraulics, and the elements of civil engineering design such as road-making, sewage disposal, railway work, instead of the theory of heat engines or of electrical transmission.

The practical training system of a civil engineer is less standardised than that of mechanical or electrical engineer, and depends upon the branch of civil engineering the student is likely to take up. In seeking an opening for a practical training it is necessary to choose one of the main sub-divisions of civil engineering such as municipal work, consulting, or contracting. In the case of the latter, the permanent-way departments of railways usually absorb a number of students.

In the formal sense, chemical engineering is a very young profession. No special course of training was laid down until the Institution of Chemical Engineers was established in 1925. The School of Chemical Engineering founded by the late Professor Gibbs definitely initiated a course of instruction in chemical engineering, but the training is still generally regarded as a post-graduate study. A student may first take a degree or diploma in chemistry at a university or technical school and then proceed to a course in chemical engineering. At present the executive posts in the large industrial firms are in the main recruited from the universities, but there is a tendency, followed for some years on the Continent and in the United States, to make chemical engineering a complete study in itself.

APPOINTMENTS FOR THE TRAINED ENGINEER

JUST as we have seen that a considerable difference exists in the training of a civil engineer on the one hand and of a mechanical or electrical engineer on the other, so the majority of the appointments which are open to the fully-trained civil engineer are of a different nature to those open to the mechanical or electrical engineer. The greatest field of appointments for the latter two categories lies in industry ; the civil engineer has his largest number of opportunities in either contracting work, such as that offered by the railway companies in this country and abroad, in Government or municipal service.

Whilst there is much civil-engineering consulting work to be done, the young engineer cannot usually purchase a partnership in a well-known firm, nor wait for the five or six years necessary before he can be established and earn money as a consulting engineer. Further, the successful consulting engineer ought to have a wide experience not only of engineering work but also of business, and this the young engineer lacks.

The career of many civil engineers might be the following : work on the staff of engineers employed by a railway company abroad where he would gain practical experience in bridge building and railway track maintenance. After similar work of this kind either at home or abroad, the next step might be the appointment to take charge of the execution of a large civil engineering project, such as the construction of a dam or the building of a road, for a firm of contracting engineers. He would probably owe this appointment to the goodwill of his first employers. Only after responsible work of this kind would a civil engineer become a consulting engineer.

It is a great advantage to the civil engineer intending to enter municipal engineering to have taken his apprenticeship training under a municipal engineer. Municipal engineering offers a definite security of tenure to the non-ambitious but competent, and a large number of openings, with certainty of employment, to the ambitious. In addition to the municipal engineer's work on the tramways, roads and bridges of his borough, there exists work to be done in sanitary engineering, refuse disposal, and sewage. In large cities special posts are sometimes allotted for this work but, in general, it is advisable for the civil engineer in municipal service to get some knowledge of chemistry and bacteriology.

WATER, GAS AND ELECTRICITY

WATER supply, gas engineering, and electricity supply are sometimes allied with and sometimes distinct from municipal engineering. The engineer in charge of a gas undertaking has usually a civil engineering training with specialised knowledge of the chemistry applying to fuels. A special training is given for this branch of engineering at most technical colleges. Electricity supply, either municipal or private company, offers one of the largest fields for the employment of electrical engineers. If the grid scheme lessens the total number of power stations, the number of electricity supply engineers engaged in the distribution and sale of electrical current is greatly increased.

Special knowledge is often useful to the modern electricity supply engineer—thus anyone to-day with a proper engineering training who has experience in agriculture is a valuable man for a municipality or company selling current in rural areas. A knowledge of business methods and of salesmanship is useful both to the gas and electricity supply engineers. Gas and electricity supply engineering both hold out numbers of good appointments to men who are not engineers but who have a good technical training ; these include responsible positions in the gas works or power station, in electricity sub-stations in the metering and service departments of gas or electrical undertakings.

THE ENGINEER IN INDUSTRY

A LARGE number of mechanical and electrical engineers obtain their first employment from the engineering company by which they were trained. To-day every production industry depends primarily upon engineering, and consequently industry in general offers the widest field of employment to every type of engineer. For instance, the textile industry, requires mechanical, electrical and chemical engineers. With the adaptation of new scientific processes to industrial work, the standard of technical knowledge required rises every year. Thus twenty years ago, the shipbuilding industry, apart from its designers, required mechanical engineers mainly. To-day the engineer in shipbuilding must have a good knowledge of processes such as those of the photo-cells, X-ray work, and welding.

The mining industry is of particular importance to this country. This industry employs a large number of mining engineers trained as surveyors, geologists and metallurgists as well as mechanical engineers, and, with the introduction of electricity for winding, coal cutting, pumping and lighting, an ever-increasing number of electrical engineers. In the case of mining and many other large power using industries, the mechanical and electrical engineers are often supplied by the company which installs the machinery.

Marine engineering is another important avenue of employment for young engineers of all types of training but with the physical characteristic of " toughness." Again, a useful opening lies in the service of engineering insurance companies where the technical and commercial experience to be gained is often very valuable.

The branch of activity which has perhaps most radically changed the world is communication engineering—the services of the telephone, the telegraph and the wireless. The largest number of jobs offered in this domain to the engineer are in the hands of the Post Office for entry into which, like other Government appointments, a special examination is necessary. A large number of engineers with an electrical training are employed by the telegraph and overseas cable companies ; as a rule these companies enrol junior engineers, train them during a probationary period and take them on their staffs for a definite number of years.

THE ENGINEER AS TEACHER

AT the beginning of their careers, many promising young engineers have a chance of obtaining a post as lecturer or teacher in universities or technical colleges. For the civil engineer these posts are few in number and have the disadvantage of not being good jumping-off points for other engineering appointments. To obtain a good post as lecturer in civil engineering requires a wide experience of practical work. Hence, like consulting engineering, it is a job for the older man.

In mechanical and electrical engineering, however, there are many more posts, fairly good salaries are paid and a secure career can be made in this branch. A great disadvantage however is the difficulty of returning to ordinary engineering work, after some years of teaching.

HOW APPOINTMENTS ARE MADE

FOR the mechanical and electrical engineer, the manufacturer at whose works the training period was spent offers the most ready source of employment, either at the works itself or with customers to whom machinery is supplied. Universities and technical colleges all have appointments boards and a real effort is made to find jobs for young engineers. For the last two years there has been a considerable amount of unemployment among young trained engineers ; but it is already diminishing, in part due to the resumption of engineering activities in the Dominions.

In certain branches of engineering such as marine engineering the outlook is definitely bad, the supply of skilled engineers far exceeding the demand. Whilst openings for British engineers in South America and in Europe are fewer than in pre-War years, any policy of Empire development and in particular of planned emigration will quite easily tend to make the demand overstep the supply. India has always offered a rich field of employment to the civil engineer, South Africa to the mining electrical engineer. By work in the Dominions is meant employment by Government or private undertakings in the Dominions rather than engineering work carried out by British companies in the Dominions.

The professional institutions to-day assist their members or associate members in the search for employment, and the engineering press is a useful medium both for employees and employers.

ENGINEERING AS A CAREER FOR WOMEN

WHILST engineering will not, for some time at least, provide a professional career for women to the same extent as does medicine, there are a number of professional women engineers in the mechanical and electrical sections of the industry. The chances of an engineering career for women are limited not so much by the academic training required as by the practical training. Many manufacturers, for instance, would not consider taking women apprentices. This is no doubt a prejudice which the course of time will remove, and there is no reason why, in the future, when many branches of engineering work will be much more closely similar to laboratory work, a large number of women should not find a place as industrial engineers.

The Women's Engineering Society was founded shortly after the War, and its membership has grown consistently. The electrical industry has a number of good posts for women which, whilst not professional posts, are recognised by the industry as a whole as definitely responsible and suitably filled by women alone. These posts are mostly in connection with demonstrating electrical appliances and teaching house-craft to the customers of the supply undertakings. The Electrical Association for Women, an entirely non-commercial association existing for the benefit both of women as con-sumers of electricity and women wishing to make a career in the electrical industry, trains women for these posts and awards certificates recognised by the industry as a whole.

SCIENTIFIC MANAGEMENT AND SALESMANSHIP

DURING works experience some engineers will have gradually found that their interests lie less with machinery and rather more with the business connected with engineering —with works administration and or with the many interesting facets of economic production. Now a trained engineer who has a real practical knowledge of engineering economics is a valuable man first of all to engineering companies, and secondly to society as a whole. In the United States and in Germany whole volumes have been written on scientific management, and if in this country we have written less we have none the less gradually realised that the engineer who has created many of the modern problems of ineffective distribution of goods and unemployment is the man who must have a bigger say in solving them.

The engineer of the future who will have a general grasp of economic problems and a particular knowledge of engineering economics—elimination of waste of material and time, special-ised knowledge of industrial power requirements, of power tariffs and such matters—will undoubtedly prove a key-man in the more highly organised state.

Yet another category of students will show special capacity for " getting business." Salesmanship is the most highly paid branch of engineering, and to-day it *is* a branch of engineering. Only an engineer can sell an oil engine or a turbo-alternator to another engineer. The man who realises that he is cut out for a salesman early in his career will of course spend much of his time in the contracts department of the works. Naturally, certain special gifts of personality are necessary to the engineering salesman.

A well-known electrical engineer told the author that, some thirty years ago when he was beginning his life-work, the possession of a degree in electrical engineering was an asset which it was often advisable to conceal from prospective employers, so strong was the prejudice against theoretical knowledge as opposed to practical. This prejudice was, however, short-sighted, quite understandable. The engineering industries had been built up by practical men, who had little book knowledge themselves, but had certainly a miraculous intuition which enabled them to make the theories of Faraday and Ampère " work." To-day, however, no amount of intuitive understanding of science can suffice for an engineer. Whatever grade in engineering a man aspires to, the theoretical knowledge is one-half of the battle.

INDEX AND PRONOUNCING GLOSSARY

Compiled by C. H. KNOWLES, B.Sc.

How to use this index.—In order to facilitate immediate reference to the principal entry on a particular subject, the page number for this entry is set in italics, thus : *258*. Subsidiary references to the subject which occur elsewhere in the book are indicated by numerals in roman type, thus : 387. References to illustrations are indicated by *the number of the figure* in roman type surrounded by square brackets thus : [151]. Cross references given in the index refer only to the index pages.

The pronouncing glossary.—Where the pronunciation of proper names and technical terms is not immediately understood from the spelling, or where the spelling may be misleading, a separate pronunciation is given after the first index entry. In simple cases a hint may be considered sufficient ; in all doubtful cases a complete phonetic re-spelling is given. The word is broken into syllables as it is spoken, and an accent mark (′) follows the syllable on which the stress is placed. The notation used for the phonetic re-spelling is as follows :

ā	m*a*te	a	p*a*t	ė	th*e*re	th	*th*in
ē	m*e*te	e	p*e*t	à	f*a*ther	TH	*th*ine
ī	m*i*te	i	p*i*t	e̱	h*er*	zh	lei*s*ure
ō	m*o*te	o	p*o*t	aw	*aw*l	ch	*ch*urch
ū	m*u*te	u	n*u*t	oi	*oi*l	g̱	*g*et
ōō	b*oo*t	oo	f*oo*t	ow	*ow*l	j	*j*am

The French nasalised *n* is denoted by italicising the vowel and the nasal concerned, thus : u*n*, bo*n*, vi*n*. The German modified ö and the similar French sounds are denoted by *oe*, the German soft ch and g by *ch*, and the guttural ch (as in Scots " loch ") by CH. The French *u* and the German modified ü are indicated by ü.